# Clifton Fadiman's
# FIRESIDE READER

*An assortment of stories,
nonfiction and verses chosen
especially for reading aloud*

## SIMON AND SCHUSTER
New York · 1961

# ACKNOWLEDGMENTS

*The author wishes to express his gratitude to the following persons and publishers for their permission to reprint stories in this anthology:*

Walter Bastian for "The Very Foreign Ambassadors," copyright 1960 by Walter Bastian.

Heywood Broun for "The Fifty-first Dragon," copyright 1941 by Heywood Hale Broun.

John Collier for "The Chaser," copyright 1940 by John Collier. Originally in *The New Yorker*.

John Davenport for "Slurvian Self-Taught," copyright 1949 by The New Yorker Magazine, Inc. Originally in *The New Yorker*.

Lester David for "The Heroic Ride of Caesar Rodney," copyright 1960 by Lester David.

John Dos Passos for "The Campers at Kitty Hawk" from *U.S.A.*, copyright 1930, 1932, 1936, 1958 by John Dos Passos.

Arthur Gordon for "The Spell," copyright 1954 by Arthur Gordon.

John McNulty for "The Television Helps, but Not Very Much," copyright 1951 by John McNulty.

5

Ogden Nash for "Every Day Is Monday," copyright 1935 by Ogden Nash.

Mrs. Kermit Roosevelt for "F.D.R. and the Great Sprout Crisis," copyright 1955 by Mrs. Kermit Roosevelt.

The Executors of the Estate of H. G. Wells for "The Pearl of Love" by H. G. Wells.

*American Mercury* for "Outer Baldonia vs. Soviet Russia" by William Bancroft Mellor, copyright 1954 by *American Mercury;* and "Pale Blue Nightgown" by Louis Golding, copyright 1950 by *American Mercury.*

Book-of-the-Month Club, Inc., for "I Admire the Human Race" by Roger William Riis, copyright 1951 by the Book-of-the-Month Club, Inc.

Dodd, Mead & Company for "My Financial Career" from *Laugh with Leacock* by Stephen Leacock, copyright 1930 by Dodd, Mead & Company.

Doubleday & Company, Inc., for "The Hack Driver" by Sinclair Lewis from *The Selected Short Stories of Sinclair Lewis,* copyright 1923 by Sinclair Lewis.

Farrar, Straus and Cudahy, Inc., for "The Great Grippe Mystery" from *Life Among the Savages* by Shirley Jackson, copyright 1952, 1953 by Shirley Jackson.

Harcourt, Brace & World, Inc., for "Private Hackleford's Big Toe" from *War Is a Private Affair* by Edmund G. Love, copyright 1951, 1959 by Edmund G. Love.

Harper & Brothers for "The Treasurer's Report" and "The Brass Cannon" from *The Treasurer's Report* by Robert Benchley, copyright 1930 by Robert C. Benchley; "Arminia Evans Avery" from *America's Growing Pains* by George R. Leighton, copyright 1936, 1937, 1938, 1939 by Harper & Brothers; and "Yes, Your Honesty!" from *Anything Can Happen* by George and Helen Waite Papashvily, copyright 1944 by George and Helen Waite Papashvily.

Holt, Rinehart and Winston, Inc., for a passage from *Brave Men* by Ernie Pyle, copyright 1944 by Holt, Rinehart and Winston, Inc.; "The Heart of a Hunter" from *The Old Man and the Boy* by Robert C. Ruark, copyright 1957 by Robert C. Ruark; and "American Names" from *Ballads and Poems* by Stephen Vincent Benét, copyright 1931, 1959 by Rosemary Carr Benét.

Alfred A. Knopf, Inc., for a passage from *Men of Good Will, Book 16: The Battle,* by Jules Romains, translated by Gerard Hopkins, copyright 1939 by Alfred A. Knopf, Inc.

J. B. Lippincott Company for a passage from *Quiet, Yelled Mrs. Rabbit* by Hilda Cole Espy, copyright 1958 by Hilda Cole Espy.

Little, Brown & Co., for "Let the Bridges Fall Down!" from *Vermont Tradition* by Dorothy Canfield Fisher, copyright 1953 by Dorothy Canfield Fisher.

The Macmillan Company for "The Lottery Ticket" from *The Wife and Other Stories* by Anton Chekhov, translated by Constance Garnett; copyright 1918 by The Macmillan Company.

McGraw-Hill Book Company, Inc., for a passage from *Thirteen Days to Glory* by Lon Tinkle, copyright 1958 by Lon Tinkle.

*The New Yorker* for "She Did Not Know How to Be Famous" by Clifton Fadiman, copyright 1937 by The New Yorker Magazine, Inc. Originally in *The New Yorker*.

Oxford University Press, Inc., for "Pericles' Funeral Oration" from *The History of the Peloponnesian War* by Thucydides, edited in translation by Sir Richard Livingstone.

Random House, Inc., for a passage from *Les Misérables* by Victor Hugo; and for "A Work of Art" by Anton Chekhov from *The Stories of Anton Chekhov*.

Charles Scribner's Sons for a passage from *Of Time and the River* by Thomas Wolfe, copyright 1935 by Charles Scribner's Sons.

Seeley, Service & Co., Ltd., for "Mr. Theodore Castwell" from *Side Lines, Side Lights and Reflections* by G. E. M. Skues, copyright 1947 by G. E. M. Skues.

Simon and Schuster, Inc., for passages from *The Longest Day* by Cornelius Ryan, copyright 1959 by Cornelius Ryan; *Mine Enemy Grows Older* by Alexander King, copyright 1958 by Alexander King; *Of Men and Music* by Deems Taylor, copyright 1937 by Deems Taylor; and *Fate Is the Hunter* by Ernest K. Gann, copyright 1961 by Ernest K. Gann.

The Viking Press, Inc., for "Small-Town Parade" from *Times Three* by Phyllis McGinley, copyright 1953 by Phyllis McGinley; "The Open Window" from *The Short Stories of Saki* (H. H. Munro); "The Standard of Living" from *The Portable Dorothy Parker*, copyright 1941, 1944 by Dorothy Parker; and "For Us, the Living" from *As You Were* by Alexander Woollcott, copyright 1943 by The Viking Press, Inc.

Walker and Company for "Amazing Lady" by Cyril Hare from *The Best Detective Stories of Cyril Hare*, copyright 1959 by Faber & Faber.

# CONTENTS

9

# INTRODUCTION

I think it was some time around the early part of 1959 that William Nichols, Editor and Publisher of *This Week* Magazine, invited me to try my hand at an experimental feature that he thought might interest his fourteen million readers, or at least a fair fraction of them. For some time he had been running, more or less regularly, new fiction—or, rather, short short stories, excellent of their kind (you will find a couple of samples in this book) but making no great pretension to high literary merit. Mr. Nichols, one of the most remarkable, ingenious and tireless editors I have ever worked under, wanted to try to replace these stories with something else. This something else he called "fiction equivalents." It was his idea for me to find brief pieces that had been printed before but with which not all of his audience might necessarily be familiar, pieces that might be straight fiction, or drawn from novels, or from history books, or indeed from any source, as long as most of them had some kind of narrative rather than expository quality. And it was his hope that many of them would turn out to have literary claims as well.

As I like to rummage in the literary treasure heaps of the past, this idea attracted me greatly. I agreed to work along these lines, but added the suggestion that I should try to keep in mind pieces that could be read aloud in the family circle, as well as silently to one's self. I had for some years been a kind of poor-man's Charles Laughton, an itinerant platform reader of stories and poems that I had found my own family liked and that I thought others might like to hear. It occurred to me that *This Week*, with its vast family circulation, might prove a better platform for my reading-aloud propaganda than any I had hitherto dared to bestride. As Mr.

Nichols himself had long been a devoted advocate of the reading-aloud idea, we had no difficulty in coming to a final agreement on the department which Mr. Nichols christened "Read It Now" and which has been running for more than two years, once every two weeks on the average.

I have not made an exact count, but I imagine that at least one half of the material in this book comes from "Read It Now," and so in a way has been pretested. The balance consists of other favorites of mine, most of which I believe to be "readaloudable."

The collection makes no claim to originality. Furthermore, while everything in it, I think, represents honest writing, not everything in it is of high literary distinction. But a good deal is. The curious thing is that it was precisely the finest selections that drew the most numerous letters of appreciation from *This Week's* readers—items such as the Funeral Oration of Pericles and Plato's description of the death of Socrates.

What I have tried to do is to compose a miscellany of good family reading, varied in tone and appeal. Most of this material can be read aloud, and it is my hope that in its small way this book may contribute to the current renaissance of that excellent tradition. But if reading aloud does not suit some particular reader's condition, he will, I think, find much here that may be read alone with some profit and pleasure.

The brief notes that precede each selection are intended to suggest its tone and mood; or, in many cases, to indicate my reason for thinking the reader may find in it some of the satisfaction it originally gave me, and still gives me.

As for family-circle reading aloud, we can say with some confidence that it is growing in popularity. I do not know the reasons: perhaps growing boredom with the entertainment offered by films and TV; perhaps the increasing need for family solidarity that is often felt in times of stress and anxiety; perhaps a natural urge to imitate such recent highly successful public readers and recitalists as Charles Laughton, Emlyn Williams, Hal Holbrook, Vincent Price; perhaps a tendency toward informal education-at-home, stimulated by our discovery that there is something radically wrong with our formal education-at-school.

However that may be, I find more and more that my neighbors are falling into the habit of regular reading aloud, and that people I meet in my junketings around the country make the same report. If you are already an old hand at this time-honored family diversion, all I can hope is that you will find in this book at least a few items that you can add with enjoyment to your repertory.

But if you are a new hand, or a would-be new hand, perhaps a few suggestions may be in order.

In every family one member will be found to be the best reader. It may be the father, the mother—or it may be a quite young child who for all his youth possesses a natural talent. But, whoever is best at it, don't let him or her monopolize the readings. If there's a member of the family who really dislikes reading aloud, that's different; but otherwise it's a good idea to give everyone a chance, not only because so many of us are hams at heart, but because reading aloud is a self-educational activity. We improve by doing. It's a particularly good idea to give your teen-age youngster—or even your ten-year-old—an opportunity to read something he has himself discovered or for which he has a special enthusiasm. It's not often that a youngster has an opportunity to make the whole family listen to him for an uninterrupted half hour or so. The experience gives him a certain confidence in himself—and it will also help him in his oral work at school, as well as giving him a sense of the weight and color of English words and sentences.

We usually associate reading aloud with the indoor months of winter; but there is no reason to confine it to the hearthside. The summer months usually bring the gift of more leisure, and surely it's just as much fun to read aloud around the barbecue or on the porch as the coolness of a summer evening steals slowly in.

Each family of course develops its own routines of living, but as a general thing I would suggest that the reading-aloud periods be made more or less regular. I don't mean that they must be scheduled rigorously, but that they be kept up with not too many long interruptions. The idea here is to break down the self-consciousness that the first few sessions may bring with them. After a few regular periods the experience will no longer seem odd, but as comfortable as an old shoe.

Don't go on too long. An hour, I've found, is maximum. Beyond that point (unless you're a trained reader with a knowledge of voice control and projection) you will tire—and so will your listeners. And if you do find that as much as an hour is enjoyable, it's better to read two or three shorter pieces rather than one long one. That's why this book contains such a jumble of material of all shapes, sizes, and reading times. On the other hand, you may find that the family is willing to take a long novel in serial gulps, as our Victorian ancestors were fond of doing. Another variation (and there are many groups around the country doing this) is to select a play and assign parts, which makes a real community affair of reading aloud. Strangely enough, it's been found by experience that Shakespeare is apt to go better than a more modern drama. I think we like the old-fashioned rolling periods, the rhetoric, the opportunity to "spout" which is often not provided by modern drama. However, Shaw goes well and so does Noel Coward—or any playwright you happen to like and admire. Most plays can be completed in two one-hour sessions, but it's perfectly practicable to do the whole affair in a single evening, because each reader by the nature of the performance is given a chance to rest his voice from time to time. The attraction of play reading is not dissimilar to that of private quartet playing: it is not perfection that is aimed at but the informal exercise, on a communal basis, of an amateur talent.

Unless you're really good at it, don't "act." Ease, informality, clearness of speech—these are more important than "expression." As every actor knows, you'll find that "expression" comes about naturally when you're really interested in what you're saying, and understand it. I mentioned clearness of speech—but that must not be taken too seriously. A certain amount of slurring is natural to our language. A reader who pronounces every *a* and *the* overzealously will sound false and makes his hearers uneasy.

The little notes that precede the selections in this book usually give an idea of their general mood and tempo. But I think you'll find it worth while, if you intend to read a piece aloud, to go over it beforehand, alone, absorbing unconsciously the atmosphere that the author is trying to create and that you will shortly re-create. Some readers are good at reading "cold," that is, from a book or script they've never seen before. But not all of us have this gift.

Another reason for prereading is to make sure that the selection is suitable for the whole family, if it is your intent to *have* the whole family listen. There is nothing in this book that will bring a blush to anyone's cheek; but there are several items that may not be easily grasped by the younger members of your family, say those under twelve.

Don't be afraid of poetry. Good poetry (not all, but most) is by its nature "readaloudable." All the poetic devices—rhythm, meter, rhyme, alliteration, assonance—gain in meaning and interest when exploited and exposed by the voice, rather than merely absorbed by the eye and the mind. Poetry originally was sung or recited, and even today, after so many centuries of development, it bears clear traces of its origin. In this collection there are not many poems, because there are other anthologies that will supply your need. One of the most recent (and excellent) is Lewis Gannett's *Family Book of Verse* (Harper). Two others I heartily recommend are Edward Hodnett's *Poems to Read Aloud* (Norton) and *Poet's Gold* (Devin-Adair), edited by David Ross who, over twenty-five years ago, when radio was more receptive to intelligence than it is today, gave pleasure to large audiences with his poetry readings. Certain poets, of course, are more rewarding when read aloud than are others: I have always, for example, found Robert Frost a good bet because his verse follows and reflects the natural intonations of the voice. The kind of poetry to avoid is the pretty-pretty kind that pleased our grandmothers, the kind that Longfellow and Tennyson, good poets at their best, wrote at their worst.

As I have noted, this book is largely prose. In general, prose that has some narrative quality responds better to the reading-aloud situation. It need not be fiction; it may be history or biography or humor. Description and analysis generally do not carry over, though I once knew a group that read Plato together for fun, treating him as what he is (among other things)—a dramatist. But on the whole I don't think reading aloud should be *consciously* educational. It should be entertainment, homemade, unambitious, relaxed. Stories with humor or suspense go well; and there are many good examples between these covers. If you can handle them, ghost and horror stories are sure-fire (but keep your audience above the ten- or twelve-year-old level—the little ones seem to be able to manufacture a sufficiency of nightmares all by themselves, without added stimulus). The essential thing to remember with this sort of tale is that you must save your best voice effects for the very end; build very gradually; and remember that reactions of horror and fear are not secured by overdramatic elocution but are often best created by a quiet, restrained, *frozen* tone of voice. Basil Davenport's *Tales to Be Told in the Dark* (Dodd, Mead) contains some wonderful chillers, together with an interesting preface telling you not how they should be read, but how they should be *retold*, which is perhaps the better way to handle them.

There's still another kind of reading-aloud program: the bits-and-pieces session. Here you simply read small, favorite passages, all mixed up, but each one perhaps sufficiently provocative to elicit comment from the audience. It's best to have these passages slip-marked in advance, to avoid fumbling. With complete immodesty I suggest that my own anthology called *The American Treasury* (Harper) is so constructed as to supply almost endless material for this kind of rag-bag reading aloud.

It is pleasant occasionally to invite a friend to your reading sessions. It puts the reader on his mettle, and it spreads the gospel. And, just as in the fence-whitewashing episode in *Tom Sawyer*, your friend will probably be burning to have his chance.

Usually the attempt to "imitate voices" fails with the amateur. Unless you have a natural gift for mimicry (some do, and never discover it till they start reading aloud) stick to your own voice even though you must handle dialogue. If you're a man, you can, by merely *gentle-ing* your voice (not raising its pitch) give the suggestion of a woman talking. If you're a woman, forget it; don't try for a distinction. Avoid dialect material unless you have a special talent; but most of us who are proud of our ability to reproduce dialect are, to tell the truth, quite dreadful at it.

I've come to the conclusion that in reading aloud, pronunciation and enunciation, while important, are less so than phrasing. Most of us read poorly because we do not know when to pause, pay too much or too little attention to marks of punctuation, and don't bother to get the "feel" of the construction of a sentence which, unless it is very short, is usually built up of parts. (Try the preceding sentence aloud to see what I mean.) Next to phrasing, the biggest stumbling block is often tempo. Some parts of any block of prose or poetry are meant to be read faster than others; the temptation for most of us is unconsciously to establish a metronome in our minds and to ticktock the reading. If you can manage to make a recording of your voice and have it played back, as I have had to do in order to learn to read passably, you will discover at once faults of which you have been unaware all your life. I found, for example, to my horror, that I tended to let my sentences "run down"—I ended all of them at a lower pitch than that at which I began them. Occasionally the sense requires this; but usually it is fatal and induces drowsiness in the listener. A large part of the art of the actor is to manipulate his voice so that the end of a line or sentence seems to invite attention to the line or sentence that is to follow. But if you worry about this sort of thing too much, you'll get into as much trouble as did the centipede when he started to reflect on which of his legs he should move next.

Remember also that you are not on a platform. You are in your own living room. To *er-r* is human; to clear your throat, to stumble, to rest a few seconds, to interrupt the reading with a comment— all are quite in keeping with the mood of home reading aloud. You are not on exhibition, but engaging in a perfectly natural pursuit, one just as natural in fact as silent reading to one's self.

Reading to small children is a specialty. It's harder than reading to grown-ups because children are quicker to detect the phony and on the other hand are not sufficiently sophisticated to overlook ordinary weaknesses in reading technique. On the other hand, once you've *got* them, they'll stick with you and give you far more of their total attention than adults will. Also, they are not competitive; they're not saying to themselves, "I could do it better." Smallish children will take verse in fairly large doses if it has humor and is strongly rhythmed; and they will take it in modest doses if it is serious, as long as it has the imaginative quality that, without knowing it, is what they are seeking. There is a good collection of Robert Frost's verse suitable for young people (Holt) and you might even try, if your youngsters seem to have in them the root of the language sense, *Poems for Youth* by Emily Dickinson, edited by Alfred Leete Hampson (Little, Brown). There are many anthologies of verse for children. A quite good one is *This Way,*

*Delight,* selected by Herbert Read (Pantheon). But far and away
the finest anthology of this kind is Walter de la Mare's *Come
Hither* (Knopf), which is meant to enchant grown-ups as well the
young. There is a most serviceable anthology called *Humorous
Poetry for Children,* edited by William Cole (World Publishing).
Our time is rich in poets who have some of the genius of Lewis
Carroll, Robert Louis Stevenson, and A. A. Milne. Perhaps the
best of them is David McCord whose *Far and Few* (Little, Brown)
supplies plenty of "readaloudables."

As for the pages that follow, I hope they may provide some
pleasures, diversions, and surprises, whether read in silence or
aloud, by adult or by child, by the habitual reader for whom the
love of literature is as natural as breathing, or by those who, in our
curious age, may come almost virgin to the delights of reading.

—Clifton Fadiman

# THE TELEVISION HELPS, BUT NOT VERY MUCH

## by John McNulty

I know this reads aloud well because I've tested it again and again on the platform, during my poor-man's-Charles-Laughton tours. If you think you can handle a colloquial Brooklyn accent, try it on the cabbie, but the story reads just as well delivered straight. There was only one John McNulty—no one could write this sort of thing as well as he could. He had a good eye, a good ear—and a fine spirit.

When I got into the cab to go down from Seventy-second and Second to Forty-fourth and Fifth, it seemed stuffy, so I gave the handle a twist and let the window down a little.

"That's O.K.," the driver said, "I'll take and close this one up, if it's all right with you."

"Oh, sure."

"If they're both open, it makes a draft on the back of my neck. I ought to be home. I got a cold."

"That's about all you can do for these colds."

"Go to bed is the best thing. Only with me, maybe I'm better off milling around in the hack. Too lonesome home. I lost my wife."

"Oh, sorry. Was it recently it happened? I mean, when did she die?"

"Pretty near a year ago at that," he said.

We were moving along Seventy-second, getting near Fifth. Traffic was slow even before we hit Fifth.

Some of them are gabby, the hack drivers. This one wasn't, even though it turned out we talked all the way. It didn't seem to be a gab. It seemed natural talk, almost as if we had known each other a long time.

"I got myself a television, for company like. The television helps, but not very much, at that."

"No kids or anything?" I asked.

"No, we didn't. We didn't have no kids at all. No in-laws even. See, we come from another city here. More than twenty years here. We made out all right. It ain't the best job in the world, but we battle along all right together, twenty years. Long time."

"Yes," I said.

"Like I say about the television, I can get interested all right, like a fight or even sometimes those cowboy movies they put on. Just the same, sooner or later the television got to wind up, don't it? I mean, it comes to the end of whatever the show is or wrassling or whatever it is."

"I know what you mean. The thing goes off," I said.

"Yeah, the thing winds up and there I am again. I'm alone again, and I maybe go to the icebox and get a beer, but it's lonesome. Do you think it wouldn't be so bad if I had kids somewheres? Even if they were grown up somewheres?"

"I don't know. I don't have any children."

"Well, they say it's different if you have kids," he said, "even if you lose your wife. That's what they say."

"Some people say that. I don't know. Did she die suddenly?"

"She was sick about two weeks, that's all," he said. "But the more I think about it, she must have been sick a long while. The doctor says she must have been. She didn't like to have doctors. Matter of fact, it was me got him finally. And I had to go to him and say to him, look, she's going to be sore at you coming in. I said, she's against you before she ever lays an eye on you, I says, so please don't mind if she acts sore. Later on, after it's all over, he tells me it was too late, the thing that was the matter with her it was too late to do anything."

"That was tough," I said.

"Thing is I keep worrying. Was it my fault maybe I wasn't more bossy and make her get a doctor? What do you think? I worry about it all the time. Like that's why I didn't stay home with this damn cold. I'd be around the house thinking maybe we'd be together just the same as always, me coming home and having supper and help with the dishes and we both sit down and have a couple beers, listen to the radio, if I made her get a doctor and never mind how much beefing, squawking she do about it. What do you think?"

"Oh, I don't know. That's a tough one to answer," I said. It wasn't that I wanted to give the driver a short answer, but there I was, thrown into the middle of a man's life, and I didn't know the man.

"You're telling me it's a tough one! Just the same, I got the notion you're kind of sensible, and after all, what harm is there? Like I tell you, I got no in-laws, no kids. I had an idea I'd talk it over with somebody. Them guys around the garage, what the hell, they're dumber than me even. What do *they* know? Know what I mean?"

"Sure."

"Like, the truth of the matter, I could get married again right away. Those guys all said don't be a sucker—don't be a sucker, they said."

"About what?" I asked.

"Well, might as well out with it. There's this girl I could get married with. Say, do you think I look forty-eight?"

"I don't know. I hardly looked at you much. Just got in the cab, hardly looked at anything except that it was a cab."

"I guess I look forty-eight all right. Well, this girl is thirty-one. She's got a little baby. I met her at a guy's house; he had me there eating Christmas dinner. Didn't want me eating in a coffeepot first Christmas I had no wife, he said."

"She divorced or what, the girl with the baby?"

"No. Thing is she was a Wac—you know, in the war they had women they called them Wacs. She was in Chicago and she married this guy, and it's only three months after and he dies on her. So in a little while she had the baby, and that's the way it is. She's a very nice woman, only—seventeen years younger. I mean seventeen years younger than me. I told you I'm forty-eight, didn't I? Well, this girl, or maybe I should say woman, she's thirty-one and got the baby and thirty-one from forty-eight, that's seventeen, see what I mean?"

"Yes," I said.

"The guys at the garage say that's too much difference, and with the kid and all. What they don't understand is I like the kid, see what I mean? I bought the kid a couple toys, and you should see how this girl appreciated it I bought toys for the kid. Don't think for a minute this is any kind of fly-around dame. She's nice. She lives with her mother now, and she works when she can get work."

"I bet she's all right."

"You can say that again. Just between ourselves, she proposed to me, you might say. Know what I mean? Honest to God, it ain't this sex stuff. That ain't the main thing at all, no matter what the guys in the garage say; they're always harping about that angle. What I mean is—well, I would like to have her around, kid and all. I like the kid. He ain't very big yet, but he could look at the television too. Like I say, it helps keep me from getting so goddam lonesome, but it don't take care of things altogether, know what I mean? Will you tell me one thing? I mean, I want you to give me your opinion—it's pretty near Forty-fourth Street after we get this light."

"O.K., what is it?" I said.

"Never mind the guys in the garage—do *you* think it'd be all right if we got married? You think it would work out?"

"You're coming at me rather suddenly with this."

"I know," he said. "I don't say I'll do what you tell me, but just the same, you got an idea now how things are, don't you?"

"Well, I think I understand."

"O.K., then, what do you think?"

"All right, you asked me," I said, and drew a deep breath. "I say go ahead and get married. That's what I say, sight unseen."

"Right!" he said, speaking loud for the first time in our rolling acquaintance. "That settles it. I guess I only needed somebody, anybody, say go ahead. Like gives me a little shove, you might say. I'm going to do it. It's too damn lonesome. And I like the kid, no fooling. . . . This is Forty-fourth. You want this corner or the downtown side?"

"This corner's all right." I got out and hollered back, "Good luck!"

"O.K., Doc." He was smiling, and now I guess he'll go ahead and get married. Probably never see him again. I didn't even look at his name beside the picture in the frame, but I hope they make out all right.

# THE DEATH OF CAPTAIN WASKOW

## by Ernie Pyle

> Ernie Pyle was not only a first-rate human-interest war correspondent but a man with a great heart. That heart is what you feel beating in this brief account of what I suppose we must call a minor episode in a vast war. You may have come across it elsewhere, yet I think it cannot be too often reprinted. Reading it aloud is a worth-while experience but not easy: too many catches in the throat.

At the Front Lines in Italy, Jan. 10 [1944] (by Wireless)—In this war I have known a lot of officers who were loved and respected by the soldiers under them. But never have I crossed the trail of any man as beloved as Captain Henry T. Waskow of Belton, Texas.

Captain Waskow was a company commander in the 36th Division. He was very young, only in his middle twenties, but he carried in him a sincerity and gentleness that made people want to be guided by him.

"After my own father, he comes next," a sergeant told me.

"He always looked after us," a soldier said. "He'd go to bat for us every time."

"I've never known him to do anything unkind," another one said.

I was at the foot of the mule trail the night they brought Captain Waskow down. The moon was nearly full, and you could see far up the trail and even part way across the valley. Soldiers made shadows as they walked.

Dead men had been coming down the mountain all evening, lashed onto the backs of mules. They came lying belly down across the wooden packsaddles, their heads hanging down on the left side of the mules, their stiffened legs sticking awkwardly from the other side, bobbing up and down as the mule walked.

The Italian mule skinners were afraid to walk beside the dead men, so Americans had to lead the mules down that night. Even the Americans were reluctant to unlash and lift off the bodies when they got to the bottom, so an officer had to do it himself and ask others to help.

The first one came early in the morning. They slid him down from the mule and stood him on his feet for a moment. In the half-light he might have been merely a sick man standing there leaning on the other. Then they laid him on the ground in the shadow of the stone wall alongside the road.

I don't know who the first one was. You feel small in the presence of dead men and you don't ask silly questions.

We left him there beside the road, that first one, and we all went back into the cowshed and sat on water cans or lay on the straw, waiting for the next batch of mules.

Somebody said the dead soldier had been dead for four days, and then nobody said anything more about him. We talked for an hour or more; the dead man lay all alone, outside in the shadow of the wall.

Then a soldier came into the cowshed and said there were some more bodies outside. We went out into the road. Four mules stood there in the moonlight, in the road where the trail came down off the mountain. The soldiers who led them stood there waiting.

"This one is Captain Waskow," one of them said quickly.

Two men unlashed his body from the mule and lifted it off and laid it in the shadow beside the stone wall. Other men took the other bodies off. Finally there were five lying end to end in a long row. You don't cover up dead men in the combat zone. They just lie there in the shadows until somebody else comes after them.

The uncertain mules moved off to their olive groves. The men in the road seemed reluctant to leave. They stood around, and gradually I could sense them moving, one by one, close to Captain Waskow's body. Not so much to look, I think, as to say something in finality to him and to themselves. I stood close by and I could hear.

One soldier came and looked down, and he said out loud, "God damn it!"

That's all he said, and then he walked away.

Another one came, and he said, "God damn it to hell, any-way!" He looked down for a few last moments and then turned and left.

Another man came. I think he was an officer. It was hard to tell officers from men in the dim light, for everybody was grimy and dirty. The man looked down into the dead captain's face and then spoke directly to him, as though he were alive, "I'm sorry, old man."

Then a soldier came in and stood beside the officer and bent over, and he, too, spoke to his dead captain, not in a whisper but awfully tenderly, and he said, "I sure am sorry, sir."

Then the first man squatted down, and he reached down and took the captain's hand, and he sat there for a full five minutes, holding the dead hand in his own and looking intently into the dead face. And he never uttered a sound all the time he sat there.

Finally he put the hand down. He reached up and gently straightened the points of the captain's shirt collar, and then he sort of rearranged the tattered edges of his uniform around the wound, and then he got up and walked away down the road in the moonlight, all alone.

The rest of us went back into the cowshed, leaving the five dead men lying in a line, end to end, in the shadow of the low stone wall. We lay down on the straw in the cowshed, and pretty soon we were all asleep.

# A WORK OF ART

## by Anton Chekhov

Once a writer becomes a "classic," he seems to acquire a reputation for sobriety, or gloominess. That's what's happened to Anton Chekhov, whose 100th anniversary was celebrated in 1960.

I maintain it isn't fair. Like most great pre-Soviet Russian writers, Chekhov was a penetrating realist, it's true. But he was a great humorist too. Here is one of his funniest stories—about a doctor who got a very unusual present from a grateful patient.

Chekhov was himself a doctor. Like many of our greatest geniuses, he has been better appreciated since his death than he was in his lifetime. New editions and translations of his stories are constantly appearing, and his plays still excite audiences on both sides of the Atlantic.

"A Work of Art" may remind you a little of our own O. Henry. I recommend reading it aloud.

Holding under his arm an object wrapped in a newspaper, Sasha Smirnov walked nervously into the office of Dr. Koshelkov.

"Well, my dear boy," exclaimed the doctor warmly, "how do you feel today? What's the good news?"

Sasha began to blink, put his hand over his heart, and stammered nervously, "My mother sends her regards and begs to thank you. You have saved my life, and we both hardly know how to thank you."

"Come, come, my young friend, let us not speak of it," interrupted the doctor, literally melting with pleasure. "I have only done what anybody else in my place would have done."

"We are poor people and consequently we are not in a position to pay you for your trouble. But Mother and I beg you to accept a token of our gratitude, this wonderful masterpiece in antique bronze."

The doctor made a grimace. "Why, my dear friend," he said, "it is entirely unnecessary. I don't need this in the least."

"Oh no, no," stammered Sasha. "I beg you please accept it!"

He began to unwrap the bundle, continuing his entreaties in the meantime, "If you do not accept this, you will offend both my mother and myself. This is a very rare work of art, an antique bronze. It is a relic left by my dead father. We have been prizing it as a very dear remembrance. My father used to buy up bronze antiques, selling them to lovers of old statuary. And now we continue in the same business, my mother and myself."

Sasha untied the package and enthusiastically placed it on the table.

It was a low candelabrum of antique bronze, a work of real art representing a group. On a pedestal stood two figures of women clad in the costume of Mother Eve and in poses that I have neither the audacity nor the temperament to describe. These figures were smiling provocatively and gave one the impression that, were it not for the fact that they were obliged to support the candlestick, they would step down from their pedestal and put on a performance which . . . my dear reader, I am ashamed to think of it!

When the doctor got a glimpse of the present, he slowly scratched his head, cleared his throat, and blew his nose.

"Yes, indeed, a very pretty piece of work," he muttered. "But—how shall I say it—not quite . . . I mean . . . rather unconventional . . . not very spiritual, is it? The devil!"

"Why?"

"If I placed such a thing on my table I would pollute my entire house!"

"Why, Doctor, what a strange idea you have of art!" cried Sasha in offended tones. "This is a real masterpiece. Just look at it! Such is its harmonious beauty that merely to contemplate it fills the soul with ecstasy and makes the throat choke back a sob! When you see such loveliness you forget all earthly things . . . Just look at it! What life, what motion, what expression!"

"I quite understand all this, my dear boy," interrupted the doctor. "But I am a married man. Small children run in and out of this room, and ladies come here continually."

"Of course," said Sasha, "if you look at it through the eyes of the rabble, you see this noble masterpiece in an entirely different light. But you certainly are above all that, Doctor, and especially when your refusal to accept this gift will deeply offend both my mother and myself. You have saved my life, and in return we give you our dearest possession."

"Thanks, friend, many thanks. Remember me to your mother and . . . But for God's sake! You can see for yourself, can't you? Children run in and out of this room, and ladies come here continually. . . . However, leave it here! There's no use arguing with you."

"Don't say another word!" exclaimed Sasha joyously. "Put the candelabrum right here, next to the vase. It's a pity I haven't got the mate to give you. But it can't be helped. Well, good-by, Doctor!"

After Sasha left, the doctor looked at the candelabrum and scratched his head.

"This is beautiful, all right," he thought. "It would be a pity to throw it away. And yet I dare not keep it. . . . Hm! Now who in the world is there to whom I can present or donate it?"

After long deliberation he hit upon a good friend of his, the lawyer Ukhov, to whom he was indebted for legal services.

"Fine!" chuckled the doctor. "Being a close friend of his, I cannot very well offer him money, and so I will give him this piece of indecency instead. And he's just the man for it . . . single, and somewhat of a gay bird too."

No sooner thought than done. Dressing himself, the doctor took the candelabrum and went to the home of Ukhov.

"Good morning, old chap!" he said. "I have come here to thank you for your trouble. . . . You will not take money, and I will therefore repay you by presenting you with this exquisite masterpiece. Isn't it a dream?"

As soon as the lawyer caught sight of it he was exhilarated with its beauty. "What a wonderful work of art!" he exclaimed. "What ideas artists get in their heads! What alluring charm! Where did you get this little treasure?"

But now his exhilaration began to fade, and he grew alarmed. Looking stealthily toward the door, he said, "But I can't accept it. You must take it right back."

"Why?" asked the doctor in alarm.

"Because . . . because . . . my mother often visits me, my clients come here, and besides, I would be disgraced even in the eyes of my servants."

"Don't say another word!" cried the doctor, gesturing wildly. "You simply have got to accept it! It would be rank ingratitude for you to refuse it! Such a masterpiece! What motion, what expression. . . . You will greatly offend me if you don't take it!"

"If only this were daubed over or covered with fig leaves."

But the doctor refused to listen to him. Gesturing even more wildly, he ran out of Ukhov's house in the thought that he was rid of the present.

When the doctor was gone, the lawyer carefully examined the candelabrum, and then he began to wonder what in the world he could do with it.

"A very beautiful object," he thought. "It's a pity to throw it away, and yet it's disgraceful to keep it. I had best present it to someone . . . I've got it! This very evening I'm going to give it to the comedian Shoshkin. The rascal loves such things, and besides, this is his benefit night."

No sooner thought than done. That afternoon the well-packed candelabrum was brought to the comedian Shoshkin.

That whole evening the dressing room of the comedian Shoshkin was besieged by men who hastened to inspect the present. And during all the time the room re-echoed with hilarious laughter which resembled the neighing of horses.

If any of the actresses approached the door and said, "May I enter?" the hoarse voice of Shoshkin was immediately heard to reply, "Oh no, no, my darling, you mustn't. I am not dressed!"

After the performance the comedian shrugged his shoulders and said, "Now what in the world am I to do with this? I live in a private apartment! I am often visited by actresses! And this isn't a photograph that one could conceal in a drawer!"

"Why don't you sell it?" suggested the wigmaker. "There is a certain old woman who buys up antique bronzes. Her name is Smirnova. You had better take a run over there. They'll show you the place all right—everybody knows her."

The comedian followed his advice. . . .

Two days later Koshelkov, his head supported on his hand, was sitting in his office concocting pills. Suddenly the door opened and into the office rushed Sasha. He was smiling and his breast heaved with joy. In his hands he held something wrapped in a newspaper.

"Doctor," he cried breathlessly, "imagine my joy! As luck would have it, I've just succeeded in getting the mate to your candelabrum! Mother is so happy! I am the only son of my mother. . . . You have saved my life."

And Sasha, quivering with thankfulness and rapture, placed a candelabrum before the doctor. The latter opened his mouth as if to say something but uttered not a word. . . . His power of speech was gone.

# PERICLES' FUNERAL ORATION

## by Thucydides

On Memorial Day we honor the men who have died in our wars and we take stock of the republic for which they gave their lives.

The greatest memorial speech in literature is ascribed to Pericles, the renowned leader of ancient Athens at the height of its glory. In it he, too, honored the dead and took stock of his country.

Athens of the Age of Pericles (about 440 B.C.) was certainly one of the most remarkable cities in history. Quite small—perhaps 170,000 people—it produced an outpouring of art, literature, science, and philosophy such as few ages or nations, however large, can boast. Much of what Athens created is lost, but what remains still enriches the world 2,400 years later: the beautiful temple of the Parthenon, the Elgin marbles, the sculpture of Phidias, the great tragedies of Sophocles and Euripides, the wisdom of Socrates, and finally the writings of two of the greatest historians who ever lived, Herodotus and Thucydides. Thanks to Thucydides, who wrote *The History of the Peloponnesian War*, we have Pericles' immortal Funeral Oration.

The speech was made at the end of the first campaign in the war between Athens and Sparta. It commemorated, in accordance with an ancient custom, the first Athenian soldiers to fall. But the speech is not only about the dead; it is about Athens, its glory, its greatness, and its idea, so akin to ours, of democracy.

I think you will want to read Pericles' Funeral Oration—somewhat condensed here—not only because it is a great and moving speech but because it presents a fresh way of thinking about our nation, our times, and ourselves.

Most of those who have stood in this place before me have commended the institution of this closing address. It is good, they have felt, that solemn words should be spoken over our fallen soldiers. I do not share this feeling. Our sense of the deserts of a number of our fellow citizens should not depend upon the felicity of one man's speech. But since the wisdom of our ancestors enacted this law, I, too, must submit and try to suit as best I can the wishes and feelings of every member of this gathering.

My first words shall be for our ancestors; for it is both just to them and seemly that on an occasion such as this our tribute of memory should be paid them. For, dwelling always in this country, they have handed it down to us free by their exertions. So they are worthy of our praises; and still more so are our fathers, while it is we ourselves who consolidated our power and secured the city's independence both in war and peace. Of the battles which we and our fathers fought I do not wish to say more. They are too familiar to you all. I wish rather to set forth the constitution and manner with which we rose to greatness. For I think . . . that these things should be called to mind in today's solemnity.

Our government is not copied from those of our neighbors. We are an example to them rather than they to us. Our constitution is named a democracy, because it is in the hands not of the few but of the many. But our laws secure equal justice for all in their private disputes, and our public opinion welcomes and honors talent in every branch of achievement.

And as we give free play to all in our public life, so we carry the same spirit into our daily relations with one another. We have no black looks or angry words for our neighbor if he enjoys himself in his own way. Open and friendly in our private intercourse, in our public acts we keep strictly within the control of law. We acknowledge the restraint of reverence; we are obedient to whomsoever is set in authority and so to the laws which offer protection to the oppressed. Yet ours is no workaday city only. No other provides so many recreations for the spirit and beauty in our public buildings to cheer the heart and delight the eye day by day. Moreover, the city is so large and powerful that all the wealth of all the world flows in to her, so that our own products seem no more homelike to us than the fruits of the labors of other nations.

Our military training, too, is different from our opponents'. The gates of our city are flung open to the world. We practice no periodical deportations, nor do we prevent our visitors from observing or discovering what an enemy might usefully apply to his own purposes. For our trust is not in the devices of material equipment but in our own good spirits for battle. So, too, with education. They toil from early boyhood in a laborious pursuit after courage, while we, free to live and wander as we please, march out none the less to face the selfsame dangers.

We are lovers of beauty without extravagance and lovers of wisdom without unmanliness. Wealth to us is not mere material for vainglory but an opportunity for achievement; and poverty we think is no disgrace to acknowledge but a real degradation to make no effort to overcome. Our citizens attend both to public and private duties and do not allow absorption in their own various affairs to interfere with their knowledge of the city's. We differ from other states in regarding the man who holds aloof from public life not as "quiet" but as useless. We decide or debate, carefully and in person, all matters of policy, holding that acts are foredoomed to failure when undertaken undiscussed. For we are noted for being at once

most adventurous in action and most reflective beforehand.
In doing good, too, we are the exact opposite of the rest of
mankind. We secure our friends not by accepting favors but
by doing them. We are alone among mankind in doing men
benefits, not on calculations of self-interest, but in the fearless
confidence of freedom.

Such, then, is the city for whom, lest they should lose her,
the men whom we celebrate died a soldier's death. Such were
the men who lie here and such the city that inspired them. We
survivors may pray to be spared their bitter hour but must disdain to meet the foe with a spirit less triumphant. Fix your
eyes on the greatness of Athens as you have it before you day
by day, fall in love with her, and when you feel her great, remember that this greatness was won by men with courage,
with knowledge of their duty.

So they gave their bodies to the commonwealth and received, each for his own memory, praise that will never die,
and with it the grandest of all sepulchers, not that in which
their mortal bones are laid, but a home in the minds of men,
where their glory remains fresh to stir to speech or action as
the occasion comes by. For the whole earth is the sepulcher of
famous men; and their story is not graven only on stone over
their native earth but lives on far away, without visible symbol,
woven into the stuff of other men's lives.

# OUTER BALDONIA
# VS. SOVIET RUSSIA

## by William Bancroft Mellor

> In case you ever decide to start your own country, this
> account of the origin and career of Outer Baldonia
> offers some useful pointers. In the literature of hoaxes
> and involved practical jokes this one will take an hon-
> orable place. I think it's a little more suitable for private
> reading than for reading aloud, and I hope that in these
> grim days of diplomatic tension it may give you a
> chuckle.

Many of Washington's keenest political observers have seen fit
to ignore the mounting tension between the Soviet Union and
the Principality of Outer Baldonia. But those in the know are
waiting with bated breath and expectant chuckles for the next
move of the Kremlin in its propaganda war with a "nation"
which exists only in the engagingly whimsical mind of Russell
M. Arundel, a Washington businessman and sportsman.

Arundel, an ardent tuna fisherman, invented "Outer Baldonia" over a bottle of bourbon one bitterly cold day in 1949,
while he and a couple of companions were out after blue fins
in the Atlantic off the Nova Scotia coast. He had just pur-
chased an uninhabited island—a barren, forty-acre mass of
rock jutting out of the sea sixteen miles southwest of Wedgeport, in the middle of some of the best tuna waters in the

39

world—and built a one-room fishing lodge on it. On your map, if it is a very large one, you will find the island listed as Outer Bald Tusket, one of a group of tiny dots scattered below the southernmost tip of Nova Scotia.

On that day in 1949 Arundel and his companions, casting about for a diversion to make them forget the chill winds which whistled through their fishing boat's drafty cabin, decided to create on the island a new and independent state— the Principality of Outer Baldonia—a nation peopled by fishermen alone and only *tuna* fisherman at that. Braced in the heaving cabin of their fishing boat, they drew up their first state document: a Declaration of Independence. It proclaimed for the citizens of the new principality the right to swear, lie, drink, and gamble and guaranteed them freedom forever from nagging, shaving, women, taxes, politics, war, cant, and inhibitions.

Arundel is mild-mannered, slight of build, and wears horn-rimmed spectacles secured by a broad black ribbon looped around the back of his neck. Seeing him sitting in his deeply carpeted Washington office, one would hardly envision him on the plunging deck of a fishing boat or astride a galloping hunter behind the foxhounds, of which he is master at Warrenton, Virginia. And certainly he is not the princely type. But beneath his proclamation, in a bold scrawl, Arundel signed himself "Russell, Rex," and proclaimed himself "Prince of Princes." Beneath his signature went those of Prew Savoy, a Washington attorney and business associate of Arundel's, who was named Prince Regent and Minister of State, and Captain Elson Boudreau, skipper of the fishing boat, who became Chancellor of the Principality.

Back in his Washington office, the Prince of Princes next ordered stationery with a gold-embossed letterhead bearing the Great Seal of Outer Baldonia, had the new nation listed on the directory of tenants in the lobby of the World Center Building where his offices are, and then hied himself to the Chesapeake & Potomac Telephone Company. Presently in the

Washington telephone book there appeared a listing for "Outer Baldonia, Principality of" (DI 7-2463)—a listing which subsequently was to occasion no little embarrassment for certain State Department fledglings who, told to make routine calls to "all foreign diplomatic missions," included Outer Baldonia on their lists.

Arundel is a busy man. His interests include a number of enterprises which allow him little time for whimsy. His spur-of-the-moment gag, however, developed such fascinating possibilities that he couldn't let go of it, and for days he devoted all his time to "affairs of state." He drew up an impressive Constitution, plastered with seals and ribbons and vesting all powers in himself—but recognizing, "for international amity," the laws of the Dominion of Canada. The document also provided that the citizenry of Outer Baldonia should consist entirely of "princes" and of "admirals of a rank no lower than six-star."

Each of the sixty-nine members of the Wedgeport Tuna Guides' Association received a formal commission as a "six-star admiral," together with notification that thenceforth his boat was to be considered a unit of the Outer Baldonian Navy. To a few tuna-fishing cronies Prince Arundel also sent embossed scrolls creating them Knights of the Order of Blue Fin and hereditary princes of the realm.

To insure the fullest possible diplomatic acceptance, the Prince of Princes appointed both an ambassador *and* a minister to Canada (Dr. Ronald Wallace, of Halifax, and Harold Lohnes, of Louisville, Kentucky), while to William DeGarthe, also of Halifax, went the post of naval attaché.

Arundel also designed passport forms, "valid forever and a day and until revoked," and had dies manufactured in preparation for the coining of his own money (the basic unit of which was to be the "tunar") and his own stamps.

Negotiations were then opened with Rand McNally & Co., the map people, and with the Interior Department's Board on Geographic Names to have Outer Baldonia shown on all future maps and charts of the Atlantic. Both requests were made on Outer Baldonia stationery over the signature of "Russell, Rex," and were phrased as royal commands.

It wasn't long before some of the Canadian newspapers blossomed out with feature stories about Outer Baldonia. The Provincial Government of Nova Scotia went along with the gag and announced to the press that it was "still undecided about recognition of the new kingdom." One of the Canadian papers, carrying a dead-pan treatment of the yarn, found its way into Germany, where the trade journal, *Industrikurier*, picked it up and printed it as a serious news dispatch. And so it got to Moscow.

On October 25, 1952, a vehement denunciation of Outer Baldonia appeared in the pages of the *Literary Gazette*, a state-controlled publication in the Russian capital. Quoting the Baldonian's constitutional right to lie, swear, and otherwise misbehave, the article unleashed a bitter tirade at the "führer" of Baldonia and declared he had "set himself the aim of turning his subjects into savages."

"In a word," the *Gazette* said, Prince Arundel had given them "the 'right' not to adhere to the ethical and moral laws which have been established by mankind."

It was several months before the *Gazette* reached the Western Hemisphere and was reprinted, tongue-in-cheek and in translation, in a Canadian Government publication.

Deeply hurt, the Prince of Princes brooded in his Washington "chancery" over this breach of diplomatic etiquette by the Russians. Then he took pen in hand.

Presently a messenger was on his way up Sixteenth Street, bearing a formal protest to the Soviet Embassy—a note which threatened severance of diplomatic relations unless amends were quickly forthcoming. Thus far there have been no further moves on either side, but Russell, Rex, and the Outer Baldonian Navy are ready.

It's your move, Malenkov.

# THE HEART OF A HUNTER

## by Robert C. Ruark

Most big-game hunters are men of leisure. Not so the author of this story. He's been writing a regular newspaper column for many years and has found time to turn out several best-selling books as well.

Possibly you saw the motion picture MGM made from his novel, *Something of Value*, with its background of Africa's bloody Mau-Mau country.

But I have chosen something that is more quiet and closer to the earth of Mr. Ruark's native North Carolina. The excerpt is from *The Old Man and the Boy*, a reminiscent book about a youngster, his grandfather, and their love of woods and streams.

This chapter will bring back memories to anyone who has made his bed beside a forest stream and been up with a frosty dawn, eager for the hunt. That, as Mr. Goldwyn might say, includes me out. But I can still enjoy Mr. Ruark's keen observation of nature at a time when the woods awaken and the small world of glade and hill comes alive.

From this boyhood world Mr. Ruark has long since moved out to taste the thrills of big-game hunting in Africa and elsewhere. Although he has now given up this sport—at present he prefers to shoot wildlife with a camera rather than a rifle—much of his hunting experience in Africa found its way into *Something of Value*.

It is always interesting to dig up the influences that
have sunk roots into a roving author, and I suspect that
a good many of Mr. Ruark's go back to the North Carolina of his boyhood, when he roamed the woods with
an Old Man.

It was awful cold when the Old Man hit me a lick in the ribs
with his elbow and said, "Get up, boy, and fix that fire." The
stars were still up, frosty in the sky, and a wind was whistling
round the corners of the tent. You could see the fire flicker just
a mite against the black background of the swamp.

Mister Howard was still snoring on his side of the pine-
needle canvas bed, and I remember that his mustache was
riffling, like marsh grass in the wind. Over in Tom and Pete's
tent you could hear two breeds of snores. One was squeaky,
and the other sounded like a bull caught in a bob-wire fence.
I crawled out, shivering, and jumped into my hunting boots.
Everything else I owned I'd slept in.

The fire had simmered down to gray ash, which was swirling
loose in the morning breeze. I kicked some of the ashes aside
and I put a couple of lightwood knots on top of the little
chunk of glowing coal, and then I dragged some live-oak logs
over the top of the lightwood. In a minute the tiny teeth of
flame opened wide to eat the oak, and in five minutes I had a
blaze going, and I was practically in it.

Pretty soon the Old Man saw the fire dancing; he woke up
Mister Howard and reached for his pipe first and his boots
next. Tom and Pete were coming out of the other tent, digging
their knuckles into sleepy eyes. Pete went down to the branch
and fetched a bucket of water, and everybody washed their
faces out of the bucket. Then Pete slapped some ham into the
pan and some eggs into the skillet, got it over the fire, set some
bread to toasting, and put the coffeepot on. I can still taste
that coffee, with the condensed milk sweet curdled on the top
and the coffee itself tasting of branch water and wood smoke.
We got up and started sorting out the guns.

"This is a buckshot day," the Old Man said, squinting down the barrel of his pump gun. "I think we'd better get us a deer today. Need meat in the camp. Howard, we'll put the boy on a stand where a buck is apt to amble by, and then you and I will drift around. One, t'other of us ought to get a buck. This crick is populous with deer."

The Old Man paused to light his pipe, and then he turned around and pointed the stem at me.

"You, boy," he said. "By this time you know a lot about guns, but you don't know a lot about guns and deer together. Many a man loses his wits when he sees a big ol' buck bust out of the bushes with a rockin' chair on his head. Trained hunters shoot each other. They get overexcited and just bang away into the bushes.

"Mind what I say. A deer ain't a deer unless it's got horns on its head and you can see all of it at once. We don't shoot does and we don't shoot spike bucks and we don't shoot each other. You mind that gun and don't pull a trigger until you can see what it is and where it is."

Tom and Pete went over to where we had the dogs tethered on a line strung between two trees, and he unleashed the two hounds, Bell and Blue. Bell was black and tan and all hound. Blue had some plain hound, some Walker hound, and some bulldog and a little beagle and a smidgen of pointer in him. He was ticked blue and brown and black and yellow and white. He looked as if somebody spilled the eggs on the checkered tablecloth. But he was a dandy deer dog.

The Old Man picked up his gun and said, "Let's go." We walked about half a mile down the swamp's edge. The light had come now, lemon-colored, and the fox squirrels were beginning to chase each other through the gum trees. We spied one old possum in a persimmon tree, hunched into a ball and making out like nobody knew he was there. We heard a turkey gobble away over yonder somewheres, and we could hear the doves beginning to moan—oooh-oohoo-oooooh.

All the little birds started to squeak and chirp and twitter at each other. The dew was staunchly stiff on the grass and on the sparkleberry and gallberry bushes. It was still cold, but getting warmer, and breakfast had settled down real sturdy in my stomach. Rabbits jumped out from under our feet. There was a lot going on in that swamp that morning.

We turned into the branch finally and came up to a track that the Old Man said was a deer run. He looked around and spied a stump off to one side, hidden by a tangle of dead brush.

"Go sit on that stump, boy," the Old Man said. "You'll hear the dogs after a while, and if a deer comes down this branch he'll probably bust out there, where that trail comes out into the open, because there ain't any other way he can cross it without leaving the swamp.

"Don't let the dogs fool you into not paying attention. When you hear 'em a mile away, the chances are that deer will be right in your lap. Sometimes they travel as much as two miles ahead of the dogs, just slipping along. And stay still. A deer'll run right over you if you stay still and the smell is away from him. But if you wink an eye, he can see it two hundred yards off."

I sat down on the stump. The Old Man and Mister Howard went off, and I could hear them chatting quietly as they disappeared. I looked all around me. Nothing much was going on now, except a couple of he-squirrels were having a whale of a fight over my head, racing across branches and snarling squirrel cuss words at each other. A chickadee was standing on its head in a bush and making chickadee noises. There were some robins hopping around on a patch of burnt ground, making conversation with each other. A towhee was scratching and making more noise than a herd of turkeys. Anybody who says woods are quiet is crazy.

This was as nice a morning as I can remember. The sun was up pretty high now and was beginning to warm the world. The dew was starting to dry, because the grass wasn't clear

wet any more but just had little drops on top. I sat on the
stump for about a half hour, and then I heard the dogs start, a
mile or more down the swamp. Bell picked up the trail first,
and she sounded as if church had opened for business. Then
Blue came in behind her, loud as an organ, their two voices
blending.

Maybe you never heard a hound in the woods on a frosty
fall morning, with the breeze light, the sun heating up in the
sky, and the "aweful" expectancy that something big was
going to happen to you. There aren't many things like it.
When the baying gets closer and closer and still closer to you,
you feel as if maybe you're going to explode if something
doesn't happen quick.

Bell and Blue held the scent firmly now, and the deer was
moving steady and straight, not trying to circle and fool the
dogs, but coming straight down the path, with me on the
other end of it.

The dogs had come so close that you could hear them panting. I kept my eyes pinned onto where the deer path opened
into the clearing.

All of a sudden there was a flash of brown and two does,
flop-eared, with two half-grown fawns skipped out of the
brush, stopped dead in front of me, looked me smack in the
face, and then gave a tremendous leap that carried them half-
way across the clearing. They bounced again, white tails carried high, and disappeared into the branch behind me. As I
turned to watch them go there was another crash ahead and
the buck tore through the clearing like a race horse. He wasn't
jumping.

This boy was running like the wind, with his horns laid
back against his spine and his ears pinned by the breeze he
was making. The dogs were right behind him. He had held
back to tease the dogs into letting his family get a start, and
now that they were out of the way he was pouring on the coal
and heading for home.

I had a gun with me, but I just watched that big buck deer run, with my mouth open and my eyes popped out of my head.

The dogs tore out of the bush behind the buck, baying out their brains and covering the ground in leaps. Old Blue looked at me as he flashed past and curled his lip. He looked as if he were saying, "This is man's work, and what is a boy doing here, spoiling my labor?" Then he dived into the bush behind the buck.

I sat there on the stump and began to shake and tremble. About five minutes later there was one shot, a quarter mile down the swamp. I sat on the stump. In about half an hour Tom and Pete came up to my clearing.

"What happened to the buck?" Pete said. "Didn't he come past here? I thought I was going to run him right over you."

"He came past, all right," I said, feeling sick, "but I never shot. I never even thought about it until he was gone. I reckon that you all ain't ever going to take me along any more." My lip was shaking and now I was about to cry.

Tom walked over and cuffed me on top of the head with the flat of his hand. "Happens to everybody," he said. "Grown men and boys, both, they all get buck fever. Forget it."

There were some footsteps in the branch where the deer had disappeared, and in a minute Mister Howard and the Old Man came out, with the dogs leashed and panting.

"I missed him clean," the Old Man said cheerfully. "That's the way it is, but there's always tomorrow. Let's us go and shoot some squirrels for the pot, and we'll rest the dogs and try again this evening. You see him, boy?"

"I saw him," I said. "And I ain't ever going to *forget* him."

After lunch we stretched out in the shade and took a little nap. Along about two I woke up, and so did Pete and Tom, and the three of us started to skin the squirrels. The whole job didn't take forty-five minutes. Then we woke up the Old Man and Mister Howard. We were going deer hunting again.

We struck off for another part of the swamp, which made a

Y from the main swamp and had a lot of water in it. I was in the process of trying to think about just how long forever was when the hounds started to holler real close. They seemed to be coming straight down the crick off to my right.

The whoo-whooing got louder and louder, and I could hear a steady swishing in the bushes. It was a buck, a big one. He was running steadily and seriously through the low bush. He had horns, what horns! It looked to me like he had a dead tree lashed to his head. I slipped off the safety catch and didn't move. The buck came straight at me, the dogs going crazy behind him.

When he got to about fifty yards I stood up and threw the gun up to my face. He kept coming, and at about twenty-five yards he suddenly saw me, snorted, and jumped left, as if somebody had unsnapped a spring in him. I shot at him like at a duck or a quail on a quartering shot—plenty of lead ahead of his shoulder. The gun said boom! but I didn't hear it. The gun kicked, but I didn't feel it. All I saw was that this monster came down out of the sky like I'd shot me an airplane. He came down flat, turning completely over and landing on his back, and he never wiggled.

The dogs started to grab him, but they had sense and knew he didn't need any extra grabbing. I'd grabbed him real good. This was *my* buck. Nobody else had shot at him. Nobody else had seen him but me. Nobody had advised or helped. He was mine.

He had fourteen points on his rack and must have weighed nearly 150 pounds undressed. His horns were as clean as if they'd been scrubbed with a wire brush, gnarled and evenly forked and the color of planking on a good boat that's just been holystoned to where the decks sparkle.

I had him all to myself as he lay there in the aromatic, crushed ferns—alone in a big cathedral of oaks and cypress in a swamp where the doves made sobbing sounds and the late birds walked and talked in the sparkleberry bush. The dogs came up and lay down. Old Blue laid his muzzle on the big buck's back. Bell came over and licked my face and wagged her tail, like she was saying, "You did real good, boy."

I didn't know then that I was going to grow up and shoot elephants and lions and rhinos and things. All I knew then was that I was the richest boy in the world as I sat there in the crushed ferns and stroked the silky hide of my first buck deer.

I was still patting him and patting the dogs when Tom and Pete came up one way and the Old Man and Mister Howard came up from another way. What a wonderful thing it is when you are a kid to have four huge, grown men come roaring up out of the woods to see you sitting by your first big triumph. "Smug" is a word I learned a lot later. Smug was modest for what I felt then.

"Well," the Old Man said, trying not to grin.

"Boy done shot hisself a horse with horns," Pete said, as proud for me as if I had just learned how to make bootleg liquor.

"Shot him pretty good too," Tom said.

"It's a very good buck, son," the Old Man said softly, "one of which you can be very, very proud."

Tom and Pete cut a long sapling, made slits in the deer's legs behind the cartilage of his knees, stuck the sapling through the slits, and slung the deer up on their backs. They were sweating through the swamp when suddenly the Old Man turned to Mister Howard and said, "Howard, if you feel up to it, we might just as well go get *our* deer and lug him into camp."

"What deer?" I demanded. "You didn't shoot this afternoon, and you missed the one you—"

The Old Man grinned and made a show of lighting his pipe. "I didn't miss him," he said. "If you hadn't shot this one—and he's a lot better'n mine—I was just going to leave him in the tree and say nothing about him. Shame to waste a deer, but it's a shame to waste a boy too."

# THE SECRET OF GENERAL DELLA ROVERE

## by Indro Montanelli

Perhaps some of my readers have seen the highly praised, prize-winning Roberto Rossellini film, *General della Rovere*, starring Vittoria de Sica. The movie is based on an almost unbelievable but true story by the outstanding Italian journalist Indro Montanelli. During World War II Montanelli was a captain in the Italian Army. As he explains in this account, he came to know and watch Della Rovere when they occupied facing cells in Milan's unsavory San Vittore Prison. So fascinated was he by this strange character that after the war he wrote a long article about him for the Italian magazine *Il Borghese*. It caused a sensation. The story that follows is a shortened version of the original article.

That wartime spring of 1944 I had been six months in San Vittore, the gloomy prison of Milan. I was a captain in the Italian Army, but because I had refused to take orders from the German invaders, I was arrested by the Gestapo and thrust into a tiny cell in the political corridor of this wretched place of despair.

By right I was entitled to an officer's honorable treatment as a military prisoner. In fact, my dignity and pride were slowly chipped away by the interrogations of the SS and the hopelessness which all of us felt. And that is how it was on the

51

morning when General Braccioforte della Rovere was escorted
down our corridor to Cell 127, opposite my own.

I was past interest in new arrivals, but something about this
man, as I gazed listlessly through the peephole in my door,
caused fibers to stir that I had not known for weeks. He was
tall and thin, with close-cropped gray hair, an aquiline nose,
a narrow mustache, and, even in that gloomy corridor, I saw
a vagrant ray of light flash off the monocle he wore in his right
eye.

Though his dress showed no insignia of rank, it was easy to
see that he was someone important. And, if other evidence
were needed, when he turned before entering his cell and spoke
to Sergeant Franz, the brutal soldier who was our particular
jailer, the German actually stood at attention as he gave his
reply. When he turned and marched down the corridor, I
saw that the door of Cell 127 had been left unlocked.

It was Ceraso, one of the Italian guards, who told me the
story of our privileged companion when he brought me my
wretched lunch. General della Rovere, he said, was on the
staff of Marshal Badoglio and was technical adviser to the
commander of the Allied troops in Italy, General Alexander.
Two nights before a British submarine had put him ashore
near Genoa, where he was to take over command of the Resistance forces in the north. But the Germans, warned by a
traitor, had trapped him. It was quite obvious what fate lay in
store for him.

Sergeant Franz returned later that afternoon and opened
the door of the general's cell. With my ear against the peephole I heard Franz announce that the prisoner would be taken
for an interrogation at five o'clock. Then the general's voice
with its note of command said that he must be shaved first. I
shifted my eye to the peephole and saw Franz hesitate a moment, then turn back down the corridor. Presently he returned
with Banchelli, a linotyper by profession, who twice a month
shaved us and cut our hair.

Banchelli remained for some time in Cell 127, alone with

the general. I wondered if he had revealed what many of us suspected, that he was one of the Partisan leaders.

When the door of Cell 127 opened again, I saw Banchelli standing at attention as he took leave. The two men seemed to exchange a long, searching look before Franz, with his usual rough manner, led Banchelli away and then marched the general off to his interrogation.

When General della Rovere came back, an hour later, there was no change in his appearance. I guessed that the SS had drawn little satisfaction from the interview.

I was astonished next morning when Ceraso unlocked the door of my cell. "General della Rovere wishes to see you," he said. I crossed the corridor to Cell 127, and as I stepped inside I saw that the room had a washstand, a chair and a cot. The rest of us slept on bare planks. The general screwed the monocle in his eye and smiled gently.

"Captain Montanelli?" he said. "I knew before I landed that you were here. His Majesty's government is keenly interested in your fate. We are confident that even when you fall before a German firing squad you will fulfill your most elementary duty as an officer." He paused for a moment.

"We officers all lead provisional lives, do we not?" he continued. "And especially in this time of our country's cruel partition. An officer is, so to speak, a bridegroom of the Goddess Death. *Novio de la muerte*, I believe the Spanish call it." Then his manner became more urgent. "You have not talked, I am sure," he said, "and I urge you to persist in this silence. But should you undergo torture—I don't mean to question your moral strength, but there are limits to physical endurance —I suggest that you give them just one name: mine. Tell them that whatever you did, you were acting under my orders. Now tell me—what are the charges against you?"

His eyes never wavered from mine as I poured out my story, and when I had finished he nodded again. "Your case is as clear-cut as mine," he told me. "Our only remaining duty is to die as officers. It should be easy to die decently."

When Ceraso came for me, I stepped back a pace and my hand came up in a smart salute which the general returned. Going back to my cell, I made Ceraso promise to send me Banchelli the next day to shave me and to cut my hair.

A curious change came over our corridor in the days that followed. I saw many prisoners enter the general's cell, and each one emerged a different man. He had retrieved something of his soldierly bearing under the eyes of this sturdy patriot whose name seemed to fit him so superbly, for "*della rovere*" means "of the oak." It was apparent from the quickened step which replaced the slouching walk of the men during their brief exercise periods in the courtyard.

But then a rumor began sifting through the corridor, and I suppose it was inevitable in that place where no one had been trusted before: the general was a stool pigeon, secretly in league with the SS. All of us had told him our inmost secrets. What was to prevent him from passing these on to the Gestapo? I could not imagine that this stern-visaged soldier was an informer. But that night I was sleepless with dread.

Even the Italian guards were infected by the rumor. They listened outside the door next morning while Della Rovere talked with a major who was supposed to know a great deal about the Partisan forces. Ceraso repeated to me later, with relief and almost with tears, what he and the others had heard the general say.

"You will undergo extreme torture," he had told the major in a stern voice which still had the kindly quality of a priest in the confessional. "Keep your mind blank. Force yourself to believe that you know nothing. If you are driven to speak, tell them that whatever you did you did on my orders."

That afternoon I passed these words to the men in the courtyard, and eyes that had been fearful became clear again—and determined, now that faith had been restored. I am convinced that from this day forward the Gestapo got no confessions from the men in San Vittore. It meant death for some. We knew that from the volleys in the courtyard.

But now these men could face death with honor and a soldier's comfort that they had not failed in their trust or in the sense of duty which General della Rovere had instilled once more in their spirits.

A few days later I underwent interrogation again, and Della Rovere's words to the major were all I heard through the barking of the SS men. They did not torture me, but I am confident that if they had I would not have broken. Ceraso brought me back, and I begged him to let me stop at Cell 127. The general put down the book he had been reading.

"Yes, that's what I expected you to do," he said after he had searched my face. "I am well satisfied, Captain!"

These were the last words I heard General della Rovere utter. The next day they took him away before dawn. It was weeks later, after I had been liberated with the others in San Vittore during the confusion of the Allied drive northward, that I learned the fate of this imperturbable man.

I could believe entirely in the story of his death in the massacre at Fossoli Prison on June 22, 1944. With sixty-seven Italian officers he was led into the courtyard where four machine guns were set up to perform the mass execution. They told me that just before the order was given to fire he screwed the monocle in his eye and spoke to his companions.

"Gentlemen, officers. As we face the ultimate sacrifice, may our thoughts turn faithfully toward our beloved country. V*iva* *l'Italia!* Long live the King!"

Yes, I could believe that this was the way the man of oak would choose to die. But even now, fifteen years later, it is hard for me to believe the rest of the story about General Braccioforte della Rovere. It is fact, so I must tell it, but it is surely one of the strangest revelations to come out of that World War.

The man who had put the oaken fiber into the San Vittore prisoners by infusing them with his uncompromising sense of an officer's duty was no general. He was not even in the army.

He was Giovanni Bertone, a jailbird, a black marketeer, a

thief. The Germans had arrested him for stealing. Once they had him in custody, they were impressed by the fact that the man was an extraordinary mimic, a superb actor. And this gave them the idea that they could use him as a stool pigeon to draw confessions from the stubborn prisoners of San Vittore.

They offered him his liberty on condition that he would serve as an informer, and Bertone readily agreed. They dressed him up—a German officer gave him his monocle—and rehearsed him in the role of the fictitious General della Rovere, friend and adviser of Badoglio and Alexander. Then they sent him off with confidence that he would trick us all into confessions.

Did Bertone accept his commission knowing even then what he intended to do? Or did the grand impersonation grow on him gradually until, in his own mind, he *became* General della Rovere? I was one of the first prisoners to talk with him, and I am convinced that he had already been transformed into a dedicated patriot. He was determined to write his death sentence by making San Vittore confession-proof.

At Fossoli on the day of the massacre, I was told by an eyewitness, a lieutenant named Tito read out the names of those who were to be executed. Each man was to step forward as his name was read. When Tito called out, "Bertone," there was no response.

The lieutenant looked up and said mockingly, "Isn't Bertone present? Then what about General della Rovere?"

At once this amazing man stepped forward, clicked his heels, and saluted.

Even though he had tricked them, the Germans evidently had the respect for Bertone which soldiers everywhere reserve for a true patriot. The monocle lay near him on the ground where it fell. As the sunlight of that June day glinted from it, someone noticed and picked it up. Before they buried him, a German soldier put it where it belonged—in the right eye of General della Rovere.

# THE FIFTY-FIRST DRAGON

## by Heywood Broun

Somebody once said that in every fat man there's a thin man clamoring to be let out. The journalist and critic Heywood Broun, who died in 1939, was not exactly fat. But he was big—a big-framed, big-hearted, shambling bear of a man, who looked, as someone phrased it, like an unmade bed. He too carried a thin man inside him, clamoring to be let out. The thin man's name was Don Quixote.

Most of us think of fairy tales as something for children, but some of them are written for adults too. Broun's "The Fifty-first Dragon" is one of them—you may remember that it figured prominently in Evan Hunter's novel, *The Blackboard Jungle*. Rick, the schoolteacher, reads it to his class of tough teen-age boys—and stirs them into some surprising realizations.

For this kidding fairy tale is backed with wisdom. What does self-confidence really spring from? From a real self-knowledge? Or from faith, a magic word, "Rumplesnitz"? In Gawaine's case "Rumplesnitz" was good for forty-nine dragons. He didn't seem to need it for the fiftieth. But how about that fifty-first?

A funny thing, self-confidence. Maybe too much truth can undermine it.

Of all the pupils at the Knight School Gawaine le Coeur-Hardy was among the least promising. He was tall and sturdy, but his instructors soon discovered that he lacked spirit. He would hide in the woods when the jousting class was called, although his companions and members of the faculty sought to appeal to his better nature by shouting to him to come out and break his neck like a man. Even when they told him that the lances were padded, the horses no more than ponies, and the field unusually soft for late autumn, Gawaine refused to grow enthusiastic. The headmaster and the assistant professor of Pleasaunce were discussing the case one spring afternoon, and the assistant professor could see no remedy but expulsion.

"No," said the headmaster, as he looked out at the purple hills which ringed the school, "I think I'll train him to slay dragons."

"He might be killed," objected the assistant professor.

"So he might," replied the headmaster brightly, but he added, more soberly, "we must consider the greater good. We are responsible for the formation of this lad's character."

"Are the dragons particularly bad this year?" interrupted the assistant professor. He always seemed restive when the head of the school began to talk ethics and the ideals of the institution.

"I've never known them worse," replied the headmaster. "Up in the hills to the south last week they killed a number of peasants, two cows, and a prize pig. And if this dry spell holds there's no telling when they may start a forest fire simply by breathing around indiscriminately."

"Would any refund on the tuition fee be necessary in case of an accident to young Coeur-Hardy?"

"No," the headmaster answered judicially, "that's all covered in the contract. But as a matter of fact he won't be killed. Before I send him up in the hills I'm going to give him a magic word."

"That's a good idea," said the professor. "Sometimes they work wonders."

From that day on Gawaine specialized in dragons. His course included both theory and practice. In the morning there were long lectures on the history, anatomy, manners, and customs of dragons. Gawaine did not distinguish himself in these studies. He had a marvelously versatile gift for forgetting things.

Afternoons he showed to better advantage, for then he would go down to the South Meadow and practice with a battle-ax. In this exercise he was truly impressive, for he had enormous strength as well as speed and grace. He even developed a deceptive display of ferocity. Old alumni say that it was a thrilling sight to see Gawaine charging across the field toward the dummy paper dragon which had been set up for his practice. As he ran he would brandish his ax and shout, "A murrain on thee!" or some other vivid bit of campus slang. It never took him more than one stroke to behead the dummy dragon.

Gradually his task was made more difficult. Paper gave way to papier-mâché and finally to wood, but even the toughest of these dummy dragons had no terrors for Gawaine. One sweep of the ax always did the business. There were those who said that when the practice was protracted until dusk and the dragons threw long, fantastic shadows across the meadow Gawaine did not charge so impetuously or shout so loudly. It is possible there was malice in this charge. At any rate, the headmaster decided by the end of June that it was time for the test. Only a night before a dragon had come close to the school grounds and had eaten some of the lettuce from the garden. The faculty decided that Gawaine was ready. They gave him a diploma and a new battle-ax and the headmaster summoned him to a private conference.

"Sit down," said the headmaster. "Have a cigarette."

Gawaine hesitated.

"Oh, I know it's against the rules," said the headmaster. "But after all, you have received your preliminary degree. You are no longer a boy. You are a man. Tomorrow you will go out into the world, the great world of achievement."

Gawaine took a cigarette. The headmaster offered him a match, but he produced one of his own and began to puff away with a dexterity which quite amazed the headmaster.

"Here you have learned the theories of life," continued the headmaster, resuming the thread of his discourse, "but after all, life is not a matter of theories. Life is a matter of facts. It calls on the young and the old alike to face these facts, even though they are sometimes unpleasant. Your problem, for example, is to slay dragons."

"They say that those dragons down in the south wood are five hundred feet long," ventured Gawaine timorously.

"Stuff and nonsense!" said the headmaster. "The curate saw one last week from the top of Arthur's Hill. He said the monster—or shall I say the big lizard?—wasn't an inch over two hundred feet. But the size has nothing at all to do with it. You'll find the big ones even easier than the little ones. They're far slower on their feet and less aggressive, I'm told. Besides, before you go I'm going to equip you in such a fashion that you need have no fear of all the dragons in the world."

"I'd like an enchanted cap," said Gawaine.

"What's that?" answered the headmaster testily.

"A cap to make me disappear," explained Gawaine.

The headmaster laughed indulgently. "You mustn't believe all those old wives' stories," he said. "There isn't any such thing. A cap to make you disappear, indeed! What would you do with it? You haven't even appeared yet. Why, my boy, you could walk from here to London, and nobody would so much as look at you. You're nobody. You couldn't be more invisible than that."

Gawaine seemed dangerously close to a relapse into his old habit of whimpering. The headmaster reassured him, "Don't worry. I'll give you something much better than an enchanted cap. I'm going to give you a magic word. All you have to do is repeat this magic charm once and no dragon can possibly harm a hair of your head. You can cut off his head at your leisure."

He took a heavy book from the shelf behind his desk and began to run through it. "Sometimes," he said, "the charm is a whole phrase or even a sentence. I might, for instance, give you 'To make the'— No, that might not do. I think a single word would be best for dragons."

"A short word," suggested Gawaine.

"It can't be too short or it wouldn't be potent. There isn't so much hurry as all that. Here's a splendid magic word— 'Rumplesnitz.' Do you think you can learn that?"

Gawaine tried, and in an hour or so he seemed to have the word well in hand. Again and again he interrupted the lesson to inquire, "And if I say 'Rumplesnitz' the dragon can't possibly hurt me?" And always the headmaster replied, "If you only say 'Rumplesnitz,' you are perfectly safe."

Toward morning Gawaine seemed resigned to his career. At daybreak the headmaster saw him to the edge of the forest and pointed him to the direction in which he should proceed. About a mile away to the southwest a cloud of steam hovered over an open meadow in the woods, and the headmaster assured Gawaine that under the steam he would find a dragon. Gawaine went forward slowly. He wondered whether it would be best to approach the dragon on the run as he did in his practice in the South Meadow or to walk slowly toward him, shouting "Rumplesnitz" all the way.

The problem was decided for him. No sooner had he come to the fringe of the meadow than the dragon spied him and began to charge. It was a large dragon, and yet it seemed decidedly aggressive in spite of the headmaster's statement to the contrary. As the dragon charged it released huge clouds of hissing steam through its nostrils. It was almost as if a gigantic teapot had gone mad. The dragon came forward so fast and Gawaine was so frightened that he had time to say "Rumplesnitz" only once. As he said it, he swung his battle-ax and off popped the head of the dragon.

Gawaine had to admit that it was even easier to kill a real dragon than a wooden one if only you said "Rumplesnitz."

Gawaine brought the ears home and a small section of the tail. His schoolmates and the faculty made much of him, but the headmaster wisely kept him from being spoiled by insisting that he go on with his work. Every clear day Gawaine rose at dawn and went out to kill dragons. The headmaster kept him at home when it rained, because he said the woods were damp and unhealthy at such times and that he didn't want the boy to run needless risks.

Few good days passed in which Gawaine failed to get a dragon. On one particularly fortunate day he killed three, a husband and wife and a visiting relative. Gradually he developed a technique. Pupils who sometimes watched him from the hilltops a long way off said that he often allowed the dragon to come within a few feet before he said "Rumplesnitz." He came to say it with a mocking sneer. Occasionally he did stunts. Once when an excursion party from London was watching him he went into action with his right hand tied behind his back. The dragon's head came off just as easily.

As Gawaine's record of killings mounted higher the headmaster found it impossible to keep him completely in hand. He fell into the habit of stealing out at night and engaging in long drinking bouts at the village tavern. It was after such a debauch that he rose a little before dawn one fine August morning and started out after his fiftieth dragon. His head was heavy and his mind sluggish. He was heavy in other respects as well, for he had adopted the somewhat vulgar practice of wearing his medals, ribbons and all, when he went out dragon hunting. The decorations began on his chest and ran all the way down to his abdomen. They must have weighed at least eight pounds.

Gawaine found a dragon in the same meadow where he had killed the first one. It was a fair-sized dragon, but evidently an old one. Its face was wrinkled, and Gawaine thought he had never seen so hideous a countenance. Much to the lad's disgust, the monster refused to charge and Gawaine was obliged to walk toward him. He whistled as he went. The dragon regarded him hopelessly, but craftily. Of course it had heard of Gawaine. Even when the lad raised his battle-ax the dragon made no move. It knew that there was no salvation in the quickest thrust of the head, for it had been informed that this hunter was protected by an enchantment. It merely waited, hoping something would turn up.

Gawaine raised the battle-ax and suddenly lowered it again. He had grown very pale. The dragon suspected a trick. "What's the matter?" it asked, with false solicitude.

"I've forgotten the magic word," stammered Gawaine.

"What a pity," said the dragon. "So that was the secret. It doesn't seem quite sporting to me, all this magic stuff, you know. Not cricket, as we used to say when I was a little dragon. But after all, that's a matter of opinion."

Gawaine was so helpless with terror that the dragon's confidence rose immeasurably and it could not resist the temptation to show off a bit.

"Could I possibly be of any assistance?" it asked. "What's the first letter of the magic word?"

"It begins with an 'r,' " said Gawaine weakly.

"Let's see," mused the dragon, "that doesn't tell us much, does it? What sort of a word is this? Is it an epithet, do you think?"

Gawaine could do no more than nod.

"Why, of course," exclaimed the dragon, "reactionary Republican."

Gawaine shook his head.

"Well, then," said the dragon, "we'd better get down to business. Will you surrender?"

With the suggestion of a compromise Gawaine mustered up enough courage to speak.

"What will you do if I surrender?" he asked.

"Why, I'll eat you," said the dragon.

"And if I don't surrender?"

"I'll eat you just the same."

"Then it doesn't make any difference, does it?" moaned Gawaine.

"It does to me," said the dragon with a smile. "I'd rather you didn't surrender. You'd taste much better if you didn't."

The dragon waited for a long time for Gawaine to ask "Why?" but the boy was too frightened to speak. At last the dragon had to give the explanation without his cue line. "You see," he said, "if you don't surrender you'll taste better because you'll die game."

This was an old and ancient trick of the dragon's. By means of some such quip he was accustomed to paralyze his victims with laughter and then to destroy them. Gawaine was sufficiently paralyzed as it was, but laughter had no part in his helplessness. With the last word of the joke the dragon drew back his head and struck. In that second there flashed into the mind of Gawaine the magic word "Rumplesnitz," but there was no time to say it. There was time only to strike, and without a word Gawaine met the onrush of the dragon with a full swing. He put all his back and shoulders into it. The impact was terrific, and the head of the dragon flew away almost a hundred yards and landed in a thicket.

Gawaine did not remain frightened very long after the death of the dragon. His mood was one of wonder. He was enormously puzzled. He cut off the ears of the monster almost in a trance. Again and again he thought to himself, "I didn't say 'Rumplesnitz'!" He was sure of that, and yet there was no question that he had killed the dragon. All the way back to the Knight School he kept rumbling about in his mind, seeking an explanation for what had occurred. He went to the headmaster immediately and, after closing the door, told him what happened. "I didn't say 'Rumplesnitz,' he explained with great earnestness.

The headmaster laughed. "I'm glad you've found out," he said. "It makes you ever so much more of a hero. Don't you see that? Now you know that it was you who killed all these dragons and not that foolish little word 'Rumplesnitz.' "

Gawaine frowned. "Then it wasn't a magic word after all?" he asked.

"Of course not," said the headmaster. "You ought to be too old for such foolishness. There isn't any such thing as a magic word."

"But you told me it was magic," protested Gawaine. "You said it was magic and now you say it isn't."

"It wasn't magic in a literal sense," answered the headmaster, "but it was much more wonderful than that. The word gave you confidence. It took away your fears. If I hadn't told you that you might have been killed the very first time. It was your battle-ax did the trick."

Gawaine surprised the headmaster by his attitude. He was obviously distressed by the explanation. He interrupted a long philosophic and ethical discourse by the headmaster with, "If I hadn't of hit 'em all mighty hard and fast any one of 'em might have crushed me like a, like a—" He fumbled for a word.

"Eggshell," suggested the headmaster.

"Like a eggshell," assented Gawaine, and he said it many times. All through the evening meal people who sat near him heard him muttering, "Like a eggshell, like a eggshell."

The next day was clear, but Gawaine did not get up at dawn. Indeed, it was almost noon when the headmaster found him cowering in bed, with the clothes pulled over his head. The principal called the assistant professor of Pleasaunce, and together they dragged the boy toward the forest.

"He'll be all right as soon as he gets a couple more dragons under his belt," explained the headmaster.

The assistant professor of Pleasaunce agreed. "It would be a shame to stop such a fine run," he said. "Why, counting that one yesterday, he's killed fifty dragons."

They pushed the boy into a thicket above which hung a meager cloud of steam. It was obviously quite a small dragon. But Gawaine did not come back that night or the next. In fact, he never came back. Some weeks afterward brave spirits from the school explored the thicket, but they could find nothing to remind them of Gawaine except the metal parts of his medals. Even the ribbons had been devoured.

The headmaster and the assistant professor of Pleasaunce agreed that it would be just as well not to tell the school how Gawaine had achieved his record and still less how he came to die. They held that it might have a bad effect on school spirit. Accordingly Gawaine has lived in the memory of the school as its greatest hero. No visitor succeeds in leaving the building today without seeing a great shield which hangs on the wall of the dining room. Fifty pairs of dragons' ears are mounted upon the shield, and underneath in gilt letters is "Gawaine le Coeur-Hardy," followed by the simple inscription, "He killed fifty dragons." The record has never been equaled.

# THE NIGHT BEFORE
# THE LONGEST DAY

## by Cornelius Ryan

Many books have already been written about D-Day, and there will be more. But for some time to come Cornelius Ryan's *The Longest Day* will stand unrivaled. I admire it because it checks all available facts, discloses some important new ones, and makes absolutely real the sensations of the individual soldier as he assumes his role in one of the most crucial events of his century.

Mr. Ryan's book has had a phenomenal career. A best seller from publication late in 1959, it sold nearly 80,000 copies in its first six months. Publication rights have been bought in eight countries.

This excerpt from his book tells how the day began, with all its vastness, its tensions, its fears, its hopes. I think it a remarkable piece of writing.

Off the French coast a little before 9 P.M. a dozen small ships appeared. They moved quietly along the horizon, so close that their crews could clearly see the houses of Normandy. The ships went unnoticed. They finished their job and then moved back. They were British mine sweepers, the vanguard of the mightiest fleet ever assembled.

For now back in the Channel, plowing through the choppy gray waters, a phalanx of ships bore down on Hitler's Europe

—the might and fury of the free world unleashed at last. They
came, rank after relentless rank, ten lanes wide, twenty miles
across, 5,000 ships of every description.

There were fast new attack transports, slow rust-scarred
freighters, small ocean liners, Channel steamers, hospital ships,
weather-beaten tankers, coasters, and swarms of fussing tugs.
There were endless columns of shallow-draft landing ships,
great wallowing vessels, some of them almost 350 feet long.
Many of these and the other heavier transports carried smaller
landing craft for the actual beach assault—more than 1,500 of
them. Ahead of the convoys were processions of mine sweepers, Coast Guard cutters, buoy layers, and motor launches.
Barrage balloons flew above the ships. Squadrons of fighter
planes weaved below the clouds. And surrounding this fantastic cavalcade of ships packed with men, guns, tanks, motor
vehicles, and supplies, and excluding small naval vessels, was
a formidable array of 702 warships.

There was the heavy cruiser U.S.S. *Augusta*, Rear Admiral
Kirk's flagship, leading the American task force—twenty-one
convoys bound for Omaha and Utah beaches. Just four
months before Pearl Harbor the queenly *Augusta* had carried
President Roosevelt to a quiet Newfoundland bay for the first
of his many historic meetings with Winston Churchill. Nearby, steaming majestically with all their battle flags flying, were
the battleships H.M.S. *Nelson*, *Ramillies*, and *Warspite*, and
U.S.S. *Texas*, *Arkansas*, and the proud *Nevada* which the
Japanese had sunk and written off at Pearl Harbor.

Leading the thirty-eight British and Canadian convoys
bound for Sword, Juno and Gold beaches was the cruiser
H.M.S. *Scylla*, the flagship of Rear Admiral Sir Philip Vian,
the man who tracked down the German battleship *Bismarck*.
And close by was H.M.S. *Ajax*, one of the trio that fought the
*Graf Spee*. There were other famous cruisers—the U.S.S. *Tus-
caloosa* and *Quincy*, H.M.S. *Enterprise* and *Black Prince*,
France's *Georges Leygues*—twenty-two in all.

Along the edges of the convoys sailed a variety of ships: graceful sloops, chunky corvettes, slim gunboats like the Dutch *Soemba*, antisubmarine patrol craft, fast PT boats, and everywhere sleek destroyers.

Slowly, ponderously this great armada moved across the Channel. It followed a minute-by-minute traffic pattern of a kind never attempted before. Ships poured out of British ports and, moving down the coasts in two-convoy lanes, converged on the assembly area south of the Isle of Wight. There they sorted themselves out and each took a carefully predetermined position with the force heading for the particular beach to which it had been assigned. Out of the assembly area, which was promptly nicknamed "Piccadilly Circus," the convoys headed for France along five buoy-marked lanes. And as they approached Normandy these five paths split up into ten channels, two for each beach—one for fast traffic, the other for slow. Up front, just behind the spearhead of mine sweepers, battleships, and cruisers, were the command ships, five attack transports bristling with radar and radio antennae. These floating command posts would be the nerve centers of the invasion.

For the troops it was good to be on the way at last, despite the discomforts and the dangers ahead. Men were still tense, but some of the strain had lifted. Now everybody simply wanted to get the job over and done with. On the landing ships and transports men wrote last-minute letters, played cards, joined in bull sessions. "Chaplains," Major Thomas Spencer Dallas of the 29th Division recalls, "did a land-office business."

One minister on a jam-packed landing craft, Captain Lewis Fulmer Koon, chaplain for the 4th Division's 12th Infantry Regiment, found himself serving as pastor for all denominations. A Jewish officer, Captain Irving Gray, asked Chaplain Koon if he would lead his company in prayer "to the God in whom we all believe, whether Protestant, Roman Catholic, or Jew, that our mission may be accomplished and that, if possible, we may be brought safely home again." Koon gladly obliged.

And in the gathering dusk, Gunner's Mate Third Class William Sweeney of a Coast Guard cutter remembers, the attack transport *Samuel Chase* blinked out a signal, "Mass is going on."

For most of the men the first few hours of the journey were spent quietly. Many grew introspective and talked of things men usually keep to themselves. Hundreds later recalled that they found themselves admitting their fears and talking of other personal matters with unusual candor. They drew closer to one another on this strange night and confided in men they had never even met before.

"We talked a lot about home and what it would all be like at the landing," Pfc. Earlston Hern of the 146th Engineer Battalion recalls. On the slippery wet deck of his landing craft Hern and a medic whose name he never learned had such a conversation. "The medic was having trouble at home. His wife, a model, wanted a divorce. He was a pretty worried guy. He said she'd have to wait until he got home. I remember, too, that the whole time we were talking there was a young kid nearby singing softly to himself. This kid made the remark that he could sing better than he ever had in the past, and it really seemed to please him."

Aboard H.M.S. *Empire Anvil,* Corporal Michael Kurtz of the U.S. 1st Division, a veteran of the invasions of North Africa, Sicily, and Italy, was approached by a new replacement, Private Joseph Steinber of Wisconsin.

"Corporal," said Steinber, "do you honestly think we've got a chance?"

"Hell, yes, boy," said Kurtz. "Don't ever worry about getting killed. In this outfit we worry about battles when we get to them."

Sergeant Bill "L-Rod" Petty of the 2nd Ranger Battalion was doing his worrying now. With his friend, Pfc. Bill Mc-

Hugh, Petty sat on the deck of the old Channel steamer *Isle of Man*, watching the darkness close in. Petty took cold comfort from the long lines of ships all about them; his mind was on the cliffs at Pointe du Hoc. Turning to McHugh, he said, "We haven't got a hope in hell of coming out of this alive."

"You're just a goddamn pessimist," said McHugh.

"Maybe," replied Petty, "but only one of us will make it, Mac."

McHugh was unimpressed. "When you gotta go, you gotta go," he said.

Some men tried to read. Corporal Alan Bodet of the 1st Division began *Kings Row* by Henry Bellamann, but he found it difficult to concentrate because he was worrying about his jeep. Would the waterproofing hold out when he drove it into three or four feet of water? Gunner Arthur Henry Boon of the Canadian 3rd Division, on board a landing craft loaded with tanks, tried to get through a pocket book intriguingly titled *A Maid and a Million Men*.

Chaplain Lawrence E. Deery of the 1st Division, aboard the transport H.M.S. *Empire Anvil*, was amazed to see a British naval officer reading Horace's odes in Latin. But Deery himself, who would land on Omaha Beach in the first wave with the 16th Infantry Regiment, spent the evening reading Symonds' *Life of Michelangelo*. In another convoy, on a landing craft which was rolling so much that nearly everybody was seasick, Captain James Douglas Gillan, another Canadian, brought out the one volume which made sense this night. To quiet his own nerves and those of a brother officer he opened to the Twenty-third Psalm and read aloud, "The Lord is my Shepherd; I shall not want. . . ."

It wasn't all solemn. There was lightheartedness too. Aboard the transport H.M.S. *Ben Machree* some Rangers strung three-quarter-inch ropes from the masts to the decks and began climbing all over the ship, much to the astonishment of the British crew. On another ship members of the

Canadian 3rd Division held an amateur night with assorted recitations, jigs and reels, and choral offerings. Sergeant James Percival "Paddy" de Lacy of the King's Regiment became so emotional listening to the "Rose of Tralee" played on the bagpipes that he forgot where he was and stood up and offered a toast to Ireland's Eamon de Valera for "keepin' us out of the war."

Many men who had spent hours worrying about their chances of survival now couldn't wait to reach the beaches. The boat trip was proving more terrible than their worst fear of the Germans. Seasickness had struck through the fifty-nine convoys like a plague.

Because of the seasickness thousands of the men lost the best meals they would see for many months to come. Special arrangements had been made to give all ships the finest food possible. The special menus, which the troops dubbed the "last meal," varied from ship to ship, and appetites varied from man to man. On board the attack transport *Charles Carroll*, Captain Carroll B. Smith of the 29th Division had a steak with eggs on top, sunny side up, and then topped it off with ice cream and loganberries. Two hours later he was fighting for a position at the rail. Second Lieutenant Joseph Rosenblatt, Jr., of the 112th Engineer Battalion ate seven helpings of chicken à la king and felt fine. So did Sergeant Keith Bryan of the 5th Engineer Special Brigade. He put away sandwiches and coffee and was still hungry. One of his buddies "lifted" a gallon of fruit cocktail from the galley, and four of them finished that.

Aboard the H.M.S. *Prince Charles*, Sergeant Avery J. Thornhill of the 5th Rangers avoided all discomforts. He took an overdose of seasick pills and slept through it all.

Despite the common miseries and fears of the men who were there, some memories are etched with surprising clarity. Second Lieutenant Donald Anderson of the 29th Division remembers how the sun broke through about an hour before dark, silhouetting the entire fleet. In honor of Sergeant Tom Ryan of the 2nd Rangers, the men of F Company gathered around him and sang "Happy Birthday." He was twenty-two. And for homesick nineteen-year-old Private Robert Marion Allen of the 1st Division it was "a night ready-made for a boat ride on the Mississippi."

All over, throughout the ships of the fleet, the men who would make history at dawn settled down to get what rest they could. As Commander Philippe Kieffer of the lone French commando unit rolled himself into his blankets aboard his landing ship, there came to his mind the prayer of Sir Jacob Astley at the Battle of Edgehill in England in 1642. "O Lord," prayed Kieffer, "Thou knowest how busy I must be this day. If I forget Thee, do not Thou forget me. . . ." He drew up the blankets and was almost immediately asleep.

# THE CONVICT
# AND THE BISHOP

## by Victor Hugo

Here is a famous excerpt from *Les Misérables,* describing the first encounter of the convict Jean Valjean with the saintly bishop, Monseigneur Bienvenu. The prose is old-fashioned and so is the translation, but I think a certain simple nobility of spirit comes through. For many years this was a favorite platform recitation in the days of our grandfathers. It is interesting to see how it will hold up today, with an audience of children accustomed to the vulgarity and violence of TV rather than to Victor Hugo's note of simple Christianity.

At this moment there was a violent knock on the door.

"Come in!" said the bishop.

The door opened.

It opened quickly, quite wide, as if pushed by someone boldly and with energy.

A man entered.

He came in, took one step, and paused, leaving the door open behind him. He had his knapsack on his back, his stick in his hand, and a rough, hard, tired, and fierce look in his eyes, as seen by the firelight. He was hideous. It was an apparition of ill omen.

Madame Magloire had not even the strength to scream. She stood trembling with her mouth open.

Mademoiselle Baptistine turned, saw the man enter, and started up half alarmed; then, slowly turning back again toward the fire, she looked at her brother, and her face resumed its usual calmness and serenity.

The bishop looked upon the man with a tranquil eye.

As he was opening his mouth to speak, doubtless to ask the stranger what he wanted, the man, leaning with both hands on his club, glanced from one to another in turn and, without waiting for the bishop to speak, said in a loud voice:

"See here! My name is Jean Valjean. I am a convict; I have been nineteen years in the galleys. Four days ago I was set free and started for Pontarlier, which is my destination; during those four days I have walked from Toulon. Today I have walked twelve leagues. When I reached this place this evening I went to an inn, and they sent me away on account of my yellow passport, which I had shown at the mayor's office, as was necessary. I went to another inn; they said: 'Get out!' It was the same with one as with another; nobody would have me. I went to the prison, and the turnkey would not let me in. I crept into a dog kennel; the dog bit me and drove me away as if he had been a man; you would have said that he knew who I was. I went into the fields to sleep beneath the stars: there were no stars; I thought it would rain, and there was no good God to stop the drops, so I came back to the town to get the shelter of some doorway. There in the square I lay down upon a stone; a good woman showed me your house and said: 'Knock there!' I have knocked. What is this place? Are you an inn? I have money; my savings, one hundred and nine francs and fifteen sous which I have earned in the galleys by my work for nineteen years. I will pay. What do I care? I have money. I am very tired—twelve leagues on foot! and I am so hungry. Can I stay?"

"Madame Magloire," said the bishop, "put on another plate."

The man took three steps and came near the lamp which stood on the table. "Stop," he exclaimed, as if he had not been understood, "not that, did you understand me? I am a galley-slave—a convict—I am just from the galleys." He drew from his pocket a large sheet of yellow paper, which he unfolded. "There is my passport, yellow, as you see. That is enough to have me kicked out wherever I go. Will you read it? I know how to read, I do. I learned in the galleys. There is a school there for those who care for it. See, here is what they have put in the passport: 'Jean Valjean, a liberated convict, native of ——,' you don't care for that, 'has been nineteen years in the galleys; five years for burglary; fourteen years for having attempted four times to escape. This man is very dangerous.' There you have it! Everybody has thrust me out; will you receive me? Is this an inn? Can you give me something to eat and a place to sleep? Have you a stable?"

"Madame Magloire," said the bishop, "put some sheets on the bed in the alcove."

Madame Magloire went out to fulfil her orders.

The bishop turned to the man.

"Monsieur, sit down and warm yourself: we are going to take supper presently, and your bed will be made ready while you sup."

At last the man quite understood; his face, the expression of which till then had been gloomy and hard, now expressed stupefaction, doubt, and joy, and became absolutely wonderful. He began to stutter like a madman.

"True? What! You will keep me? you won't drive me away? a convict! You call me *Monsieur* and don't say 'Get out, dog!' as everybody else does. I thought that you would send me away, so I told first off who I am. Oh! the fine woman who sent me here! I shall have a supper! a bed like other people with mattress and sheets—a bed! It is nineteen years that I have not slept on a bed. You are really willing that I should stay? You are good people! Besides, I have money: I will pay well. I beg your pardon, Monsieur Innkeeper, what is your name? I will pay all you say. You are a fine man. You are an innkeeper, aren't you?"

"I am a priest who lives here," said the bishop.

"A priest," said the man. "Oh, noble priest! Then you do not ask any money? You are the curé, aren't you? the curé of this big church? Yes, that's it. How stupid I am; I didn't notice your cap."

While speaking, he had deposited his knapsack and stick in the corner, replaced his passport in his pocket, and sat down. Mademoiselle Baptistine looked at him pleasantly. He continued:

"You are humane, Monsieur Curé; you don't despise me. A good priest is a good thing. Then you don't want me to pay you?"

"No," said the bishop, "keep your money. How much have you? You said a hundred and nine francs, I think."

"And fifteen sous," added the man.

"One hundred and nine francs and fifteen sous. And how long did it take you to earn that?"

"Nineteen years."

"Nineteen years!"

The bishop sighed deeply.

The man continued: "I have all my money yet. In four days I have spent only twenty-five sous which I earned by unloading wagons at Grasse. As you are an abbé, I must tell you, we have an almoner in the galleys. And then one day I saw a bishop; monseigneur, they called him. It was the Bishop of Majore from Marseilles. He is the curé who is over the curés. You see —beg pardon, how I bungle saying it, but for me, it is so far off! you know what we are. He said mass in the center of the place on an altar; he had a pointed gold thing on his head that shone in the sun; it was noon. We were drawn up in line on three sides, with cannons and matches lighted before us. We could not see him well. He spoke to us, but he was not near enough, we did not understand him. That is what a bishop is."

While he was talking, the bishop shut the door, which he had left wide open.

Madame Magloire brought in a plate and set it on the table.

"Madame Magloire," said the bishop, "put this plate as near the fire as you can." Then turning toward his guest, he added: "The night wind is raw in the Alps; you must be cold, monsieur."

Every time he said this word monsieur, with his gently solemn and heartily hospitable voice, the man's countenance lighted up. *Monsieur* to a convict is a glass of water to a man dying of thirst at sea.

"The lamp," said the bishop, "gives a very poor light."

Madame Magloire understood him and, going to his bedchamber, took from the mantel the two silver candlesticks, lighted the candles, and placed them on the table.

"Monsieur Curé," said the man, "you are good; you don't despise me. You take me into your house; you light your candles for me, and I haven't hid from you where I come from, and how miserable I am."

The bishop, who was sitting near him, touched his hand gently and said: "You need not tell me who you are. This is not my house; it is the house of Christ. It does not ask any comer whether he has a name, but whether he has an affliction. You are suffering; you are hungry and thirsty; be welcome. And do not thank me; do not tell me that I take you into my house. This is the home of no man, except him who needs an asylum. I tell you, who are a traveler, that you are more at home here than I; whatever is here is yours. What need have I to know your name? Besides, before you told me, I knew it."

The man opened his eyes in astonishment.

"Really? You knew my name?"

"Yes," answered the bishop, "your name is my brother."

"Stop, stop, Monsieur Curé," exclaimed the man. "I was famished when I came in, but you are so kind that now I don't know what I am; that is all gone."

The bishop looked at him again and said:

"You have seen much suffering?"

"Oh, the red blouse, the ball and chain, the plank to sleep on, the heat, the cold, the galley's crew, the lash, the double chain for nothing, the dungeon for a word—even when sick in bed, the chain. The dogs, the dogs are happier! nineteen years! and I am forty-six, and now a yellow passport. That is all."

"Yes," answered the bishop, "you have left a place of suffering. But listen, there will be more joy in heaven over the tears of a repentant sinner than over the white robes of a hundred good men. If you are leaving that sorrowful place with hate and anger against men, you are worthy of compassion; if you leave it with good will, gentleness, and peace, you are better than any of us."

# SMALL-TOWN PARADE,
# DECORATION DAY

## by Phyllis McGinley

Many good judges think Pulitzer-Prize-winner Phyllis McGinley the best writer of light verse in this country. She combines technical skill with warm humor and a seriousness of feeling that light verse often does not possess. This poem reads aloud well on May 30. But so does it on any other day.

Below the lawns and picket fences,
    Just past the firehouse, half a block,
Sharp at eleven-five commences
    This ardent and memorial walk
    (Announced, last night, for ten o'clock).

Solemn, beneath the elmy arches,
    Neighbor and next-door neighbor meet.
For half the village forward marches
    To the school band's uncertain beat,
    And half is lined along the street.

O the brave show! O twirling baton!
    O drummer stepping smartly out!
O mayor, perspiring, with no hat on!
    O nurses' aid! O martial rout
    Of Bluebird, Brownie, Eagle Scout!

And at the rear, aloof and splendid,
    Lugging the lanterns of their pride,
O the red firemen, well attended
    By boys on bicycles who ride
    With envious reverence at their side!

The morning smells of buds and grasses.
    Birds twitter louder than the flute.
And wives, as the procession passes,
    Wave plodding husbands wild salute
    From porches handy to the route.

Flags snap. And children, vaguely greeted,
    Wander into the ranks awhile.
The band, bemused but undefeated,
    Plays Sousa, pedagogic style,
    Clean to the Square—a measured mile.

Until at last by streets grown stony,
    To the gray monument they bring
The wreath which is less testimony
    To Death than Life, continuing
    Through this and every other spring.

# PINK TIES

## by Alexander King

This episode is drawn from Alexander King's strange
and diverting book of memoirs, *Mine Enemy Grows
Older*. The essence of his talent lies in his ability to tell
wonderful anecdotes. For me this is the best one in the
book, funny and touching.

There was one curious aspect to my life during all those years,
from 1917 to 1948, which I have somehow or other forgotten
to mention to you before—that for more than thirty years I
wore only pink neckties. Not ever any other color, under any
circumstances. It finally got to be an identifying trade-mark
for me, although, heaven is my witness, I never intended anything of the sort when I first started wearing them. In fact, I
got into this pink-tie addiction when I was only seventeen
years old, and believe me, any boy or man who was willing to
wear such an unorthodox color back in those dark days of
somber men's attire had to have plenty of guts or plenty of
stupidity, or plenty of both, to get away with it.

Of course I stumbled into it all, as I fell into most things,
by strictly minding my own business and by just carefully putting one foot in front of the other.

I was working on the New York *Sunday World* when I was
seventeen, and I was also doing some cartooning jobs for the

*Big Stick,* a Jewish joke paper that I already told you about. My salary on the *World* was twenty-five dollars a week, and I generally took long, leisurely walks every Friday afternoon, just to give myself, and those twenty-five bucks a luxurious airing. These walks often included window-shopping tours ranging from Nassau Street and lower Broadway to Forty-second Street and Fifth Avenue up as far as the Plaza.

Well, then, loaded as I was, one of those Friday afternoons I happened to stop in front of Sulka's window, somewhere in the Forties or Fifties, and I noticed that they were having a sale of neckties. Six dollars a tie. I wondered what in hell they could possibly have charged for them before the sale. I felt myself getting even a little indignant about the whole thing. However, in spite of my simmering annoyance I found that I was deliberately walking into their cool, expensive-smelling store.

It stands to reason, doesn't it, that I wasn't planning to buy anything, and the clerk, whose face looked just like a shinbone with eyebrows, knew this as well as I did. But, like two idle dogs of the same gender who can't resist their pointless browsing, this clerk and I forthwith proceeded to give the stock a judicious fingering; which means that I sneered disparagingly at the tie racks, while he kept on constructing smart four-in-hand knots in mid-air, just to show off his really stupendous manual dexterity and also to make me feel like a cheap piker.

This went on for about twenty minutes or so, and I was just about to call off the whole silly ballet by making my exit, when the clerk, who was obviously a pansy, suddenly said to me, "You know, we have some colors that are much less popular, and those ties cost only one dollar apiece. Would you care to see any of them?"

"Why not?" I said. "As long as I'm here, anyway. What sort of colors are they?"

"I'll show them to you. To tell you the truth," he said with a confidential smirk, "I'm saving some of them especially for my friends."

This, of course, instantly alarmed me, because I was quite sure that any friend of his was bound to be a leaping faggot, but just the same I decided to take a look. He pulled a box off the shelf, removed the lid, and exposed about two dozen crepe-de-Chine ties, all of them pink.

"Not a very great selection," I said. "How much are they, did you say?"

"A dollar apiece," he said. "They cost us more than that wholesale."

Now, then, who really knows what dark and sinister impulses are crouched and coiled in the recesses of man's unconscious? Who can guess what terrible unfulfilled longings in a man's heart are just waiting for the right word, or the right moment, to spring into instant, demoniacal action, for the sake of a long-deferred secret appeasement?

In short, I bought six of those pink crepe-de-Chine neckties, and, believe it or not, I even had a certain feeling of high accomplishment out of this demented proceeding. It was as if I'd pulled a particularly cute caper, not just on Sulka and Company, but on all the goddamned expensive shops up and down Fifth Avenue.

And that's how it happened that I came to wear a pink tie to work the next day. I labored, at the time, in the tower of the old Pulitzer Building, down on Park Row, and when I first took off my coat, the screams, the whistles, the yowls, and the yodelings all around me stopped all human activity on that floor for the next ten minutes.

But, since I was seventeen years old and a man of my convictions, I ignored this racket and quietly went about my business. My business was to make some black-and-white line sketches for the Sunday magazine section, and so I was able, for a while at least, to bend zealously over my drawing board without having to meet anybody's eye. This was certainly a help, but even so it was hard for me to ignore the mad cavortings of the office boys and the various younger staff members, who made it their pleasure to pass my desk forty times an hour in that special mincing gait which has ever been the immemorial hallmark of the camping fairy.

I don't know how I lived through that first morning. At any rate, right before lunch I took off my tie and hung it in a metal closet where I usually kept only a pair of torn rubbers. When I got ready to quit work that evening, I had a shocking surprise waiting for me. Somebody on that floor had dipped my tie in a large glue vat that was permanently stationed near the fire exit. The glue had completely dried up and left the tie with a texture like a smoked kipper; but since I knew that a lot of furtive eyes were certainly watching me at that moment, I just dropped my violated neckpiece casually into the garbage can and went home.

Fools! I thought. Just a pack of crude, conventional fools. Ah well, they believed I was routed, did they? They thought they had me down for the count, eh? Well, they'd soon learn different. Damned soon, too! I'd show those mushheads a thing or two—or even five, if it came to that, because, as you perfectly well know, I still had five more of those ties hanging at home in my closet, ready and waiting to be launched whenever the spirit moved me.

I was determined to teach all those dopes a lesson, to teach them to respect a man's right to wear whatever the hell he goddamned well pleased. And so the battle lines were drawn, and no mercy was given or expected.

I wore my pink ties every day from then on, and, do you know, as the tense weeks went by a very funny thing happened. In about a month or so I couldn't help but notice that slowly, ever so slowly, the fury and the clamor were beginning to die down. In fact, by the time I'd gotten around to wearing the third of my ties, somebody from the business office, who had never before seen my colorful haberdashery and was just about to launch himself into the gibbering state of epilepsy that the occasion seemed to call for, was stupefied into silence when a few of my nearby colleagues told him to shut his trap and to mind his own goddamn business.

You see, the young journalists on my floor had not only become used to my pink ties, they had developed a certain comradely state of tolerance toward my special eccentricity. They had come to consider it *their* peculiar privilege to razz me for acting out of line, but they all stood defensively by me if any unlicensed outsider ever decided to put me down.

In short, after six months of nothing but pink ties, nobody around me seemed any longer to notice that I was wearing anything out of the ordinary at all.

And then came a real crisis. I gave five of my ties away to be cleaned, in a store on West Eighth Street, and when I came back a few days later to reclaim them, I found to my horror that the place had been completely gutted by fire.

It was a real calamity for me, as you can plainly understand. Those pink ties were the symbols of my individuality, weren't they? And, to a certain extent, they had even become the tangible pennants that I had tremblingly fluttered before a hostile world, to announce my freedom of choice. I just couldn't let myself down now. I simply couldn't make my appearance at the office wearing some dark, practical colors, not after all I'd already been through, could I? If I did, all would be lost again.

Oh yes, I could just see all those blubberheads on the paper saying, "Well, you've finally got yourself straightened out! Decided to rejoin the human race again, eh? Good for you boy!"

No, no, no! It was out of the question. Eternal vigilance was the price of freedom! That was the basic rule of the game, and I damn well knew it.

And so, in this frightening emergency, I quickly hustled up to B. Altman's on Thirty-fourth Street and bought myself three yards of candy-pink crepe-de-Chine material. Afterward I consulted a classified phone directory and found that the Acme Tie Company, right nearby, on Thirty-sixth Street, was prepared to make neckties in small quantities to private order.

I had myself quite a time finding that goddamned tie place, too, because it was located in one of those depressing blocks between Eighth and Ninth avenues, where there weren't even any drugstores or lunchrooms to break up the solid façade of grim wholesale manufacturing. I did find it at last, and it was literally, just a very small hole in a very thick and forbidding wall.

Mr. Aron Buxbaum, the owner, turned out to be a neat little bearded elderly Jew who wore a black skullcap and satin sleeve garters and who showed no surprise whatever at the unusual color of my material.

"I'm in a terrible hurry about these ties," I told him as I unwrapped the stuff. "How soon can I possibly have them?"

"Day after tomorrow," said Mr. Buxbaum. "We generally like to have more time, but, if it's an emergency, we'll just do the best we can."

"Fine," I said. "I'll pick them up around lunch time on Friday."

When I returned, two days later, Mr. Buxbaum handed me a pretty good sized package and a bill for fifteen dollars.

I nearly fainted. "How come, fifteen dollars?" I said. "You're charging me a fortune. After all, I supplied the material, didn't I?"

Mr. Buxbaum looked hurt. "We do very fine work here," he said. "You just take a look at those ties, and you'll see what you're getting for your money. You're getting a big bargain."

"Never mind," I said. "I haven't got time now. I have to get back to work. I don't get through until four o'clock."

Luckily, because it was payday, I had a twenty-dollar bill on me, and so I was able to square myself.

"Wear them in good health!" said Mr. Buxbaum, when I finally stood in the open doorway.

"Thanks," I said. "By the way, how many ties did you manage to get out of that material anyway?"

"Exactly sixty-two," he said. "If you had bought just a quarter of a yard more, you could have had sixty-five."

And that's how it was.

Ties, I later learned, are cut on the bias and really require very little material. And so, at one stroke, I had added to my wardrobe a matter of more than five dozen pink ties.

They lasted for quite a while, too, and when they finally wore out I just bought some more material and had a new batch made up for myself over at Buxbaum's. And that's how it happened that I came to march through the ages as a peculiarly necktied man.

And then, sometime in 1947, all of my luggage was lost by one of the airlines, and I arrived in New York with only one pink necktie to my name, the one that I was wearing. Well, I naturally went straight up to Altman's to get myself three and a quarter yards of fresh pink crepe de Chine. I'd made these trips and these purchases quite often during the past thirty years, and I no longer had the slightest difficulty in locating the Acme Tie Company on West Thirty-sixth Street.

But when I finally got there, old man Buxbaum wasn't anywhere in sight. Instead, a sort of young and beardless caricature of him was sitting against the back wall and making entries in a huge ledger.

"You're Mr. Buxbaum's son, aren't you?" I said.

"Yes," he said. "I'm George Buxbaum. And you, I believe, must be Mr. King."

"I am," I said. "But how in the world did you know that?"

"Because," said George Buxbaum, "my father is now dead, and you used to be his only customer."

"What?" I said. "You mean that I alone have kept his whole enterprise going?"

"If you want to put it that way," he said. "Actually the matter is a little more complicated than that. You see, my brothers and I are probably the largest wholesale tie manufacturers in America. In fact, we own this building, which houses one of our four factories."

"And what about this store?" I said.

"Ah well, that was all my father's wish," he said, "You see, he came to this country as an immigrant and started to sell ties out of a cigar box on Orchard Street. My mother used to make those ties on a foot-pedal sewing machine at home. Later on he got a pushcart, and by the time my brothers and I were going to high school he'd managed to get himself a nice little store on Second Avenue near Twelfth Street. Well, to make a long story short, we all of us somehow or other got into the necktie business, and we did so well in it that after a while the whole family kept pleading with my father to retire, to take it easy, or at least to take some kind of an executive position in one of our plants. But, for some reason or another, he just never had any real confidence in our success. It was all too big and much too vague for him. Everything was done by bank drafts and checks, and in our places of business he never saw any real money changing hands. And so, every time we expanded, or opened a new factory, he just got more worried about us.

"Finally one day he pleaded with us to fix him up this little retail place right here, where he at least could go on making a real visible dollar across the counter. I think he felt that he was prepared to save the family from absolute ruin, when we had all smashed up with our grand and highfalutin notions. So we built this store for him, and for a while he even had a couple of dozen customers that used to trade here steadily. But for the last eight or ten years the only jobs that came his way were your pink ties.

"And that brings me to still another point," he said. "You see, Mr. King, the whole family always gets together for dinner in my mother's house on Friday nights, and my father and my brothers and I, we would spend hours and hours, wondering and speculating what could possibly be the meaning of all those pink ties. Some of us thought it must be the emblem of some secret society. Others had the idea that maybe it had a certain religious significance or something. But my father—you must excuse me for telling you this—my father was convinced that you were an artist and that you painted naked girls on those ties and that you sold them at stag parties."

"Your father overestimated my talents," I said. "No, I had those ties made for other good and sufficient reasons." And then I told young Buxbaum, briefly, the gist of my story.

"Well," he said, "I'm very glad you've explained it at last, because if my father's spirit is anywhere at all, it certainly must be hovering around this little store where he spent so many years of his life."

He opened a small desk file, and I could see that it contained only one single card. George Buxbaum showed me what his father had written on it. It was in Yiddish.

ONLY PINK TIES.
WHY?

The children think he is some kind of a bolshevik, but I'm sure he only makes a few harmless dirty pictures. He is a good and steady customer. May God preserve him from mischief. And from the police.

On the bottom of this card young Buxbaum now wrote *Account Closed*.

"So you are finally giving up the store," I said.

"Yes," he said. "By the end of next week the door and window will be walled up and the premises will have been absorbed by the rest of the building. But don't worry, for old time's sake we'll make you this last batch of ties from the material you just brought. You'll just have to call for them on the seventh floor."

And that was the end of the Acme Tie Company, and that was the last of my pink ties, too, because I never had the heart to take my business to anybody else.

# A LOVE AFFAIR WITH LIFE

There's a poetic ferment, perhaps even a poetic renaissance, in full swing. Its weirdest aspect is the beatnik poets, mainly in San Francisco, reciting their way-out verse to a jazz accompaniment. But it has healthier aspects. Young people, for instance, are no longer ashamed to be caught reading poetry—or even writing it. In paperback anthologies good verse sells by the hundred thousands. New poets by the score are being published. Our greatest living poet, Robert Frost, has become the property of all of us—millions, particularly among our youth, know and love his work. More and more magazines are devoting pages to the poetry renaissance. On radio, television, and on records one can hear fine verse finely read.

Recently Dorothy Stickney, one of Broadway's brightest stars and the wife of playwright Howard Lindsay, made her own glowing contribution to the current poetry revival. Out of the letters and poems of Edna St. Vincent Millay, one of America's great lyric poets, and the first woman to win a Pulitzer Prize, Miss Stickney fashioned a moving three-act dramatization in which the star and the entire cast is Miss Stickney herself. Produced at the Hudson Theater in New York, A Lovely Light drew plaudits from the critics. Miss Stickney plans to present it on platforms from coast to coast. I hope my readers will have a chance to see and hear her.

What follows is a selection of the letters and poems

through which Dorothy Stickney made Miss Millay live again. I've made my own selections from the dramatization and provided narrative bridges where necessary, sometimes using Miss Stickney's words, sometimes my own.

We could dip into the play almost anywhere, but let's pick it up in the second act, a month after Edna Millay had returned from Europe in the spring of 1923. She is back in Greenwich Village, where some of her finest verse was written—poems which had already won her a Pulitzer Prize. She had been happy in Greenwich Village in the years after Vassar—happy as she tasted the carefree, rebellious life of New York's literary quarter—and sometimes sad . . .

"My candle burns at both ends,
It will not last the night.
But Ah my foes, and Oh my friends,
It gives a lovely light!"

*Now she is back in the familiar place again, writing to her mother in Maine where she was born in 1892:*

". . . Darling, do you remember meeting Eugen Boissevain one day in Waverly Place? It was only for a moment and possibly you don't remember. But anyway, you will like him very much when you know him, which will be soon. And it is important that you should like him—because I love him very much and am going to marry him—THERE! We shall be married sometime this summer."

"Being young and green, I said in love's despite;
Never in the world will I to living wight
Give over—air my mind to anyone,
Hang out its ancient secrets in the strong wind

To be shredded and faded . . .
Oh, me, invaded
And sacked by the wind and the sun!"

*Eugen Boissevain was a well-to-do coffee importer from
Holland. The first thing people noticed about him was his
kindness and abundant vitality. They were married in July
1923.*

*Very few of their letters exist, because very few were ever
written. They were almost never separated. One of the rare
exceptions was during the first year of their marriage. A reading
tour had already been contracted for, and the obligation had to
be fulfilled. Vincent, as family and friends had always called
the poet, wrote to her husband from Cedar Rapids, Iowa, in
February 1924:*

"My dear: All your letters came, even the ones that forgot to
say Iowa . . . It's amusing to think how entirely, *totally, absolutely* different everything would be if you were here beside
me. It makes me laugh, it's so funny that there could be such a
difference. Oh, it will be so lovely when we go around the
earth together! I told some people yesterday that we are going
to Java and China in March. Why not? For we are, we are!
Aren't we?"

*And they did. By July she was writing her mother in a letter
dated from Hong Kong Harbor.*

"All day almost the spray of the ship was full of bright rainbows—and last night the phosphorus made the edge of the
waves all like green electric light—and there was heat lightning,
and I said, 'Oh, Eugen, rainbows by day and phosphorus by
night—I can hardly bear it.' And he said, 'If you should see a
rainbow at night I don't think you could bear it.' And just at
the moment he finished speaking there was a flash of lightning,
and across the phosphorescent crest of the wave a beautiful,

perfect rainbow appeared, bright for a moment and instantly was gone. *And I did bear it! . . . "*

*When they came back, Miss Stickney's narrative continues, they bought a home high in the Berkshire Hills of New York State. Eugen took the overgrown and neglected land and turned it into a prosperous and paying farm. They named it Steepletop after a tall, pink wild flower that grows there. In June she wrote her mother:*

"Here we are in one of the loveliest places in the world, I'm sure, working like Trojans, dogs, slaves, etc.—Having chimneys put in and plumbing put in and a garage built.—And we found a brook—an extra one that we didn't know was there."

> "I know not how such things can be;
> I only know there came to me
> A fragrance such as never clings
> To aught save happy living things;
> A sound as of some joyous elf
> Singing sweet songs to please himself,
> And through and over everything
> A sense of glad awakening."

*Winter came to Steepletop in full abundance, and Vincent wrote:*

"We have been snowed in—I mean hermetically—four weeks today. Five miles on snowshoes, that means, to fetch the mail or to post a letter. And the thermometer at zero again this morning . . . All the old beams and boards that were no good for anything else have been sawn up and stacked in the most beautiful woodpile you ever saw."

> "Pile high the hickory and the light
> Log of chestnut struck by the blight.
> Welcome in the winter night."

*But spring brought new wonders:*

"The young wrens who have their house under the peak of
the icehouse are flying today. And what a to-do, and what
beautiful singing from their father, as if to say:

" 'Someday you'll have as handsome feathers as I, and a tail
that sticks straight up behind your rump, and a song as beautiful as mine.' "

*In 1936 the poet had an accident which seriously injured
the nerves of her back. She was leaning against the door of her
station wagon. It burst open suddenly and she was thrown out
to roll down a gully. For four years she suffered almost constant pain; three operations were performed in an attempt to
cure her.*

*In March 1941 she was writing to her publishers, Harper &
Brothers, of another tragedy:*

"Once again I must ask my publishers to come—running—
to my aid. What it comes to is this. Because of the war Eugen
has lost everything he had. There is not a penny he can get at,
so for the time being it is up to me.

"Now, however, I think the answer to the pain may have
been hit on. I shall probably get well soon and be able to get
back to work."

*Vincent had always loved the sea. It was the thing she had
often longed for during the years on her wooded mountainside.
So—they bought a small island off the coast of Maine. It was
called Ragged Island. Here is a note she left one September
day in 1947 for her husband to find:*

"Darling, come up from the harbor. The sea is making—at
least it looks so, and anyway the wind is coming up N.W. by
N.—I think. Don't go out, please. We have everything here
. . . Dearest—I'm going topside. Maybe I'll sleep, maybe not."

"The hills may shift, the waters may decline,
Winter may twist the stem from the twig that bore it,
But never your love from me, your hand from mine."

*They stayed late on Ragged Island, and she wrote to an editor in New York:*

"It looked for a time as if we should have to spend the winter there as well. We stayed on much later than usual and got caught in the autumn storms, the sea becoming so rough that it was impossible to cross the four miles of open water to the mainland . . . We didn't get back to Steepletop until damn near time to slide the Thanksgiving turkey into the oven."

*It was just two years later, on December 10, 1949, that she wrote to a friend:*

"You feared that I might be ill. I am far worse than ill. My husband has died. I cannot write about it, nor about anything else. And I cannot answer questions. But I wanted to get some word to you, you were so distressed by my silence."

*She returned to Steepletop to live—alone. Her friends protested, but she went anyway. That was what she wanted.*

"As to some lovely temple, tenantless
Long since, that once was sweet with shivering brass,
Knowing well its altars ruined, and the grass
Grown up between the stones,—yet from excess
Of grief hard driven, or great loneliness
The worshipper returns—and those who pass
Marvel his crying on a name that was."

*That same December she wrote to two friends in New York:*

"Dear Margaret and Alice: If you chaps are determined to give me a Christmas present . . . nothing I can say will stop you—I'll tell you what I would like.

"A—Three typewriter ribbons.

"B—Six composition books—the kind with stiff covers so that I can pick one up and prop it against my knee and scribble in it . . . Oh, I should feel so rich, so reinforced, so sassy with a new ribbon in each of my three typewriters."

*She was writing again. She was working on a sonnet. On some brilliant October morning she must have stepped through the doorway unprepared, when wonder sprang out at her again. For these are the words that were found in the composition book:*

"Never before, perhaps, was such a sight;
Only one sky (my breath) and all that blue!
Creation blue—world's morning, and room too
For clouds, long sprays of Egret thin and bright
And dumpling clouds, horizon bunched, thick white—"

"I will control myself or go inside.
I will not flaw perfection with my grief.
Handsome this day—no matter who has died!"

*Her last letter, dated October 19, 1950, was left for the maid who found her on the stair landing, curled up like a tired child. She had died apparently of heart failure.*

"Dear Lena: The iron is set too high. Don't put it on where it says 'Linen' or it will scorch the linen. Try it on 'Rayon' and then perhaps on 'Woolen.' And Lena, be careful not to burn your fingers when you shift it from one heat to another.

"It is five-thirty and I have been working all night. I am going to bed.

"GOOD MORNING."

# PALE BLUE NIGHTGOWN

## by Louis Golding

Most of us have heard about the poet Coleridge and
how one day he fell asleep, and dreamed the lines of a
whole poem, and awoke, and began writing them down,
and was interrupted by a visitor, and so the wonderful
poem "Kubla Khan" that we all read in school was never
finished. But have you ever heard of a writer dreaming
*a whole short story*, complete with plot and characters?
The only case I know of is that of the late Louis Golding, author of *Magnolia Street* and other novels. He
also wrote this strange, little-known tale called "Pale
Blue Nightgown." Here's what the English author, Mr.
Golding, himself says about it:

"I dreamed this tale, as I have dreamed tales before
and decided to write them. But I have never actually
done so till now. For the fact was that they proved to
be nonsense, as most dreams are, with no coherence in
episode and character and with no finale.

" 'Pale Blue Nightgown' was unlike them. The characters are as real to me now as they were when I
dreamed them. The central situation still terrifies me as
it terrified me the night it evolved between a bed sheet
and a pillowcase drenched with sweat. The denoue-
ment has as much 'surprise' as any tale I have composed in my *waking* moments.

"I remember two things in that night dreaming, the appalling vividness of the events themselves, and my insistence throughout, 'What a good story this will make.'

"At the same time I was consumed with curiosity. 'How,' I asked myself, 'is it going to end?' The ending was as startling and terrifying to myself as it has been to my friends since, if I am to believe them."

Mr. Dofferty was tall and thin and had big hands and feet. The small boys called him "Lampy," which was an abbreviation of "Lamppost." He hated the small boys calling him "Lampy," not only because he was sensitive about his appearance, but because he hated small boys. He would rather have taken the top form in a refined girls' school and would have got on very well there. He could have talked about Swinburne with the girls, and about his foreign travels. "Was there ever really a Dolores, Mr. Dofferty?" "Do the young warriors in Kashmir still go out to battle with roses behind their ears?" He would have been very happy in such a place.

But it had not worked out that way. He was getting on in years by the time he got his teacher's certificate, and he could not pick and choose. He became a pupil-teacher at a boys' school in Doomington. They were common boys. In the course of time he became headmaster.

He knew that he deserved better things. He let it be known that he had traveled about the East quite a lot in his young days; and it was true, for he had been the son of a noncommissioned officer out in India. Later, he was employed on a tea plantation in Ceylon. When that failed, he came to England to take up teaching.

He was very proud of having traveled in the East. His "sanctum," as he called it, was cluttered with Eastern curios. There were prayer wheels and fly whisks, curtains and cushions, elephants carved in ebony, ash trays and pen trays of

Benares ware, a Malay kris he used as a paper knife, a soap-stone Buddha he used as a paperweight. It was not very suitable furniture for a headmaster's room in a poor boys' school in Doomington, but it put people in their place. It put him in his place too. He was a traveler, an empire builder.

He did not feel so sure of himself when he went out into the playground. He would have preferred to stay in his sanctum, but he had a feeling that the small boys took to talking and laughing about him when they got together. He would stand for a long time, quite still, behind the windows of one of the classrooms, and then, all of a sudden, he was a few inches behind you. For a person with such large feet, he moved very quickly and quietly over the gravel.

The school day came to an end at half-past four. It was bad enough when the boys collected in the play intervals between lessons, but when the last lesson was over, there was absolutely no excuse for them to be hanging about, whispering and pointing with their thumbs over their shoulders. On the day in Mr. Dofferty's history with which this tale is concerned there was an unusually large troop of boys assembled near the woodwork room, at the bottom end of the playground. Mr. Dofferty happened to be at the top end of the playground. He observed that only one of the boys was talking, a small, pale boy named Albert Hewitt. The rest were listening. At least they were listening in the intervals of laughing. The narrative with which Albert Hewitt was regaling them seemed to entertain them mightily, though Albert himself seemed not at all amused. On the contrary, his spotty little face seemed paler than usual; his eyes seemed to stand quite a long way out of his head.

Mr. Dofferty did not like Albert Hewitt; he thought him a soapy, sneaky sort of boy. He had had occasion more than once to take him into his sanctum and use the cane on him. What was the boy doing, holding forth at this time of day, when well-behaved boys should be making tracks for home, with

their heads filled with the night's homework? What and who
was there to talk about that was so frightfully funny?

Of course; Mr. Dofferty could swear to it . . . "Lampy,"
and once again, "Lampy." It was a long way from the bottom
end to the top end of the playground, but Mr. Dofferty had ex-
traordinarily acute hearing. "Lampy" again, and a roar of
laughter. The boy was talking about his headmaster; he was
making jokes about his headmaster. Mr. Dofferty's lips set thin
and hard.

Mr. Dofferty made a sort of sideways movement on a seg-
ment of a wide circle toward the group of boys. He looked a
bit like a huntsman keeping to windward of his quarry. The
maneuver was successful. He had come up to within a few
yards of them, always in the rear of Albert Hewitt, before the
boys became aware of him. Then, suddenly, the boys caught
sight of him: all but Albert Hewitt. One moment later they
had scuttled away, like a warren-full of rabbits shocked into a
hedge by a footstep. A hand came down heavily on Albert
Hewitt's shoulder.

"You were talking about me, I think," said Mr. Dofferty.
His voice was gentle.

Albert Hewitt's body quivered under the great hand. He
did not dare to turn round.

"No, sir, Mr. Dofferty, I wasn't" said the small boy.

"You were referring to me by another name," pointed out
Mr. Dofferty.

"No, sir, Mr. Dofferty, I wasn't," the small boy said again.
His voice was hardly more than a whisper.

Mr. Dofferty removed his hand from Albert Hewitt's
shoulder.

"Perhaps you'll turn around, Albert," he suggested.

Albert turned round. He did not dare to look up into Mr.
Dofferty's face, cold and remote. The thin thighs of the headmaster seemed to soar into space, like trees. The playground
was appallingly empty but for himself and the soft voice that
came down from so high.

"I would like you to look into my face," requested Mr. Dofferty. "Will you?"

The small boy did as he was told.

Mr. Dofferty continued. "Excellent, Albert. Now, I feel quite certain you won't lie to me. You *were* referring to me by a name which I have forbidden the school to use. Is that not so, Albert?"

"Yes, sir," whispered the small boy. His lips started quivering. He found it as difficult not to lower his eyes from Mr. Dofferty's eyes as it had been difficult a moment ago to raise them.

"Now, now." Mr. Dofferty wagged his finger almost playfully. "Don't make an exhibition of yourself. No harm will come to you, so long as you're a good boy and speak up. What was it you were saying to those boys, Albert? Come, come, Albert, what was it?"

The boy said not a word. He stared up into Mr. Dofferty's eyes, as if he had neither ears nor tongue.

"What are you staring at me like that for?" barked Mr. Dofferty. "Is there anything wrong with me?"

The boy's head sagged suddenly toward his chest.

"Well, Albert!" The headmaster's voice had become gentle as a dove's again. "Are you going to tell me what it was you were saying about me?"

"I wasn't saying nothing," Albert said. His lower lip projected a little.

"Obstinate, eh?" said Mr. Dofferty, quite gaily now. "You know, Albert," he almost wheedled, "it will be a lot better for you if you tell me what you were saying."

"I wasn't saying nothing," Albert repeated.

"I see," Mr. Dofferty said shortly. He raised his eyes to roof level and joined his hands behind his back. He seemed to be communing with himself. Then he spoke again. His tone was very matter-of-fact. "If you go on disobeying me, I'll take you into the sanctum and thrash you. Do you hear?"

"Yes, sir," the boy mumbled.

"Very well, then. Are you going to tell me what you were saying?"

"No, sir."

"I'll take you into the sanctum and thrash you within an inch of your life. Are you going to tell me?" Again silence. "Are you going to tell me?" Mr. Dofferty reached down and got his fingers round the boy's arm.

With a quick involuntary gesture the boy wrenched his arm free.

"It was only a dream!" he cried. "Let me go home!"

"Oh, it was only a dream?" said Mr. Dofferty, easily. "Why didn't you say so before, you silly boy?" His heart felt curiously lighter. He took his watch out of his waistcoat pocket. "You're right!" he exclaimed. "It's time we were both going home!"

"Oh, thank you, thank you very much, sir!" cried Albert. "Good afternoon, Mr. Dofferty." The boy was already scampering off.

"Oh, by the way!" the headmaster called after him.

The boy turned. "Yes, sir?" he asked fearfully.

Mr. Dofferty did not say anything for a moment or two. He realized, in fact, he had nothing to say. He was merely aware that he did not like the boy going off like that, as if he had not used the forbidden nickname, as if he were innocent as the shorn lamb. Then he found his lips uttering a question concerning which his mind had no curiosity at all. For, after all, what interest was it to Mr. Dofferty, headmaster, Mr. Dofferty, world traveler, what dream a sniveling, little elementary schoolboy might dream?

"What did you dream about, Albert?"

The boy's jaw fell. The faint flush of color that had come up into his face went out completely.

"Nothing," he muttered.

"Nonsense!" said Mr. Dofferty. "You were dreaming about me, weren't you?"

Then, suddenly, Mr. Dofferty remembered how amused all

the small boys had been while Albert Hewitt had been holding forth. He had been telling them his dream, of course, a dream about their headmaster. Mr. Dofferty blushed. It was in the last degree undignified for a person in his position to insist on ferreting out a small boy's dream, whatever the dream was about. But he could not bear the way the boy was lying to him. If the boy would only own up simply and honestly, they could go home, both of them.

"Well, are you going to say something?" asked Mr. Dofferty.

The boy was as silent as a lump of wood.

Mr. Dofferty, suddenly, lost patience. "Very well, then. You will please come along with me."

He strode forward toward the big door in the middle of the building. The boy hesitated for one moment. He looked round wildly. It was impossible to get away from those long legs.

The sanctum was a room on the right-hand side of the main corridor. Mr. Dofferty took out his bunch of keys and unlocked the door.

"This way," he said frigidly.

The boy followed. He knew the way well enough. There was a faint smell in the air which turned his stomach, as it had been turned once or twice before. Mr. Dofferty burned joss sticks, now and again, when his nostalgia for the East got him badly.

The headmaster went over to the table in the middle of the room and carefully removed two or three of his oriental knick-knacks—the soapstone Buddha he used as a paperweight, the ivory-handled Malay kris he used as a paper knife, the heavy, brass, Chinese seal. He sat down in the space thus cleared and reached casually along the table for his cane.

"Stand here," he ordered the boy. The boy came and stood beside him. "What was your dream about?"

The boy stood obdurate.

"You're not going to tell me?" Mr. Dofferty roared. "So,

you're not going to tell me?" He lifted the cane high in the air, ready to strike.

"I'll tell you!" the boy shouted suddenly. "Please, sir, I'll tell you!"

Mr. Dofferty's face was as white as a tablecloth; his lips were almost as white. "Very well, then! Go on!"

"I—I—dreamed—" the boy whimpered—"I—I dreamed— that I——" Then he looked up beseechingly. "I *can't* tell you, sir!" he wailed.

"I think you can," said the other.

The boy swallowed hard. "I dreamed in my dream, sir, you was wearing—you was wearing——"

"Go on!"

"You was wearing a long nightgown, sir. It was a silk one, sir, pale blue silk. And—and——" Again the words stuck in the boy's throat.

Mr. Dofferty was not aware of the boy's discomfort. He was aware only of his own. He knew he had never felt so ridiculous in all his life before.

"Go on!" he said thickly. "Anything more?"

"Yes, sir!" blubbered the boy. "You was wearing a wreath of daisies round your head!"

"I see," whispered Mr. Dofferty.

But he did not mean that he himself saw. He meant that the small boys saw, the small boys who had laughed uproariously when Albert had told them his dream. He saw with their eyes his own unspeakable grotesqueness—pale blue nightgown and wreath of daisies.

Why didn't the small boy get to hell out of it? What was the blob of dirt hanging about for? He must take himself in hand. He must not let the boy realize how naked he had left him, shivering in the whistling blackness, with only a pale blue nightgown round his skinny body, a wreath of daisies for headgear.

"Is that all?" he asked with a deadly attempt at casualness.

Then the boy gave tongue, with a voice so shrill and terrible that it seemed to pierce the eardrums.

"That's all!" he screamed. "I tell you that's all. I didn't dream nothing more! Nothing at all!"

The eyes glared. The jaw was so rigid that the words came through with the effect of ventriloquy.

For the first time in the encounter Mr. Dofferty's intellectual interest was aroused. He forgot his anger with the boy and his shame of himself. He was conscious only of an exceeding curiosity. What more was it the boy had dreamed, the terror of which made him a gibbering idiot? What on earth could it be?

"Listen, Albert," he said coaxingly. "Don't be frightened. I know you dreamed something more. I'd like to know what it was. Won't you tell me?"

"Nothing more! I didn't dream nothing more!" The boy stamped his feet.

"I assure you, you're going to tell me!" Mr. Dofferty said. "You might as well tell me now, as later."

He was not going to have the struggle start all over again. He was feeling completely worn out. He got down from the table. The cane had fallen to the floor. He reached down and lifted it. He swished it through the air. "Won't you tell me, Albert?" he asked once again.

The boy said nothing.

Then the man's patience snapped. The cane went hissing into the air and came screaming down again. He did not know where it landed, on the boy's hands, body, or face.

The boy did not know, either. He knew nothing more excepting that the whole world was a blackness with a great wind roaring in it. Then, at last, the wind ceased roaring and there was light in the world again. He became aware that he was in the sanctum of Mr. Dofferty, his headmaster. He became aware of Mr. Dofferty's body extended interminably between his own legs and the legs of the table. The Malay kris that Mr.

Dofferty used as a paper knife stuck out from between his ribs.

The boy leaned forward, pointing toward the ivory handle, where the blood gushed above the blade.

"That's what I dreamed!" his lips went. "That's what I dreamed!"

# I ADMIRE THE HUMAN RACE

## by Roger William Riis

> Whenever the morning newspaper, with its picture of
> our follies and our failures, makes us despair of the
> future of humanity, it's a good idea to raise our sights
> and take the longer view. These few but inspiring para-
> graphs may help.

I admire the human race. I do, indeed. Everybody is busy
running us down these days for the mess they say we have
made here and there and everywhere. Pshaw! That's short-
range stuff, a worm's-eye view of our world. Over the march-
ing and abundant centuries we haven't made any mess. Far
from it!

We have done and are doing a better job than anyone has
any right to expect. We're all right!

From the beginning we found ourselves alone in a vast universe, and not only alone but the only living thing on this
planet which could realize its loneness. We realized it, gave it
a good close look, and then turned our attention to making
something practical and useful out of an unprecedented
situation.

First of all, we found for ourselves a Light, a God, and we
got a sense of direction, a goal to work toward. This was
pretty clever of us, if you think of it carefully.

We proceeded to set up standards for our living together. Early in our experience we made the revolutionary discovery that gentleness and kindliness were more practical than brute strength. No other species has ever found that out and used it as a model and practical code of conduct.

We have in actual fact no one we need answer to, beyond ourselves, and yet we observe our ideal standards in remarkable degree. We are honest and trustworthy one with another so that it is the exception, it is news, when we commit a theft. We are decent 99 per cent of the time, when we could easily be vile.

With silence and mystery behind us and ahead of us, we make up gay little songs and whistle them, and our feet keep jig time to them. We look life and fate in the eye and smile. I like that, and I admire the people who do it.

Alone among living things we have discovered Beauty, and we cherish it and create it for eye and ear. Alone among living things, we have the power to look at our environment and criticize it and improve it.

Finding it necessary to live together by the millions, we created for ourselves governing systems covering vast geographical spaces. Now we actually have the thrilling and terrific idea of a world government, a global government to bring justice to white and black, to Eskimo and Afrikaner, rich and poor, not because any tribe is powerful and can exact justice, but because we have conceived and created the ideal of justice and plan it for all men. This is great. This is not the act of a little animal or a mean animal. This is possible only to a great animal. We think in global terms. We inhabit a star, and we know it.

Finding that we have to work to stay alive, we work with ability beyond imagining.

Out of the earth we take food and improve that food year by year; we take heat and light, so that darkness which lay upon the face of the earth is dispelled by man-made light. We enjoy all the myriad products of our unparalleled ingenuity.

Every morning the necessity for the day's work faces us. And we go and do a day's work, with an over-all average effectiveness and perseverance that is amazing, considering many of the jobs.

Of a persistence, a daring and ingenuity impossible to surpass, we find ways to move easily under the water and through the air. Now we speculatively eye our neighboring planets. It should astound no one if man one day begins to move among these planets. How shall I not admire such a creature? Daunted by nothing, his horizons constantly recede, the territories of his possession and use expand and expand.

Whenever he comes to an impassable obstacle, an apparently final barrier, he goes to work at it and, in due time, surpasses it. If he has limits, I do not see where they are. I do not think he has limits. I think he is a child of the universe who inherits eternity. I think he is wonderful. I am his devoted partisan, and I am proud indeed to be one of him.

# THE HEROIC RIDE
# OF CAESAR RODNEY

## by Lester David

Perhaps some of my readers will spend next Independence Day in Washington. You might find yourself visiting the National Archives Exhibition Hall, reflecting on how it all started, as you examine the document of the Declaration of Independence. Look at the list of signers. In the fourth column, third line from the bottom, you will make out a name: Caesar Rodney. Behind that signature lies a suspense-packed true story of the Revolution's other rider.

The facts of that story were unearthed by Lester David who obtained much of his information from Federal Judge Richard S. Rodney, a descendant of the uncle of the man whose ride, as you will see, may now be added to those of Paul Revere and General Phil Sheridan.

Judge Rodney's home in New Castle, Delaware, is on the route of Caesar Rodney's dramatic journey. On one wall is a military commission signed by Washington. Scattered about is furniture that once formed part of the Dover farmhouse from which Judge Rodney's ancestor started out on the dark early morning of July 2, 1776.

Today you can travel by car from Dover to Philadelphia, virtually following Rodney's route, in just under two hours. It took Rodney eleven hours to gallop and splash his way up to the front door of the State House in Philadelphia—and make history.

This little-known chapter in the national annals is not only worth reading. It is worth remembering.

A dust-caked messenger drew rein at "Poplar Grove," Caesar Rodney's rambling farmhouse on the outskirts of Dover in the colony of Delaware. It was almost two in the morning of July 2, 1776, and the house was quiet and dark as the starless night.

Moments later lights flickered and Rodney himself—farmer, militia commander, and delegate to the Continental Congress —turned the huge lock with its five-inch key and swung open the door.

The rider spoke. "I have an urgent message for Caesar Rodney."

"I am Rodney," said the man at the door. "What is it?" The messenger fumbled in his pouch and pulled out a letter. Rodney read quickly, then drew in his breath.

He was needed in Philadelphia at once. Congress, in session there, was preparing to vote on the question of independence, perhaps before this very day ended. And because of a division of opinion between his two fellow Delaware delegates, Rodney's vote was indispensable.

Rodney was stunned. He had not remained in Philadelphia as the other delegates had. News had reached him that loyalists were raising men and arms in Delaware to fight on England's side. And as head of the Delaware militia he had rushed back home. He had thought he could quell the uprising and be back in Philadelphia in plenty of time.

But the question of independence was coming up sooner than he had expected, much sooner. He had to be there that day.

Turning, he thanked the messenger and snapped a command to a servant, "Saddle the brown. I'm leaving now." The man dashed past him and out the door. Rodney ran upstairs to dress, while the tired messenger set out for a bed at the tavern.

Less than ten minutes later Rodney was striding to the stable, his candle lantern cutting a glow into the blackness. He wore spurs and riding boots, heavy knee breeches, and a waist-coat over a white, collarless shirt. His black cocked hat was pulled low over his small head, and he carried a riding crop. Around his disease-ravaged face—he had an ulceration diagnosed as cancer that wouldn't heal—he had knotted a dark green cloth.

His mount was ready, a bigboned stallion with proven courage and endurance. The delegate from Delaware swung himself into the saddle and wheeled toward the road. There he paused and looked at the sky. It was black and the wind was southerly. A heavy rain would make the roads almost impassable. Already they were muddy from earlier rains.

Those roads northward toward Philadelphia were narrow, winding and pocked with holes where one false step could send a horse and man hurtling. There were unbridged streams to ford and dangerous quagmires where horses could founder in black mud up to their bellies.

Caesar Rodney leaned forward, lightly touched spurs to flanks, and whispered, "Go." The big horse leaped forward. Rodney began riding through the night to Philadelphia, eighty miles away. . . .

The day before, July 1, the gavel had banged for order in the Continental Congress shortly after 9 A.M. Slender, beak-nosed Thomas McKean of Delaware sat frustrated and gloomy. McKean, like Caesar Rodney, was heart and soul for independence. But George Read, Delaware's third delegate, was implacably opposed. With Rodney at home, Delaware's vote could not be cast for liberty—and a unanimous vote was essential.

Leaders backing the independence resolution were sure of

nine of the thirteen colonies. Two of the remaining four, South Carolina and Pennsylvania, were swinging over. New York's delegation was awaiting instructions from home which were virtually certain to be favorable. That left only Delaware. And even one colony refusing to indorse independence would seriously weaken the patriot cause.

Suddenly McKean rose, left the hall, and crossed the State House yard. He hurried down Walnut Street to the express-rider station.

"How soon can a rider reach Dover?" he asked.

"In twelve hours, if there's no rain."

"Then send a rider with this message—and tell him in God's name to hurry!"

Would Rodney arrive in time? Rodney didn't know himself. Ten miles of hard riding from the farm brought him to the two forks of Little Duck Creek, each of which cut across the road, neither of which had a bridge. At each he eased the stallion into the water and, with practiced hands and knees born of years in the saddle, guided him expertly to the other side. Then he plunged into the scrub forest which stretched for the next ten miles.

Suddenly, nearing a bend, the stallion stumbled. Rodney pitched forward and nearly fell. But the horse regained his footing and the rider kept his seat. He urged his mount on, leaning low over his neck to whisper quiet, encouraging words.

After the forested area the road widened. When the first glimmerings of daylight came, Rodney was approaching Cantwell's Bridge at Appoquinimink River. He had allowed his horse only brief rests and himself only occasional pulls from the West India rum he carried. Now he reined in at a wayside inn.

He knocked loudly and roused the sleeping keeper. "My apologies for waking you," Rodney said. Then, nodding toward his horse, "Could you provide us with a breakfast?"

It was six in the morning and he had come twenty-five

miles. The day was dawning cloudy and close. Rodney didn't tarry.

At nine that morning most of the delegates were in their seats at the State House for the final vote.

By now every man knew the farmer from Delaware had been sent for, but nobody was certain when he would arrive—or if he would. Stocky John Adams of Massachusetts, whose red-rimmed eyes and shaky hands revealed all too plainly that he was on the point of exhaustion from his heroic efforts of the past few months, held a whispered conference with young Thomas Jefferson of Virginia. The sandy-haired, brilliant Jefferson, only thirty-three, had finished his draft of the Declaration of Independence, and it lay at that moment on the table before the presiding officer. Discussion of the Declaration was the next order of business, following the vote on the resolution.

Adams looked up, caught Colonel McKean's eye, and waved him over. He asked, "Will he come in time?"

"Look at the sky," McKean said.

Caesar Rodney was looking at the sky also. Blackness told him he must hurry. There were thirty miles to go.

After breakfasting quickly, he had entered upon the lonely, rolling hills of St. Georges. At 8 A.M. he had stopped to water his horse at the Red Lion, a crossroads tavern.

For the next stretch the road was excellent, and the rain still held off. Rodney galloped at full speed for whole stretches; by nine o'clock he was clattering over the cobbles of New Castle, past its lovely greens and tall-spired churches, with Chester twenty miles off.

There he knew his friend William Kerlin, host of the Pennsylvania Arms Tavern, could provide him with a fresh horse. The big stallion was faltering.

And then the heavens opened, and in less than a minute Rodney was soaked and the road was sliding, oozing mud. The weary stallion staggered and slowed, but Rodney, crouching low, dug in his spurs.

The lightning flashed. Behind him a tree exploded with a loud report. A wind gust now tore away the green cloth covering Rodney's face, and the rain drove shafts of pain into the open sore. But he rode on, through the thunder and rain, into the bustling port town of Wilmington.

Toward eleven he clattered over a crude bridge across Chester Creek and pulled up wearily at the Pennsylvania Arms. His good friend Kerlin rushed out, looked with astonishment at the mud-splashed rider, and exclaimed, "By God, you must have ridden all night!"

For reply Rodney said, "I must go on—let me take a fresh horse, William, your stoutest and fastest. And have this brave fellow cared for." He himself would eat and rest while the second horse was made ready. And he would appreciate some dry clothing. Not long after Rodney mounted again and was on his way. Philadelphia was still fifteen miles to the northeast.

At the State House the vote still had not come.

At noon the Congress recessed for lunch, and the delegates scuttled through the rain to eat at nearby taverns and private homes. Voting on the resolution would be the first order of business at the afternoon session.

One hour to go, and Rodney hadn't appeared.

At one o'clock the first of the delegates returned. In ten minutes the room was half-filled. Five minutes later the door to the chamber was closed. Benjamin Harrison of Virginia, as chairman of the Committee of the Whole, was presiding. He banged his gavel.

McKean was still outside, waiting at the State House door.

Then the sound came—hoofbeats on the cobblestones of Walnut Street, on the other side of the wall. Mud-spattered and rain-soaked, Rodney rode into the yard.

A great surge of relief and gladness went through McKean as Caesar Rodney climbed from his mount and walked to the plain front doorway.

McKean tried to speak, but no words would come other

than a brief, "Thank God you're here," as he extended a hand. The two men walked arm in arm to the meeting room. The delegates turned and looked as Rodney sank wearily into his seat. Many waved—Jefferson smiled; old Benjamin Franklin, now seventy, beamed; tired John Adams threw him a grateful glance.

The voting began. Balloting was in geographical order, northern colonies called first, each delegate polled individually.

New Hampshire, Massachusetts Bay, Rhode Island—all voted aye. (New York abstained temporarily while waiting for final instructions, but there was no doubt that the state would vote yes. Approval came soon after.) Connecticut, New Jersey, Pennsylvania also thundered "ayes." And then Delaware was called. McKean, "aye." Read, a firm "nay." Rodney?

He stood, riding crop still in his hand, boots and spurs still on his feet, and mud on his clothes, and spoke in loud, clear tones, "As I believe the voice of my constituents and of all sensible and honest men is in favor of independence, my own judgment concurs with them. I vote for independence."

The great resolution had been carried without a dissenting state. And the colonies were united as one before the whole world.

# THE WIT OF OSCAR WILDE

Oscar Wilde's tragic and controversial life has been the subject of two recent movies; his stories and poems are in anthologies and schoolbooks; his plays are frequently revived. A musical version of *The Importance of Being Earnest* won acclaim off-Broadway a season or so ago. But the world remembers Oscar Wilde, above all, for being one of the wittiest men who ever wrote—or talked.

Here are some of the most remarkable samples of Wilde's urbane and unexpected wit. Some of these you may have heard, perhaps without knowing it was Oscar Wilde who said them. I think they show why he is still one of the most quoted of all celebrities.

"A cynic is a man who knows the price of everything and the value of nothing."

"Duty is what one expects from others—it is not what one does oneself."

"Nothing is so dangerous as being too modern; one is apt to grow old-fashioned quite suddenly."

"I can resist everything except temptation."

"Give me the luxuries, and anyone can have the necessaries."

"A Russian who lives happily under the present system of government in Russia must either believe that man has no soul, or that, if he has, it is not worth developing."

"There are things that are right to say, but they may be said at the wrong time and to the wrong people."

"I always pass on good advice. It is the only thing to do with it. It is never any use to oneself."

"Alcohol, taken in sufficient quantities, produces all the effects of intoxication."

"The British cook is a foolish woman—who should be turned for her iniquities into a pillar of salt which she never knows how to use."

"If you wish for reputation and fame in the world and success during your lifetime, you are right to take every opportunity of advertising yourself."

"We have really everything in common with America nowadays, except, of course, language."

"Consistency is the last refuge of the unimaginative."

"A man who does not think for himself does not think at all."

"Work is the curse of the drinking classes."

"In modern life nothing produces such an effect as a good platitude. It makes the whole world kin."

"I dislike arguments of any kind. They are always vulgar, and often convincing."

"Whistler is indeed one of the very greatest masters of painting in my opinion. And I may add that in this opinion Mr. Whistler himself entirely concurs."

"Would you like to know the great drama of my life? It is that I have put my genius into my life—I have put only my talent into my works."

# WHY VERDUN STILL STANDS

## by Jules Romains

> Jules Romains is the author of a many-volumed chron-
> icle of French life called *Men of Good Will*. This ex-
> tract is from perhaps the best of the volumes, *Verdun*.
> In it young Jerphanion is explaining to his friend Jallez
> how, in World War I, men could face the German ar-
> tillery bombardment of Verdun and not go mad. I be-
> lieve it to be a classic account of what takes place deep
> inside the minds of many soldiers, a statement of their
> private mythologies or illusions or faiths which enable
> them to endure inhuman tests of their humanity. I
> have always thought it very beautiful.

"My real point is this: that for the men in the trenches—for
all of them, that is, who are above the purely animal level, for
whom, as you must see for yourself, it is most necessary to find
an explanation—the idea that they must stay where they are
and get on with their job because there is no real alternative
is not enough to keep them in spirits, to prevent their moral
collapse. Each one of them has got to find some effective suggestion that will touch him personally, some thought, some
fixed idea, the secret of which is known to him alone, the essence of which he can absorb drop by drop. Sometimes he has
several among which he can take his choice. No sooner does

one begin to lose its potency than he can change over to others. Take my own case, for instance. For quite a while I managed very comfortably on the idea that I was the kind of man who could 'rise superior to circumstances'—the circumstances in question being partly composed of mental distress, partly of bodily discomfort. 'I'd like,' said I, 'to see those circumstances to which I could not rise superior!' While shrapnel pattered round me (it was at the time when a good deal of shrapnel was being used), I would recite to myself, like a sort of magic formula, those terrific lines of Horace:

> *Si fractus illabatur orbis*
> *Impavidum ferient ruinæ. . . .*

It really is a magic formula. And then, one day, it no longer worked. My mental distress became too great; my fear became too great, and I just wanted to burst into tears and cry 'Mamma!' like a little boy. . . . Then take the young second lieutenant fresh from Saint-Cyr, all innocence and splendid bravery, who says to himself, 'If France is conquered, life will be impossible. I shall feel personally dishonored. Far rather would I have my name on a headstone with the words, "Died on the field of honor," than live on disgraced.' Another example is that of the reservist with a taste for serious reading and an equipment of large-hearted ideals, the kind of man who says to himself, 'This is the war that will end war. We are bringing peace to the whole world. Thanks to our sacrifice, our children will be spared knowledge of such horrors.' Standing next to him in the same trench will be some fellow who thinks, 'This is the end of the world. We're all in for it. What does it matter if I get killed a little sooner or a little later?' Another there may be who believes in a coming reign of justice, who is still convinced that victory for the democracies will mean freedom for the oppressed everywhere in the world, the end of the domination of money and social iniquity, who would be will-

ing even to die if only he could be sure that his death would
mean greater happiness for men yet unborn. Then there's the
sentimentalist, for whom nothing counts but personal relationships, whose world is made up of just a few dear friends, who
argues, 'Most of my pals are dead. If they all go, what is there
left to live for?' There's the man whose wife left him as soon as
he was called up and ran off with someone else, who gets no
letters and no parcels, who feels himself too old to start life
afresh, who would just as soon be dead, for whom the very
fact of danger is a distraction, because it gives him the illusion
that life is still sweet. There is the man who exists in a world
of dreams and takes things as they come. 'Everything is pre-
destined,' says he. 'I always knew it. No use fighting against
fate. We must just go with the tide.' There is the man who
has never had a chance, who has always felt himself to be the
victim of injustice and insult, who has always envied the good
fortune of others, who so relishes the taste of equality bred of
a general misery that he pays but lip service to the desire for
peace with all the bitterness that it will bring for him in its
train. Close beside him is another in whom the war has waked
a deep-seated strain of pessimism, who thinks sincerely, 'The
universe is a foul absurdity. It was always pretty obvious, but
the war has proved it beyond the shadow of a doubt. Why
cling to a foul absurdity?' or, 'Humanity is the work of the
Devil, a blot on the face of the earth, born for murder and
self-slaughter. So much the worse for humanity (and for me,
who am part of humanity and so of the whole putrescent
mess).' There is the fanatical Catholic, who thinks, 'This is
God's punishment wrought on a corrupt and faithless generation. If God has decided that I, too, must pay the penalty,
even for the faults of others, who am I to question His will?'
There is the gentle Catholic who carries tucked away in his
pack a tiny edition of the *Imitation*, who, when night falls, says
his prayers in his shellhole, very quietly, so that no one shall
notice him, and murmurs, 'Let me suffer, as You suffered, Jesu

mine. Why should I be spared, since You suffered a thousand deaths hanging on Your cross? Give me strength that I may be not too unworthy of You.' Finally, there is the man"—and Jerphanion made a gesture toward Notre Dame, which was now immediately opposite them, across the river, its pinnacles just touched by the fading day—"who says, 'All that matters to me in this world is the language of France, the cathedrals of our French countryside, the quays of the Seine, landscapes that can be found nowhere else in the world, a way of life that is unique. If all that is to be taken away, life has no longer any point. If, by dying, I can ensure that all these things will live on after me, then death is right and proper. . . .' Picture to yourself trench after trench filled with men thinking such thoughts, and you will find the answer to your question. . . . That is why Verdun still stands."

# THE GREAT GRIPPE MYSTERY

## by Shirley Jackson

Shirley Jackson writes eerie horror stories. She also writes very funny books about her large and lively family. This hilarious episode (well, I think it's hilarious anyway) is drawn from her *Life Among the Savages*, which you should get and read at once.

We are all of us, in our family, very fond of puzzles. I do double-crostics and read mystery stories; my husband does baseball box scores and figures out batting averages and says he knows the odds against drawing a fourth ace; Laurie is addicted to the kind of puzzle which begins, "There are fifty-four items in this picture beginning with the letter C"; Jannie does children's jigsaws, and Sally can put together an intricate little arrangement of rings and bars which has had the rest of us stopped for two months. We are none us, however, capable of solving the puzzles we work up for ourselves in the oddly diffuse patterns of our several lives, and along with such family brain-teasers as "Why is there a pair of rollerskates in Mommy's desk?" and "What is *really* in the back of Laurie's closet?" and "Why doesn't Daddy wear the nice shirts Jannie picked out for Father's Day?" we are all of us still wondering nervously about what might be called the Great Grippe Mystery. As a matter of fact, I should be extremely grateful if anyone could solve it for us, because we are certainly very short of blankets, and it is annoying not to have *any* kind of an answer. Here, in rough outline, is our puzzle:

Our house is, as I have said, large, and the second floor has four bedrooms and a bathroom, all opening out onto a long, narrow hall which we have made even narrower by lining it with bookcases so that every inch of hall which is not doorway is books. As is the case with most houses, both the front door and the back door are downstairs on the first floor. The front bedroom, which is my husband's and mine, is the largest and lightest and has a double bed. The room next down the hall belongs to the girls and contains a crib and a single, short bed. Laurie's room, across the hall, has a double-decker bed and he sleeps on the top half. The guest room, at the end of the hall, has a double bed. The double bed in our room is made up with white sheets and cases; the baby's crib has pink linen, and Jannie's bed has yellow. Laurie's bed has green linen, and the guest room has blue. The bottom half of Laurie's bed is never made up, unless company is going to use it immediately, because the dog traditionally spends a large part of his time there and regards it as his bed. There is no bed table on the distaff side of the double bed in our room. One side of the bed in the guest room is pushed against the wall. No one can fit into the baby's crib except the baby; the ladder to the top half of Laurie's double-decker is very shaky and stands in a corner of the room; the children reach the top half of the bed by climbing up over the footboard. All three of the children are accustomed to having a glass of apple juice, to which they are addicted, by their bedsides at night. Laurie uses a green glass; Jannie uses a red glass; Sally uses one of those little flowered cheese glasses, and my husband uses an aluminum tumbler because he has broken so many ordinary glasses trying to find them in the dark.

I do not take cough drops or cough medicine in any form.

The baby customarily sleeps with a half dozen cloth books,

an armless doll, and a small cardboard suitcase which holds the remnants of half a dozen decks of cards. Jannie is very partial to a pink baby blanket which has shrunk from many washings. The girls' room is very warm, the guest room moderately so; our room is chilly, and Laurie's room is quite cold. We are all of us, including the dog, notoriously easy and heavy sleepers; my husband never eats coffee cake.

My husband caught the grippe first, on a Friday, and snarled and shivered and complained until I prevailed upon him to go to bed. By Friday night both Laurie and Sally were feverish, and on Saturday Jannie and I began to cough and sniffle. In our family we take ill in different manners; my husband is extremely annoyed at the whole procedure and is convinced that his being sick is somebody's fault; Laurie tends to become a little lightheaded and strew handkerchiefs around his room; Jannie coughs and coughs and coughs; Sally turns bright red, and I suffer in stoical silence, so long as everyone knows clearly that I am sick. We are each of us privately convinced that our own ailment is far more severe than anyone else's. At any rate, on Saturday night I put all the children into their beds, gave each of them half an aspirin and the usual fruit juice, covered them warmly, and then settled my husband down for the night with his tumbler of water and his cigarettes and matches and ash tray; he had decided to sleep in the guest room because it was warmer. At about ten o'clock I checked to see that all the children were covered and asleep and that Toby was in his place on the bottom half of the double-decker. I then took two sleeping pills and went to sleep in my own bed in my own room. Because my husband was in the guest room I slept on his side of the bed, next to the bed table. I put my cigarettes and matches on the end table next to the ash tray, along with a small glass of brandy, which I find more efficacious than cough medicine.

I woke up some time later to find Jannie standing beside the bed. "Can't sleep," she said. "Want to come in *your* bed."

"Come along," I said. "Bring your own pillow."

She went and got her pillow and her small pink blanket and her glass of fruit juice, which she put on the floor next to the bed, since she had got the side without any end table. She put her pillow down, rolled herself in her pink blanket, and fell asleep. I went back to sleep, but sometime later Sally came in, asking sleepily, "Where's Jannie?"

"She's here," I said. "Are you coming in bed with us?"

"Yes," said Sally.

"Go and get your pillow, then," I said.

She returned with her pillow, her books, her doll, her suitcase, and her fruit juice, which she put on the floor next to Jannie's. Then she crowded in comfortably next to Jannie and fell asleep. Eventually the pressure of the two of them began to force me uneasily toward the edge of the bed, so I rolled out wearily, took my pillow and my small glass of brandy and my cigarettes and matches and my ash tray and went into the guest room, where my husband was asleep. I pushed at him and he snarled, but he finally moved over to the side next to the wall, and I put my cigarettes and matches and my brandy and my ash tray on the end table next to *his* cigarettes and matches and ash tray and tumbler of water and put my pillow on the bed and fell asleep. Shortly after this he woke me and asked me to let him get out of the bed, since it was too hot in that room to sleep and he was going back to his own bed. He took his pillow and his cigarettes and matches and his ash tray and his aluminum glass of water and went padding off down the hall. In a few minutes Laurie came into the guest room where I had just fallen asleep again; he was carrying his pillow and his glass of fruit juice. "Too cold in my room," he said, and I moved out of the way and let him get into the bed on the side next to the wall. After a few minutes the dog came in, whining nervously, and came up onto the bed and curled himself up around Laurie, and I had to get out or be smothered. I gathered together what of my possessions I could and made my way into my own room, where my husband was asleep with Jannie on one side and the baby on the other. Jannie woke up when I came in and said, "Own bed," so I helped her carry her pillow and her fruit juice and her pink blanket back to her own bed.

The minute Jannie got out of our bed the baby rolled over and turned sideways, so there was no room for me. I could not get into the crib and I could not climb into the top half of the double-decker, so since the dog was in the guest room I went and took the blanket off the crib and got into the bottom half of the double-decker, setting my brandy and my cigarettes and matches and my ash tray on the floor next to the bed. Shortly after that Jannie, who apparently felt left out, came in with her pillow and her pink blanket and her fruit juice and got up into the top half of the double-decker, leaving her fruit juice on the floor next to my brandy.

At about six in the morning the dog wanted to get out, or else he wanted his bed back, because he came and stood next to me and howled. I got up and went downstairs, sneezing, and let him out and then decided that since it had been so cold anyway in the bottom half of the double-decker I might as well stay downstairs and heat up some coffee and have that much warmth at least. While I was waiting for the coffee to heat Jannie came to the top of the stairs and asked if I would bring *her* something hot, and I heard Laurie stirring in the guest room, so I heated some milk and put it into a jug and decided that while I was at it I might as well give everybody something hot, so I set out enough cups for everyone and brought out a coffee cake and put it on the tray and added some onion rolls for my husband, who does not eat coffee cake. When I brought the tray upstairs Laurie and Jannie were both in the guest room, giggling, so I set the tray down in there and heard Sally talking from our room in the front. I went to get her and she was sitting up in the bed talking to her father, who was only very slightly awake. "Play card?" she was asking brightly, and she opened her suitcase and dealt him, onto the pillow next to his nose, four diamonds to the ace, jack, and the seven of clubs.

I asked my husband if he would like some coffee, and he said it was terribly cold. I suggested that he come down into the guest room, where it was warmer. He and the baby followed me down to the guest room, and my husband and Laurie got into the bed and the rest of us sat on the foot of the bed and I poured the coffee and the hot milk and gave the children coffee cake and my husband the onion rolls. Jannie decided to take her milk and coffee cake back into her own bed, and since she had mislaid her pillow she took one from the guest-room bed. Sally, of course, followed her, going first back into our room to pick up *her* pillow. My husband fell asleep again while I was pouring his coffee, and Laurie set his hot milk precariously on the headboard of the bed and asked me to get his pillow from wherever it was, so I went into the double-decker and got him the pillow from the top, which turned out to be Jannie's, and her pink blanket was with it. I took my coffee cake and my coffee into my own bed and had just settled down when Laurie came in to say cloudily that Daddy had kicked him out of bed and could he stay in here. I said of course, and he said he would get a pillow and he came back in a minute with the one from the bottom half of the double-decker which was mine. He went to sleep right away, and then the baby came in to get her books and her suitcase and decided to stay with her milk and her coffee cake, so I left and went into the guest room and made my husband move over and sat *there* and had my coffee. Meanwhile Jannie had moved into the top half of the double-decker, looking for her pillow, and had taken instead the pillow from Sally's bed and my glass of brandy and had settled down there to listen to Laurie's radio. I went downstairs to let the dog in and he came upstairs and got into his bed on the bottom half of the double-decker, and while I was gone my husband had moved back over onto the accessible side of the guest-room bed so I went into Jannie's bed, which is rather too short, and I brought a pillow from the guest room and my coffee.

At about nine o'clock the Sunday papers came and I went down to get them, and at about nine-thirty everyone woke up. My husband had moved back into his own bed when Laurie and Sally vacated it for their own beds, Laurie driving Jannie into the guest room when he took back the top half of the double-decker, and my husband woke up at nine-thirty and found himself wrapped in Jannie's pink blanket, sleeping on Laurie's green pillow and with a piece of coffee cake and Sally's fruit-juice glass, not to mention the four diamonds to the ace, jack, and the seven of clubs. Laurie, in the top half of the double-decker, had my glass of brandy and my cigarettes and matches and the baby's pink pillow. The dog had my white pillow and my ash tray. Jannie in the guest room had one white pillow and one blue pillow and two glasses of fruit juice and my husband's cigarettes and matches and ash tray and Laurie's hot milk, besides her own hot milk and coffee cake and her father's onion rolls. The baby in her crib had her father's aluminum tumbler of water and her suitcase and books and doll and a blue pillow from the guest room, but no blanket.

The puzzle is, of course, what became of the blanket from Sally's bed? I took it off her crib and put it on the bottom half of the double-decker, but the dog did not have it when he woke up, and neither did any of the other beds. It was a blue-patterned patchwork quilt and has not been seen since, and I would most particularly like to know where it got to. As I say, we are very short of blankets.

# THE DEATH OF SOCRATES

## by Plato

Everyone has heard of the ancient Athenian philosopher Socrates. He devoted most of his life to thinking and talking about how life should best be lived. When he was seventy he was charged with irreligion and "corrupting the young"—that is, forcing them to question established ideas. He was condemned to die by drinking hemlock.

The story of Socrates' death has come down to us in the words of his greatest pupil, Plato, who was twenty-eight when Socrates died. The scene is the prison cell at Athens, where the philosopher is attended by a few followers. He has been talking calmly about the immortality of the soul and how we may live on earth lives worthy of that immortality.

The reverence in which Plato held Socrates is revealed by this famous quotation:

"I thank God," Plato wrote, "that I was born Greek and not barbarian, free man and not slave, man and not woman, but above all, that I was born in the age of Socrates."

The "age of Socrates" has extended a long time—right into our own century. Not only are the words of this wise man still taught in our colleges and universities, but he's universally quoted in newspapers, magazines, books.

133

> I think Plato's account will leave you with the best of
> reasons why Socrates goes on living today. It has been
> called "possibly the finest piece of narrative ever writ-
> ten."

It seemed to us as if we were going to lose a father and to be
orphans for the rest of our life.

When Socrates had bathed, and his children had been
brought to him—he had two sons quite little and one grown
up—and the women of his family were come, he spoke with
them in Crito's presence and gave them his last commands.
Then he sent the women and the children away and returned
to us.

Presently the servant of the governing council which had
condemned him to death came and stood before him and said,
"I know that I shall not find you unreasonable like other men,
Socrates. They are angry with me and curse me when I bid
them drink the poison because the authorities make me do it.
But I have found you all along the noblest and gentlest and
best man that has ever come here; and now I am sure that you
will not be angry with me, but with those who you know are
to blame. And so farewell, and try to bear what must be as
lightly as you can; you know why I have come." With that he
turned away, weeping, and went out.

Socrates looked up at him and replied, "Farewell—I will do
as you say." Then he turned to us and said, "How courteous
the man is. And the whole time that I have been here, he has
constantly come in to see me, and sometimes he has talked to
me, and has been the best of men; and now, how generously
he weeps for me. Come, Crito, let us obey him—let the poison
be brought if it is ready; and if it is not ready, let it be prepared."

Crito replied, "Nay, Socrates, I think that the sun is still
upon the hills—it has not set. Besides, I know that other men

take the poison quite late, and eat and drink heartily, and even enjoy the company of their chosen friends, after the announcement has been made. So do not hurry; there is still time."

Socrates replied, "And those whom you speak of, Crito, naturally do so; for they think that they will be gainers by so doing. And I naturally shall not do so for I think that I should gain nothing by drinking the poison a little later, but my own contempt for so greedily saving up a life which is already spent. So do not refuse to do as I say."

Then Crito made a sign to his slave who was standing by, and the slave went out and after some delay returned with the man who was to give the poison, carrying it prepared in a cup. When Socrates saw him, he asked, "You understand these things, my good sir, what have I to do?"

"You have only to drink this," he replied, "and to walk about until your legs feel heavy, and then lie down, and it will act of itself."

With that he handed the cup to Socrates, who took it quite cheerfully, without trembling, and without any change of color, or of feature, and looked up at the man with that fixed glance of his, and asked, "What say you to pouring out a libation to the gods from this draught? May I or not?"

"We only prepare so much as we think sufficient, Socrates," he answered.

"I understand," said Socrates. "But I suppose that I may, and must, pray to the gods that my journey hence may be prosperous. That is my prayer—be it so."

With these words he put the cup to his lips and drank the poison quite calmly and cheerfully. Till then most of us had been able to control our grief fairly well. But when we saw him drinking, and then the poison finished, we could do so no longer. My tears came fast in spite of myself, and I covered my face and wept for myself—it was not for him, but at my own misfortune in losing such a friend. Even before that Crito had been unable to restrain his tears and had gone away. And

Apollodorus, who had never once ceased weeping the whole time, burst into a loud cry and made us one and all break down by his sobbing and grief, except only Socrates himself.

"What are you doing, my friends?" he exclaimed. "I sent away the women chiefly in order that they might not offend in this way, for I have heard that a man should die in silence. So calm yourselves and bear up."

When we heard that we were ashamed, and we ceased from weeping. But he walked about, until he said that his legs were getting heavy, and then he lay down on his back, as he was told. And the man who gave the poison began to examine his feet and legs from time to time. Then he pressed his foot hard and asked if there was any feeling in it, and Socrates said, No. And then his legs, and so higher and higher, and showed us that he was cold and stiff.

And Socrates felt himself, and said that when it came to his heart, he should be gone. He was already growing cold about the groin, when he uncovered his face, which had been covered, and spoke for the last time.

"Crito," he said, "I owe a cock to Asclepius; do not forget to pay it."

"It shall be done," replied Crito. "Is there anything else that you wish?"

He made no answer to this question, but after a short interval there was a movement, and the man uncovered him, and his eyes were fixed. Then Crito closed his mouth and his eyes.

Such was the end of our friend, a man, I think, who was the wisest and justest and the best man I have ever known.

# AMAZING LADY

## by Cyril Hare

This story has a charming girl, romance, money, and mystery. The truth about Hermione may surprise you.

When Richard Armstrong, explorer and mountaineer, disappeared in a blizzard in the Karakoram, his only daughter Hermione was just turned twenty. He bequeathed her a good deal of unusual experience from remote parts of the world but very little else.

For more tangible aids to living she had to look to her uncle Paul, who was in a position to supply them on a very lavish scale. Paul Armstrong had confined his explorations to the square mile of the earth's surface lying east of London's Temple Bar and found them extremely fruitful.

Hermione was a slender, fragile creature with observant blue eyes, a determined chin, and a small mouth that remained closed unless speech was absolutely necessary. She gave her aging uncle and aunt no sort of trouble, submitted quietly to the horseplay which passed for humor with her tall, athletic cousins, Johnny and Susan, and kept her own counsel. In that cheerful, noisy household she passed almost unobserved.

In the following winter Susan Armstrong was killed by a fall in the hunting field. Six months later Johnny, playing a

137

ridiculous game of leapfrog with Hermione on the springboard of his parents' swimming pool, slipped, crashed into the side of the pool, and broke his neck.

Paul and his wife had worshiped their children with uncritical adoration. The double blow deprived them of all motive for living, and when, shortly afterward, they fell victims to an influenza epidemic, they made not the slightest resistance. Though Hermione herself insisted on ministering to them, refusing the doctor's suggestion that professional nurses be engaged, their end was but briefly delayed.

Even with death duties at their present level, Hermione was a considerable heiress. With the calm deliberation that had always characterized her she set about to look for a husband suitable to her station in life. After carefully considering the many applicants for the post she finally selected Freddy Fitzhugh.

It was an altogether admirable choice. Freddy was well-to-do, well connected, good-looking, and no fool. Their courtship was unexciting but satisfactory; the engagement was announced, and on a fine spring morning they went to Bond Street to choose a ring.

Freddy took her to Garland's, those aristocrats among jewelers, and the great Mr. Garland himself received them in his private room behind the shop. Hermione examined the gems which he showed her with dispassionate care and discussed them with an *expertise* that astonished Freddy as much as it delighted Mr. Garland. She ended by choosing a diamond as superior to the rest as Freddy had been to his rival suitors, and they took their leave.

Meanwhile the shop itself had not been idle. Shortly after Freddy and his beloved had passed through the door of Mr. Garland's private room, two thickset men entered and asked the assistant at the counter to show them some diamond bracelets. They proved to be almost as difficult to please as Hermione, without displaying her knowledge of precious stones, and before long there were some thousands of pounds' worth of brilliants on the counter for their inspection.

To the bored assistant it began to seem as though they would never come to a decision. Then, just as Mr. Garland was bowing Freddy and Hermione out of the shop, everything began to happen at once. A large limousine slowed down in the street outside and paused with its engine running. At the same moment one of the men with lightning speed scooped up half a dozen bracelets and made for the door, while his companion sent the doorkeeper flying with a vicious blow to the stomach.

Freddy, who had stopped to exchange a few words with Mr. Garland, looked around and saw to his horror that Hermione was standing alone in front of the doorway, directly in the path of the man. She made no attempt to avoid him as he bore down on her. It flashed across Freddy's mind that she was too paralyzed by fear to move. Hopelessly he started to run forward as the man crashed an enormous fist into Hermione's face.

The blow never reached its mark. With a faintly superior smile, Hermione shifted her position slightly at the last moment. An instant later the raider was flying through the air to land with a splintering of glass, head first against the showcase. The whole affair had only occupied a few second of time.

"You never told me you could do jujitsu, Hermione," said Freddy, when he eventually left the shop.

"Judo," Hermione corrected him. "My father had me taught by an expert. It comes in handy sometimes. Of course, I'm rather out of practice."

"I see," said Freddy. "You know, Hermione, there are quite a number of things that I didn't know about you."

They parted. Hermione had an appointment with her hairdresser. Freddy went for a quiet stroll in the park. Then he took a taxi to Fleet Street, where he spent most of the afternoon browsing in the files of various newspapers.

They met again at dinner that evening. Freddy came straight to the point.

"I've been looking at the reports of the inquest on your cousin Johnny," he said.

"Yes?" said Hermione with polite interest.

"It was very odd the way that he shot off the springboard onto the edge of the pool. How exactly did it happen?"

"I explained it all to the coroner. I just happened to move at the critical moment, and he cannoned off me."

"Hard luck on Johnny."

"Very."

"Hard luck on that chap this morning that you just happened to move at the critical moment. I don't think you told the coroner that you could do this judo stuff?"

"Of course not."

"Hard luck on Susan, too, taking that fall out hunting."

"That," said Hermione flatly, "was pure accident. I told her she couldn't hold the horse."

Freddy sighed. "I'll have to give you the benefit of the doubt over that one," he said. "But I'm afraid the engagement's off."

Hermione looked at the diamond on her finger and screwed her hand into a tight little fist.

"I can't stop you breaking it off, Freddy," she said. "But you'll find it very expensive."

He did. It was very expensive indeed. But he thought it well worth the money. As has been said, Freddy was no fool.

# OCTOBER HAS COME AGAIN

## by Thomas Wolfe

If, like me, you suffer from that very human weakness—affection for the sound of one's own voice—here is a first-rate opportunity for your vocal cords. The novelist Thomas Wolfe could do wonderful things with language, though occasionally there was not much thought behind the fireworks. This passage has always seemed to me one of his most beautiful, and a good male voice that is sensitive to Wolfe's swinging rhythms can make something overpoweringly effective out of it.

October had come again, and that year it was sharp and soon; frost was early, burning the thick green on the mountainsides to massed brilliant hues of blazing colors, painting the air with sharpness, sorrow, and delight—and with October.

Doing something different is an adventure in itself. So, while the seasons have passed for six successive years, I have found increasing pleasure in my insect sanctuary. I have come to know intimately each square inch of the hillside. In August sunsets and in dusty September days, during the cool of June dusks and when blizzards of varicolored autumn leaves swept across the garden, I have observed the little events around me.

Down the slope from the barn to the marsh, across the hill from the line of cedars to the wild-cherry tangle, back and forth, my feet have worn thin trails through the grass. In this small area I have watched closely all the intermeshing cogs of life. There I saw the rounded whole; the beginning, the middle, and the end; the reiterated cycle instead of the fragmentary and fleeting. The life story in a succession of generations unfolded around me as the years passed. And I grew to know the plants and birds and the trees as well as the insects.

I saw fruit, which I had known a few weeks before as blossoms, burden the limbs of the apple trees. I saw dead twigs appear on the branches like new wrinkles on a familiar face. I observed the orchard trees under varying conditions of the year—on summer mornings when they stretched long shadows up the slope; on autumn days when they sprinkled the browning grass with red and yellow, striped and speckled fruit; in winter gales when they gripped the earth with widespread roots. Their fate, their adventures with wind and storm and sleet became increasingly important to me.

Similarly, different sections of the garden took on individuality, and I began to think of them by names that fitted best their character. There are Chlorophyll Mountains of the wildcherry tangle; the Knothole Cavern in the trunk of one of the Northern apple trees; the Hills of Lilliput amid the sand of an open stretch; the Swamp Walk; Dragonfly Hollow; the Beetles' Burying Ground; the Lincoln Tree.

Names on the colored face of a map—magic names like Enchanted Pond, Mad River, Lake of Northern Lights—bring a sudden lift to the imagination. They conjure up faraway, enticing places and recall youthful dreams. And for some of us they bring to life that buried heritage of generations of restless pioneers—a yearning, ever-recurring, to follow the Romany Road of exploratory adventure.

Sometimes, and often, there was warmth by day, an ancient drowsy light, a golden warmth and pollenated haze in afternoon, but over all the earth there was the premonitory breath of frost, an exultancy for all the men who were returning, a haunting sorrow for the buried men and for all those who were gone and would not come again.

Now October has come again which in our land is different from October in other lands. The ripe, the golden month has come again, and in Virginia the chinkapins are falling. Frost sharps the middle music of the seasons, and all things living on earth turn home again. The country is so big you cannot say the country has the same October. In Maine, the frost comes sharp and quick as driven nails; just for a week or so the woods, all of the bright and bitter leaves, flare up: the maples turn a blazing bitter red, and other leaves turn yellow like a living light, falling about you as you walk the woods, falling about you like small pieces of the sun so that you cannot say where sunlight shakes and flutters on the ground and where the leaves.

Meanwhile the Palisades are melting in massed molten colors, the season swings along the nation, and a little later in the South dense woodings on the hill begin to glow and soften, and when they smell the burning wood smoke in Ohio children say, "I'll bet that there's a forest fire in Michigan." And the mountaineer goes hunting down in North Carolina, he stays out late with mournful flop-eared hounds; a rind of moon comes up across the rude lift of the hills: what do his friends say to him when he stays out late? Full of hoarse innocence and laughter, they will say, "Mister, yore ole woman's goin' to whup ye if ye don't go home."

Oh, return, return!

October is the richest of the seasons: the fields are cut, the granaries are full, the bins are loaded to the brim with fatness, and from the cider press the rich brown oozings of the York Imperials run. The bee bores to the belly of the yellowed grape, the fly gets old and fat and blue, he buzzes loud, crawls slow, creeps heavily to death on sill and ceiling, the sun goes down in blood and pollen across the bronzed and mown fields of old October.

The corn is shocked: it sticks out in hard yellow rows upon dried ears, fit now for the great red barns in Pennsylvania, and the big stained teeth of crunching horses. The indolent hooves kick swiftly at the boards, the barn is sweet with hay and leather, wood and apples—this, and the clean dry crunching of teeth is all: the sweat, the labor and the plow is over. The late pears mellow on a sunny shelf; hams hang to the warped barn rafters; the pantry shelves are loaded with three hundred jars of fruit. Meanwhile the leaves are turning, turning, up in Maine the chestnut burrs plop thickly to the earth in gusts of wind, and in Virginia the chinkapins are falling.

There is a smell of burning in small towns in afternoon, and men with buckles on their arms are raking leaves in yards as boys come by with straps slung back across their shoulders. The oak leaves, big and brown, are bedded deep in yard and gutter: they make deep wadings to the knee for children in the streets. The fire will snap and crackle like a whip, sharp acrid smoke will sting the eyes, in mown fields the little vipers of the flame eat past the black coarse edge of burned stubble like a line of locusts. Fire drives a thorn of memory in the heart.

The bladed grass, a forest of small spears of ice, is thawed by noon: summer is over but the sun is warm again, and there are days throughout the land, of gold and russet. But summer is dead and gone, the earth is waiting, suspense and ecstasy are gnawing at the hearts of men, the brooding prescience of frost is there. The sun flames red and bloody as it sets, there are old red glintings on the battered pails, the great barn gets the ancient light as the boy slops homeward with warm foaming milk. Great shadows lengthen in the fields, the old red light dies swiftly, and the sunset barking of the hounds is faint and far and full of frost: there are shrewd whistles to the dogs, and frost and silence—this is all. Wind stirs and scuffs and rattles up the old brown leaves, and through the night the great oak leaves keep falling.

Trains cross the continent in a swirl of dust and thunder, the leaves fly down the tracks behind them: the great trains cleave through gulch and gully, they rumble with spoked thunder on the bridges over the powerful brown wash of mighty rivers, they toil through hills, they skirt the rough brown stubble of shorn fields, they whip past empty stations in the little towns and their great stride pounds its even pulse across America. Field and hill and lift and gulch and hollow, mountain and plain and river, a wilderness with fallen trees across it, a thicket of bedded brown and twisted undergrowth, a plain, a desert, and a plantation, a mighty landscape with no fenced niceness, an immensity of fold and convolution that can never be remembered, that can never be forgotten, that has never been described—weary with harvest, potent with every fruit and ore, the immeasurable richness embrowned with autumn, rank, crude, unharnessed, careless of scars or beauty, everlasting and magnificent, a cry, a space, and ecstasy! —American earth in old October.

And the great winds howl and swoop across the land: they make a distant roaring in great trees, and boys in bed will stir in ecstasy, thinking of demons and vast swoopings through the earth. All through the night there is the clean, the bitter rain of acorns, and the chestnut burrs are plopping to the ground.

And often in the night there is only the living silence, the distant frosty barking of a dog, the small clumsy stir and feathery stumble of the chickens on limed roosts, and the moon, the low and heavy moon of autumn, now barred behind the leafless poles of pines, now at the pinewoods' brooding edge and summit, now falling with ghosts' dawn of milky light upon rimed clods of fields and on the frosty scurf on pumpkins, now whiter, smaller, brighter, hanging against the steeple's slope, hanging the same way in a million streets, steeping all the earth in frost and silence.

Then a chime of frost-cold bells may peal out on the brooding air, and people lying in their beds will listen. They will not speak or stir, silence will gnaw the darkness like a rat, but they will whisper in their hearts:

"Summer has come and gone, has come and gone. And

now—?" But they will say no more, they will have no more to say: they will wait listening, silent and brooding as the frost, to time, strange sticking time, dark time that haunts us with the briefness of our days. They will think of men long dead, of men now buried in the earth, of frost and silence long ago, of a forgotten face and moments of lost time, and they will think of things they have no words to utter.

And in the night, in the dark, in the living sleeping silence of the towns, the million streets, they will hear the thunder of the fast express, the whistles of great ships upon the river.

What will they say then? What will they say?

# SLURVIAN SELF-TAUGHT*

## by John Davenport

> On account of the spellings this is funnier read than heard. I include it just because I like it.

Listening to a well-known Hollywood radio commentator some time back, I heard her say that she had just returned from a Yerpeen trip and had had a lovely time nittly. I at once recognized her as an accomplished Slurvian linguist and, being a student of Slurvian, readily understood that she had just returned from a European trip and while there (in Yerp) had had a lovely time in Italy.

Slurvian is coming into common use in the United States, but I am, so far as I know, the only scholar to have made a start toward recording it. There is no official written Slurvian language, but it is possible, by means of phonetic spelling, for me to offer a brief course of instruction in it. In a short time the student can learn enough to add immeasurably to his understanding and enjoyment of conversation wherever he travels in the country.

I first heard pure Slurvian fluently spoken by a co-worker of mine who told me that his closest friend was a man named Hard (Howard). Hard was once in an automobile accident, his car, unfortunately, cliding with another, causing Hard's

* Originally appeared in The New Yorker

wife Dorthy, who was with him, to claps. Dorthy didn't have much stamina but was a sweet woman—sweet as surp.

I soon discovered I had an ear for Slurvian, and since I began to recognize the language, I have encountered many Slurvians. At ball parks, they keep track of hits, runs, and airs. On farms, they plow furs. In florist shops they buy flars. When hard up they bar money from banks and spend it for everything from fewl for the furnace to grum crackers for the children.

When Slurvians travel abroad, they go to visit farn (or forn) countries to see what the farners do that's different from the way we Murcans do things. While in farn countries, they refer to themselves as Murcan tersts and usually say they will be mighty glad to get back to Murca. A Slurvian I once met on a train told me he had just returned from a visit to Mexico. He deplored the lack of automobiles down there and said that the natives ride around on little burrs.

A linguistic authority of my acquaintance, much interested in my work in Slurvian, has suggested to me the possibility that the language may be related to, or a variation of, the one still spoken in England of which such a contraction as "Chumley," for "Cholmondeley," is a familiar example. However, I think the evidence insufficient for drawing such a conclusion. Surnames cannot be considered subject to the ordinary rules of pronunciation. In fact, the only one I have positively identified in Slurvian is Faggot, the name of the American admiral who won the Battle of Mobile Bay.

The name Faggot brings me to a discussion of what I designate as "pure" Slurvian. This includes those Slurvian words that, when spelled exactly as pronounced, also make good English words (such as "Faggot," "burr," and "claps"). The day I can add to the lexicon such a word, hitherto unrecorded, is a happy day for me. Here are some examples of pure Slurvian, alphabetically listed:

> BEAN, *n.* A living creature, as in *human bean.*
> CACTUS, *n. pl.* The people in a play or story.

COURSE, *n.* A group of singers.

FISCAL, *adj.* Pertaining to the body, as opposed to the spurt.

FORM, *n.* Gathering place of the ancient Romans.

GNOME, *n.* Contraction for *no, ma'am. Colloq.*

LINE, *n.* The king of beasts.

LORE, *n.* The more desirable of the two berths in a Pullman section.

MYRRH *n.* A looking glass.

PAR, *n.* An attribute of strength, as in *the par and the glory.*

PLIGHT, *adj.* Courteous.

SEARS, *adj.* Grave intent.

SPORT, *v.t.* To hold up, to bear the weight of.

WRECKERS, *n. pl.* Discs on which music is recorded for phonographs.

I am presently engaged in compiling a dictionary of Slurvian words, which I hope will prove to be the definitive work on the subject. The help of any interested students is welcomed, but I must caution such students to be certain the words are genuine Slurvian and not merely regional speech, such as that of Alabama, Texas, or New England.

Let me close with a final example, to make my meaning clear. Wherever you may be in the United States, if you hear the word "tare," the speaker probably is not referring to a Biblical weed growing in the wheat. More likely he is describing the sensation of extreme fear expressed by a movie fan watching Borse Karloff in a harr picture.

# "LET THE BRIDGES
# FALL DOWN!"

## by Dorothy Canfield Fisher

If you visit the Hall of Fame at New York University you'll find an inscription under the name of educator Horace Mann. It says: THE COMMON SCHOOL IS THE GREATEST DISCOVERY EVER MADE BY MAN. That's an extremely American statement.

We tend to take our public school system a little too much for granted, as we take so many of our finest institutions. Because I don't think we should take it for granted I hope you'll read "Let the Bridges Fall Down!" —preferably aloud, to the whole family.

This story is a true one. It was written just as it happened. There's something about it, I've always thought, that shows the average American at his finest. That's why I'm glad it has appeared in translation in so many foreign countries.

Dorothy Canfield Fisher died November 9, 1958, at her home in the little town of Arlington, Vermont. She was a good novelist and critic. She was a tireless crusader for better education for all Americans. And she was one of the purest and bravest characters I have ever known. In this heart-touching tribute to our free public school system there's a lot of Dorothy Canfield Fisher.


High school graduation in our town is a big event. It is held in the evening so that wage-earning elders can be there. The ritual is always the same. The tall boys and girls march in very slowly while the school band plays—rather loudly for indoors. They mount solemnly to the platform, remembering not to knock their toes on the steps and not to trip over their floating academic robes. These are rented for the night and worn to hide any differences in clothing which might mark differences in income.

They take their places in the semicircle of chairs on the stage. In the glare of the footlights their young faces look blank with inexperience of life.

We have all known them since they were born, while they grew up in our communal past. Now we have come together to celebrate the moment when they become part of our future.

The man to the right of you, the man to your left, the men and women beyond them—every man and woman in the twilight assembly room gazes up at the lighted stage.

The program begins, the glee club, the valedictorian, the "speaker of the day," the awarding of scholarships (these go only to a few).

Singing again. The national anthem. It is the end. Everybody stands up. The decisive moment has passed. Before our eyes they have turned the corner. The big boys and girls are no longer children in our school but young citizens of life. They file carefully down the steps, holding those hired academic robes out of their way. They look intensely serious.

The woman next to you begins, very quietly, gently, and joyfully, to cry. The man on the other side presses his lips together and stares straight ahead—at what? Perhaps he does not see it clear. But it is there.

The assembly room is a fine one; the school is a good one. Astonishing how this smallish group of not rich men and women have achieved it.

Perhaps those fixed eyes of the man next to you are staring back to another gathering of citizens years ago, when the seed for tonight's celebration was planted. Perhaps he is remember-

ing—as you are—every detail of that crucial town meeting
when we argued over whether to build this school. The group
was divided then—not logically, coolly, reasonably, but con-
vulsed, like a human heart, torn by the passionate wrestling of
opposed desires.

On one side was the feeling that the old, venerated community life pattern must not be touched.

Against this massive spiritual immobility the future struggled, as always, to come to birth.

This was no academic discussion group debating the abstract
proposition: "Resolved, that every child has the right to four
years' schooling beyond the eighth grade." This was a fight.

The voters who believed the town could never raise the extra
money required for building and upkeep were sincere in their
mournful conclusions. What with that wretched train service,
and the lack of automobiles, the nearest existing public high
school might almost as well be fifty miles off, rather than the
actual twelve miles of unplowed winter snowdrifts and spring
mudholes. With bitter sincerity they listed the community's
urgent material needs. The hill roads should be resurfaced, or
they would wash out to stony trails. Care for the sick and the
poor was more costly every year. But above all—the bridges!

In a mountain town with flash floods roaring over the banks
after hard rains, bridges have an imperious priority. Our
bridges needed reinforcement, not only from recurring high
water, but against the great tonnage of modern traffic. It would
be dangerous *not* to rebuild them. It would take all the resources of a poor mountain town to keep our bridges in repair.
To add to that expense the enormous cost of a new school—
insane!

The tangible needs of the body and the impalpable needs of
the mind stood up to see which was the stronger. The material
needs, real and actual, outshouted the ideal. The little flickering flame of responsibility for the future of the town's children
died down to a faint glimmer in the hearts of the men and

women whose votes would in a few moments make the decision. Those who had longed and worked for the school sat silent—the crashing of the bridges loud in their ears. What could be said against that?

Then up sprang Patrick Thompson—yes, you are right in guessing from his name that he was Irish. He was only one generation away from those who drank stinking water from the ship's barrel, as they struggled on toward the New World and Vermont. He had worked his way up to partnership in one of our two grocery stores. What education he had—and it was sound—he had received in our public schools. We usually saw him in a white apron, standing behind the counter, selling sugar and tea.

We have never forgotten and we never will let our children forget how he looked that day, his powerful shoulders squared, his hands clenched. We still remember his exact words, intense as the flame of a blowtorch: "We are being told that our town cannot afford to keep its bridges safe and *also* to provide for its children a preparation for life that will give them a fair chance alongside other American children.

"That's what we are being *told*. Not one of us really believes it. We just can't think what to say back. But suppose it were true. Then I say, if we have to choose, 'Let the bridges fall down!' What kind of a town would we rather have, fifty years from now—a place where nitwit folks go back and forth over good bridges? Or a town with well-educated people capable of holding their own in life? You know which of those two is really wanted by every one of us here. I say '*Let the bridges fall down!*'"

He took his seat in silence, the American citizen, the Celt, whose grandparents had lived in enforced ignorance.

It was a turning point in the life of our town. We knew it was. So we spoke not a word.

Presently the moderator said, "Any further discussion?" The silence was unbroken. Then, "Forward your ballots." In a silent line the grave-faced voters moved slowly toward the ballot box, each hand holding a white paper.

The school was built. Years later it burned and was replaced, almost without opposition, by an even better one. The first battle had been conclusive. As we old-timers look at the building, our hearts bursting with thanksgiving, we can see clearly, as if actually carved on the lintel, the words *"Let the bridges fall down!"*

Patrick Thompson has long been in his grave. But he still walks at the head of every graduating class in our high school . . . a school for poor as well as rich, open to every race, to every creed, to everybody.

# THE MONSTER

## by Deems Taylor

This remarkable account of a monster whose monstrosity no longer matters was originally delivered by the
distinguished music critic and composer, Deems Taylor,
as a radio talk. That was many years ago, when radio
still assumed that its audience might be intelligent, sensitive, and responsive to fine English well spoken. I
don't know of a more vivid picture of Richard Wagner
drawn in as few words.

He was an undersized little man, with a head too big for his
body—a sickly little man. His nerves were bad. He had skin
trouble. It was agony for him to wear anything next to his skin
coarser than silk. And he had delusions of grandeur.

He was a monster of conceit. Never for one minute did he
look at the world or at people except in relation to himself. He
was not only the most important person in the world, to himself; in his own eyes he was the only person who existed. He believed himself to be one of the greatest dramatists in the
world, one of the greatest thinkers, and one of the greatest
composers. To hear him talk, he was Shakespeare, and Bee-
thoven, and Plato rolled into one. And you would have had
no difficulty in hearing him talk. He was one of the most exhausting conversationalists that ever lived. An evening with

him was an evening spent in listening to a monologue. Sometimes he was brilliant; sometimes he was maddeningly tiresome. But whether he was being brilliant or dull, he had one sole topic of conversation: himself. What *he* thought and what *he* did.

He had a mania for being in the right. The slightest hint of disagreement, from anyone, on the most trivial point, was enough to set him off on a harangue that might last for hours, in which he proved himself right in so many ways, and with such exhausting volubility, that in the end his hearer, stunned and deafened, would agree with him, for the sake of peace.

It never occurred to him that he and his doings were not of the most intense and fascinating interest to anyone with whom he came in contact. He had theories about almost any subject under the sun, including vegetarianism, the drama, politics, and music; and in support of these theories he wrote pamphlets, letters, books . . . thousands upon thousands of words, hundreds and hundreds of pages. He not only wrote these things and published them—usually at somebody else's expense—but he would sit and read them aloud, for hours, to his friends and his family.

He wrote operas; and no sooner did he have the synopsis of a story, but he would invite—or rather summon—a crowd of his friends to his house and read it aloud to them. Not for criticism. For applause. When the complete poem was written, the friends had to come again and hear *that* read aloud. Then he would publish the poem, sometimes years before the music that went with it was written. He played the piano like a composer, in the worst sense of what that implies, and he would sit down at the piano before parties that included some of the finest pianists of his time and play for them, by the hour, his own music, needless to say. He had a composer's voice. And he would invite eminent vocalists to his house and sing them his operas, taking all the parts.

He had the emotional stability of a six-year-old child. When he felt out of sorts, he would rave and stamp or sink into suicidal gloom and talk darkly of going to the East to end his days as a Buddhist monk. Ten minutes later, when something pleased him, he would rush out of doors and run around the garden, or jump up and down on the sofa, or stand on his head. He could be grief-stricken over the death of a pet dog, and he could be callous and heartless to a degree that would have made a Roman emperor shudder.

He was almost innocent of any sense of responsibility. Not only did he seem incapable of supporting himself, but it never occurred to him that he was under any obligation to do so. He was convinced that the world owed him a living. In support of this belief, he borrowed money from everybody who was good for a loan—men, women, friends, or strangers. He wrote begging letters by the score, sometimes groveling without shame, at others loftily offering his intended benefactor the privilege of contributing to his support, and being mortally offended if the recipient declined the honor. I have found no record of his ever paying or repaying money to anyone who did not have a legal claim upon it.

What money he could lay his hands on he spent like an Indian rajah. The mere prospect of a performance of one of his operas was enough to set him to running up bills amounting to ten times the amount of his prospective royalties. On an income that would reduce a more scrupulous man to doing his own laundry, he would keep two servants. Without enough money in his pocket to pay his rent, he would have the walls and ceiling of his study lined with pink silk. No one will ever know—certainly he never knew—how much money he owed. We do know that his greatest benefactor gave him $6,000 to pay the most pressing of his debts in one city and a year later had to give him $16,000 to enable him to live in another city without being thrown into jail for debt.

He was equally unscrupulous in other ways. An endless procession of women marches through his life. His first wife spent twenty years enduring and forgiving his infidelities. His second wife had been the wife of his devoted friend and admirer, from whom he stole her. And even while he was trying to persuade her to leave her first husband he was writing to a friend to inquire whether he could suggest some wealthy woman—*any* wealthy woman—whom he could marry for her money.

He was completely selfish in his other personal relationships. His liking for his friends was measured solely by the completeness of their devotion to him or by their usefulness to him, whether financial or artistic. The minute they failed him— even by so much as refusing a dinner invitation—or began to lessen in usefulness, he cast them off without a second thought. At the end of his life he had exactly one friend whom he had known even in middle age.

He had a genius for making enemies. He would insult a man who disagreed with him about the weather. He would pull endless wires in order to meet some man who admired his work and was able and anxious to be of use to him—and would proceed to make a mortal enemy of him with some idiotic and wholly uncalled-for exhibition of arrogance and bad manners. A character in one of his operas was a caricature of one of the most powerful music critics of his day. Not content with burlesquing him, he invited the critic to his house and read him the libretto aloud in front of his friends.

The name of this monster was Richard Wagner. Everything that I have said about him you can find on record—in newspapers, in police reports, in the testimony of people who knew him, in his own letters, between the lines of his autobiography. And the curious thing about this record is that it doesn't matter in the least.

Because this undersized, sickly, disagreeable, fascinating little man was right all the time. The joke was on us. He *was* one of the world's great dramatists; he *was* a great thinker; he *was* one of the most stupendous musical geniuses that, up to

now, the world has ever seen. The world did owe him a living.
People couldn't know those things at the time, I suppose; and
yet to us, who know his music, it does seem as though they
should have known. What if he did talk about himself all the
time? If he had talked about himself twenty-four hours every
day for the span of his life he would not have uttered half the
number of words that other men have spoken and written
about him since his death.

When you consider what he wrote—thirteen operas and
music dramas, eleven of them still holding the stage, eight of
them unquestionably worth ranking among the world's great
musico-dramatic masterpieces—when you listen to what he
wrote, the debts and heartaches that people had to endure
from him don't seem much of a price. Eduard Hanslick, the
critic whom he caricatured in *Die Meistersinger* and who
hated him ever after, now lives only because he was caricatured
in *Die Meistersinger*. The women whose hearts he broke are
long since dead; and the man who could never love anyone
but himself has made them deathless atonement, I think, with
*Tristan und Isolde*. Think of the luxury with which for a time,
at least, fate rewarded Napoleon, the man who ruined France
and looted Europe; and then perhaps you will agree that a few
thousand dollars' worth of debts were not too heavy a price to
pay for the *Ring* trilogy.

What if he was faithless to his friends and to his wives? He
had one mistress to whom he was faithful to the day of his
death: Music. Not for a single moment did he ever compromise with what he believed, with what he dreamed. There is
not a line of his music that could have been conceived by a
little mind. Even when he is dull, or downright bad, he is dull
in the grand manner. There is greatness about his worst mistakes. Listening to his music, one does not forgive him for what
he may or may not have been. It is not a matter of forgiveness.
It is a matter of being dumb with wonder that his poor brain
and body didn't burst under the torment of the demon of

creative energy that lived inside him, struggling, clawing, scratching to be released; tearing, shrieking at him to write the music that was in him. The miracle is that what he did in the little space of seventy years could have been done at all, even by a great genius. Is it any wonder that he had no time to be a man?

# PRIVATE HACKLEFORD'S BIG TOE

## by Edmund Love

> There are many pieces in this rag bag of a book that
> seem funny to me, and all I can hope is that they will
> seem funny to you. This wacky story makes me laugh
> every time I reread it. It's pretty long for a reading-
> aloud session, but give it a try anyway.

It was the rule to promote all privates to private, first class after
a battle. The difference in pay between the two ranks was
negligible; it was a matter of prestige. Like a pledge in a
college fraternity, the private could display his new title as the
badge of his initiation and acceptance as a veteran soldier. No
man was ever really accepted in the infantry rifle company
without it. Yet there was one private who won four Purple
Hearts—and still remained a private. I know it's not possible,
but there it is.

Private William Hackleford had joined Item Company,
106th Infantry, as a replacement after the battle for Eniwetok.
He was small, wiry, and quick. He was eighteen years old. His
one hope in life was to become a full-fledged member of the
group to which he had been assigned. In the training period
before the battle for Saipan he was something of an eager
beaver, volunteering for everything that came along and doing
his best to ingratiate himself to everyone he met. Most of the

older men regarded him with some humor and some affection. They dubbed him "the Kid" and made things just a little harder for him than for the rest of the recruits. He was the victim of many practical jokes, the object of good-natured ribbing, and the gullible listener for most of the tall stories. Hackleford never resented any of this. He never bragged to anyone about what he was going to do once he got into battle, but anyone could look at him and see what he was thinking.

Item Company landed on Saipan on June 20, 1944, and Hackleford set out at once to be a hero. Early on the morning of June 21 his platoon was ordered out on sniper patrol through the hilly area north of an airfield. The mission was a simple one. The patrol was to ferret out Japanese stragglers. During that whole first morning the platoon poked around farmhouses, looked into clumps of bushes, and checked culverts without finding a single enemy soldier. Then, about noon, while the men were taking a break for lunch, Hackleford began looking for action on his own initiative. There was a steep hill nearby and he climbed it, gradually circling around to the back, out of sight of the others. Soon the men in the platoon heard shooting and scrambled cautiously up the slope to see what the trouble was. They found Hackleford trapped in a cave by five Japanese soldiers. It didn't take the patrol long to dispatch the enemy and rescue Hackleford, but when someone remonstrated with him for having allowed himself to get trapped in a cave, he became quite indignant. It soon developed that he was in the cave on purpose. When he had first come upon the Japanese, *they* were in the cave. He had thrown a smoke grenade so that they would get out and let him in.

"Hell," he said, "I reckoned I was better off in there where there was some cover than if I was outside and the Japs had the cover."

This rather unorthodox approach to warfare had everyone but the company commander scratching his head. The captain was neither bemused by the logic nor amused by the maneuver. On Hackleford's second morning at Saipan he was serving as a helper on one of the company's supply jeeps. But he had not given up the idea of being a hero. The jeep was sent back to the beach for a load of rations and water. While the driver was negotiating with the beachmaster, Hackleford wandered into an adjacent Marine area and found a pile of boxed ten-in-one rations. There was Virginia baked ham, hamburgers, and roast beef. Hackleford could see no reason why the Marines should eat this type of thing while Item Company subsisted on K rations. He picked up two boxes and started back for the jeep. A Marine sentry challenged him and he challenged right back. The next thing anyone knew, Hackleford was in a fight with three brawny Marines. A few soldiers rushed to his rescue and a few Marines joined the other side. Soon the beachmaster had to call in a whole platoon of MPs. That night the company commander of Item Company summoned Gordon Hall, the company aid man, and gave him instructions.

"That kid's going to get himself killed if he's not careful," he said. "Just keep an eye on him until he gets the ants out of his pants. Every time he starts doing something foolish, you stop him."

Early the next morning, June 23, Item Company moved up to the front line as the reserve for the 3rd Battalion, 106th Infantry. During most of the next twenty-four-hour period the company occupied a woods, directly behind a wide, coverless valley where heavy fighting was taking place. It was not a woods such as one finds in America. The trees were about twelve feet high, spindly, and close together so that a man had to twist and turn to make his way through them. Over the whole area a thick canopy of leaves spread, unbroken. This woods had been the scene of much heavy fighting. The floor was littered with the debris of war. Helmets, packs, broken rifles, and empty ammunition boxes were scattered about. And, as usual, a few stray Japanese soldiers had been left behind. Most of these stragglers were looking only for a chance to escape back to their own lines, but the temptation to shoot at something often got the best of them. All of them had crawled up into the thick foliage, and a rifle occasionally poked out from the leaves and surreptitiously got off a shot at an American.

The sniping was annoying but not dangerous. Item Company was the most annoyed. The men had been lolling about, leaning up against the trees, or lying in the grass on the edge of the woods. One officer had been shot through the hand while he was smoking a cigarette. One of the BAR men had been nicked neatly in the ear while squatting over a latrine. A jeep had been shot in the rear tire. Twice, during the twenty-four-hour period, a patrol had gone into the woods but had found nothing.

At about ten o'clock on the morning of June 24 William Hackleford had opened a box of K rations, extracted an envelope of instant coffee, and boiled a canteen cup of water over a fire that someone had built on the edge of the woods. He had carried his cup of steaming hot coffee over to a group that was stretched out on the grass in the nearby field and sat down with his back up against the trunk of a tree to drink it. Two other men were leaning up against the same tree, each facing in a different direction. No one was talking very much. When the canteen cup of coffee was about one third gone, Hackleford had perched it up on the top of his knees and was dreamily looking off into the distance. At that precise moment two holes suddenly appeared in the cup. A bullet had gone in one side and out the other.

"I didn't even notice it at first," Hackleford said later. "I didn't hear no shot. There wasn't no noise when the bullet hit the cup. The first thing I knew, coffee began leaking down my pants. I looked up and saw the holes. I was going to jump up and tell the other guys, and then I got this here idea. I hadn't moved that damned cup one little whit. If I lined it up,

real careful like, I reckoned I could probably tell right where
that little bastard was shooting from. I reckoned that he could
see me, and I reckoned that if he saw what I was doing, or if
he saw me get excited, he might move. I just made up my
mind to be real cagey. I was going to figure out where he was
and then I was going to go get him. I wasn't going to disturb
nobody, least of all him."

Hackleford lined up the two holes with three easily distinguishable landmarks in the woods. Then, as calmly as he
could, he finished the coffee in one gulp, got up lazily from
the base of the tree, stretched, and moved around behind the
trunk. While standing there, he casually put the canteen back
in its cup, refastened it to his pistol belt, checked his rifle, re-
loaded it, and walked off, almost in a direction directly opposite to that from which the bullet had come. After moving
about forty yards, he turned abruptly and stalked into the
woods. Only one man had seen him go. That was Gordon
Hall, the company aid man.

"The minute I saw that little bastard squinting through
his canteen cup, I knew he was up to something," Hall said
later. "Then I saw him march out into the field like he was
passing in review, do a by-the-right-flank, and I decided I better go get him. Hell, he couldn't have fooled nobody. My only
trouble was that I didn't get started quick enough. He had
a head start on me, and it took me a little while to find him in
them woods."

Hackleford didn't find the going easy. He had to twist and
turn, then stop and peer around for the landmarks, but he
finally reached the spot directly in line with the three trees he
had marked. When he finally had himself all lined up, he
stopped, crouched, and looked through the trees. Then he
moved on for twenty feet, stopped, crouched, and looked
again. Without realizing it, the second time he stopped he
was directly beneath the tree where his intended quarry was
perched. The Japanese soldier had been aware, for some time,

that Hackleford was looking for him. He seems to have tried
to get his rifle into position to fire, but he also seems to have
realized that he had only one shot to do the business. The
tangle of leaves and branches, the desire to keep from giving
away his position, and the necessity of making the most of his
one opportunity, all contrived to keep that shot from being
fired until it was absolutely certain to take effect. When
Hackleford stopped beneath the tree, there was no use in waiting longer. Very carefully the Japanese lowered the barrel of
his rifle down through the branches until it was pointing
directly at the top of Hackleford's helmet, a few inches away.
It was at this precise moment that Hackleford straightened
out of his crouch. The helmet clanked against the rifle barrel,
and several things happened at once.

"The minute I heard that metal clank on my helmet, I
knew I was in trouble for sure," Hackleford said afterward. "I
jumped. Maybe I just fell. Just about the time I moved was
when he pulled that trigger. When that rifle went off, it was
right up against my ear. I never heard such a loud noise."

Hackleford had fallen sideways and backwards and fell flat
on his back. In some way the bullet from the Japanese rifle
crossed the front of his body and "took me in the big toe." He
was not entirely aware that he had been hit.

"If I was thinking at all," he recalls, "I was thinking about
that little bastard up there in that tree. I knew he had a clip
in that rifle of his, but I knew it wasn't no M-1. He had to
work a bolt before he could get off another shot, and I didn't
aim to give him no chance to do *that*. So, while I was sprawled
out there on my back, I just pulled up my rifle and give him
the whole clip. The next thing I knew, he come down out of
there, head first."

The Japanese helmet is made of steel. The dead man landed
squarely in the middle of Hackleford's stomach. The blow
knocked the wind out of Hackleford and he could do nothing
but lie on the ground, gasping for breath. At the same time

the sight of the Japanese soldier's rifle had raked across Hackleford's forehead, leaving a thin scratch in which the blood slowly began to form, then trickle to one side. Hackleford was not aware that he was bleeding. All he knew was that a Japanese soldier was lying across his chest. His one idea was to get out from under the body and get out of the woods quickly. He groped around on the ground for his helmet and his rifle. He found a helmet, all right, but it wasn't his. The helmet he grabbed and clamped on his head was a helmet that belonged to another American soldier who had been wounded in a previous action. The wound suffered by the other man was a head wound. There was a jagged hole in the helmet, near the forehead.

Gordon Hall had been looking frantically for Hackleford when the shots rang out. By proceeding in the direction of the sound of the shots, Hall managed to fight his way through the tree trunks, just in time to see Hackleford clamp the helmet on his head. It was an awesome sight to behold. Hackleford was struggling to sit upright. His forehead had blood trickling down it. He was groggy. He had a shattered, torn helmet on his head. A dead Japanese soldier was draped across his chest.

"Lay down," Hall yelled, as he came running up. "Lay back down, you bastard. Don't you know enough not to get up? You might be hurt bad."

"The hell with you," Hackleford yelled back.

Hall never let Hackleford finish getting up. He grabbed Hackleford by the shoulders and threw him back on the ground, then sat astride of him.

"My God!" Hall kept muttering over and over. He reached down into the first-aid kit that he carried on his hip and pulled out a box of sulfa powder and a roll bandage. Then, knocking off the battered helmet, he quickly sprinkled some of the powder on Hackleford's hair and forehead and started wrapping the bandage around and around. He still kept muttering, "My God!"

Hackleford had not ceased to struggle. He managed to get himself up to his elbows several times. Each time Hall would push him back.

"Let me up, you son of a bitch," Hackleford yelled at him. "What are you trying to do to me anyway?"

"My God, man!" Hall said. "You're shot in the head. Don't you feel nothing?"

"The hell I'm shot in the head," Hackleford said.

"The hell you ain't shot in the head," Hall retorted. "Just look at here!" He reached out and handed the torn, battered helmet to Hackleford. It was covered with the dried blood from the old wound, and it was wet with the new blood from Hackleford's scratch.

"This ain't my helmet," Hackleford said, after turning it over and over and looking at it.

"It was on your head," Hall said. "The trouble with you is that you been knocked goofy. You don't know where you are or what's going on."

Hackleford subsided and tried to think when he'd been shot in the head. Hall continued to wrap the bandage until he'd finished, then he reached into the kit again and brought out a large white tag. He filled it out and tied it to the front of Hackleford's fatigues. "Gunshot wounds (GSW), in head." Hall stood up.

"Now I got to find a way to get you out of here," Hall said, looking around. "I don't know whether it's safe to leave you here while I go back and get a litter or not."

Hackleford struggled up to his elbow again.

"If you'd fix my toe," he said, "I'd walk."

"What toe?" Hall asked him.

Hackleford pointed and Hall knelt down.

"How'd this happen?"

"That son of a bitch, there, shot me," Hackleford said, pointing at the dead Japanese soldier.

Hall examined the wound thoughtfully, then suddenly dropped the leg from his knee.

"To hell with it," he said. "It ain't serious, and it ain't going to kill you for a while. It's your head I'm worried about. Your brains are liable to start leaking out any minute, and I got to get you someplace where a doc can look at you. Here!" He extended his hand to help Hackleford up. "I'll carry you back to the battalion aid station. It's as close as the company and you don't weigh much. If I can just keep you from bumping your goddamned head against a tree, we're all right."

It took Hall ten minutes to carry his patient through the woods to the battalion aid station. When he emerged into the clearing where the battalion command post had been set up, one of the aid men shouted at him.

"Your old man's looking all over hell for you, Hall," the man said. "Jay Company's going in the line and he wants you back. You better get your ass back over there."

"Okay! Okay!" Hall said with some irritation, "but I got a bad hurt man here. He might be a mortal case."

"Put him under the tree over there by the tent. I'll get to him in a minute," the battalion aid man said.

Hall carried Hackleford over to the tree, propped him up, took a cigarette out of his pocket, lit it, and stuck it between the patient's lips, then said goodbye and disappeared back into the woods. The 3rd Battalion, 106th Infantry was a busy battalion on June 24, 1944. Two of the companies were suffering heavy casualties, and wounded men had been pouring into the battalion aid station in a steady stream all morning. At least twenty men besides Hackleford were awaiting attention in the tent and outside it.

"We had one surgeon on duty at each battalion," a doctor told me afterward. "On a day like that there was just too much for one man to do. There was only one solution. When things got too thick, we took care of the most seriously wounded. The rest we sent back to regiment or one of the division stations where there were more doctors."

Hackleford leaned against his tree for a half hour or more. No one paid any attention to him at all.

"Medics was running all over the place," he said later. "They were busy, but my toe was starting in to hurt something furious. I wanted somebody to fix it. After a while I began yelling at every medic that went by. They didn't pay any attention at all."

"Sure, Hall told me about a guy he brought in," one 3rd Battalion medic told me afterward. "Hall said the guy was hurt bad. This guy that was leaning against the tree didn't look like he was in very bad shape. I didn't connect him with the guy Hall brought in at all. Anway, I knew the guy against the tree wasn't going to die right away, and I had a couple of guys that looked like they might be going to, so I took care of them."

A doctor finally emerged from the aid tent, lit a cigarette, took a long puff, looked up at the sky, threw the cigarette away, and turned to go back inside. Hackleford bellowed at him. The doctor turned to him, looked, then walked over to the tree.

"Who are you?" the doctor said, kneeling. Then he looked at the tag. He lifted the edge of the bandage. "No bleeding now," he said, then turned. "Sergeant!" he yelled. "This man shouldn't be sitting up with a head wound. Put him on a litter and cover him with a blanket," the doctor said. "I want him on the first jeep going back to regiment. I think he'll be all right, but get him somewhere where someone can do him some good." He turned to Hackleford. "You feel all right?"

"That doc was out on his feet," Hackleford said later. "I felt sorry for him, and I felt guilty about bothering him over that little old toe. I was going to tell him that I'd be all right if some first-aid man would just fix it. I started to get up from the tree. The only trouble was that I touched that damned toe on the ground, and I liked to passed out. It hurt. I reached out and grabbed the tree and hung on. The doc put out his hands. 'Steady, boy, steady,' he said. The sergeant grabbed me by the shoulders and lowered me down to the ground and made me stretch out. The doctor lifted my eyelid. 'No sign of shock, but we'll give him plasma anyway,' he said. 'Rig up the bottle and get him on that jeep.' The sergeant said he would and went away. The doctor looked at my dog tags and yelled out after him, 'Type O,' then he turned back to me again. He wanted to know what happened, so I told him about going out in the woods and the sniper sticking the rifle by my ear and pulling the trigger."

"Which ear?" the doctor said.

"This one." Hackleford pointed.

The doctor bent over and looked closely, then turned to the tent again.

"Sergeant!" he yelled.

The sergeant stuck his head out of the tent.

"Yes, sir," he said.

"Bring along that tube of ointment and put some on this man's face," the doctor said. "He has second- or third-degree powder burns on his cheek. Put a new tag on him while you're at it. The aid man didn't notice it."

A new jeepload of wounded roared into the CP area at this moment and the doctor looked at it wearily, patted Hackleford on the shoulder, and walked away.

A medical jeep-ambulance arrived at the battalion aid station a few moments later, and two aid men emerged from the tent in a businesslike manner, lifted Hackleford onto a litter, strapped him to it, lifted the litter to the jeep, attached a plasma bottle to the bracket of the litter rack, stuck a tube in Hackleford's arm, covered him with a blanket, and bid the jeep driver bon voyage.

"We drove about a mile and a half, over a very rough road," Hackleford recalled. "The other guys on that jeep had been doped up, so they didn't say much. I was the only guy that could talk and I kept telling the driver that my toe hurt. I guess the driver was used to guys raving while he drove them along, and I guess he'd heard about guys who had their legs cut off and still yelled about their toe hurting. He was pretty squeamish, I guess, and he wasn't going to lift that blanket to look, but he sure imagined the worst. He just hunched over the steering wheel and drove harder."

The regimental aid station was as busy as the battalion aid station had been. As soon as the jeep drove into the yard of the farmhouse where it was located, a doctor strode out of a building, clip board in hand. He moved from patient to patient, looking at the tags, examining each man, and issuing instructions. When he came to Hackleford, he stuck a thermometer in his mouth, copied the data from the two tags tied to the fatigue blouse, looked at the dog tags, checked the plasma bottle, lifted the edge of the bandage, rubbed his finger through the smear of ointment, and felt for the pulse.

"Shock retarded. Pulse normal. Temperature normal," the doctor said to himself, then turned to his assistants. "This man's all right to go back to the beach. Leave him on the jeep. Take the others inside and bring out those three men I had marked for the ship."

The jeep driver whispered something to the doctor, pointing at Hackleford. The doctor lifted the blanket and looked under it.

"You're all right, soldier," he said to Hackleford. "You've got both arms and both legs. Stop fretting about things."

Hackleford recalls that he was a little exasperated at this point.

"Maybe I *did* yell too hard," he said later, "but I was mad because they wouldn't fix my toe. I asked that doc if he was going to listen to what I had to say because I had something important to tell him. He just stepped over, calm like, and put his hand over my mouth and told me to quiet down, that I didn't have to yell at the top of my voice, he could hear me all right. He asked me if I thought everybody was deaf. I said I guessed they were because they weren't hearing me very well. He seemed to think after that, then all of a sudden he stepped over and looked at those tags again."

"How did you get those powder burns, soldier?" the doctor said in a loud voice.

"A Jap stuck his rifle by my ear and pulled the trigger," Hackleford said.

The doctor bent over and looked at Hackleford's face closely, then turned his head and tried to look into the ear. "I want you to put another tag on this man," he said, when he straightened up. "He's been shot by a weapon held close to his ear. He's obviously having trouble with his auditory processes. Put down, 'Possible injuries to eardrum.' And you might write that we recommend sedation."

Hackleford's next stop was a large, Chautauqua-like tent that had been erected near Blue Beach Two. When the jeep pulled up in front of it, the litters were lifted off and carried into the tent. A few minutes after their arrival a doctor came along the aisle, accompanied by several orderlies. The doctor stopped at each stretcher, looked briefly at the tags, then turned to issue instructions to his assistants. When he came to Hackleford, he went through the same routine as the other doctors.

"This man may be seriously injured," he said to one of the orderlies. "I think the best thing we can do is get him out to the ship at once. Put him on the first boatload." He patted Hackleford's hand. "How do you feel, boy?" he asked.

It was at this point that Hackleford became aware of the fact that he had been strapped to the litter. He tried to raise himself up on his elbows as he answered the doctor's question. The strap pressed hard against the spot where the Japanese soldier's head had hit him in the stomach. He winced and fell back. The doctor saw the grimace of pain.

"Where's that hurt?" the doctor said.

"In my stomach," Hackleford said.

"Stomach?" the doctor said, and threw back the blanket, tore open the fatigue jacket, looked a moment, then tapped Hackleford's abdomen with his fingers. "That hurt?" he asked.

"You're damned right it hurts," Hackleford said. "It's sore as hell."

"I don't wonder it hurts. You've got a nice big bruise there," the doctor said. It'll be black and blue in the morning."

"Listen, Doc," Hackleford said, trying to raise himself again. "I don't care about no goddamned black-and-blue spot. I'm practically bleeding to death."

The doctor looked at the three tags now tied to the front of Hackleford's fatigues.

"There's nothing here about stomach injuries or internal hemorrhages," he said.

"I don't know nothing about eternal whatever it was you said," Hackleford exploded. "It's my toe that's bleeding."

"Your toe?" The doctor looked at him sharply.

"Aw, hell," Hackleford said, dropping back, exhausted. "I don't know what it is any more. I lost track a long time ago."

The doctor put his hand on Hackleford's forehead, then turned to the orderly beside him.

"I think you'd better give this man the recommended sedation," he said, "and, Sergeant—"

"Yes, sir," the orderly said.

"You'd better put another tag on him. I don't like this bleeding business. Say-er-ah, 'Severe abdominal bruises. Possibility of internal hemorrhages.'"

Hackleford recalled little of what happened to him next. An enlisted aid man came by and jabbed him in the arm with a hypodermic needle and he went to sleep.

"I was tired, anyway," he recalled later.

When Hackleford awoke, it was to find himself aboard the hospital ship *Solace*. The ship was already two hours at sea, en route to the Hawaiian Islands. There were three white-coated doctors gathered around him, and Hackleford noted, with some relief, that they were all looking at his foot. One of the three doctors glanced up and saw that the patient was awake. He came to stand at the head of the bed.

"How did this happen, soldier?" the doctor asked.

Hackleford started at the beginning and told everything that had happened since he got up to go into the woods.

"Then you think there is nothing the matter with you except the foot?" the doctor asked him.

"I know there's nothing the matter with me except the foot. I been trying to tell everybody," Hackleford said.

"I don't think you tried very hard," the doctor said, somewhat cynically.

The doctors worked on Hackleford's foot, bandaged it, and put it in a temporary cast.

"Nobody on that boat treated me very good," Hackleford recalled later. "The doctors wouldn't talk to me, and the nurses wouldn't come near me. They was babying hell out of everybody else, but after a couple of days they gave *me* a cane and put *me* on KP. It took us more than two weeks to get back to Honolulu, and some of the other guys that got up and around was talking about having some fun when they got ashore. All the guys that was able was supposed to get three-day passes. They didn't give me no three-day pass. When I got off the boat, they put me in a truck, and the next damned thing I know I am on an airplane, headed back to Saipan. By the time I get back and find what is left of Jay Company, the battle is all over with and I missed the whole damn thing."

A month after the battle was over the battalion commander distributed medals in Item Company.

"He came down the line and pinned a Purple Heart with three Oak Leaf Clusters on me," Hackleford recalled. "That's four Purple Hearts. One was for getting shot in the head, which I didn't. One was for getting a busted eardrum, which I didn't. One was for a bleeding stomach, which wasn't bleeding at all. And one was for burns on the face, which just might have been true. I didn't get anything for getting shot in the toe, but I sure heard about that toe, I can tell you. About a month after I got all those Purple Hearts, an MP came down to the company and told me I was under arrest for shooting myself in the toe. He told me I was going to be court-martialed for cowardice in the face of the enemy. It was one of them doctors on the ship that jumped to conclusions and turned me

in. I spent about a day in the stockade and then they take me
right in to see the general. He makes me stand at attention
while he reads me the riot act about what kind of a bastard
will shoot himself in the toe to keep from doing his duty for
his country. Then, when he is all done with the lecture, he
holds up my service record. 'I see by this,' he says to me, 'that
you have been wounded in action four different times. If it
wasn't for that, I *would* court-martial you. As it is, I am returning you to duty, but I am going to recommend that your
promotion to private, first class, be withheld until you prove,
in battle, that you deserve it.' "

# AMERICAN NAMES

## by Stephen Vincent Benét

During the Second World War, together with thousands of other writers, I worked on war propaganda. Of all the writers who co-operated in this effort none offered himself with a purer devotion than the poet, novelist, and short-story writer Stephen Vincent Benét. He died in the middle of the war, at the sadly early age of forty-four. What the American historian Henry Steele Commager said is literally true: "He loved his country passionately, gave his life to singing her beauty and her glory."

You probably know, perhaps from TV or some other medium, his classic tale, "The Devil and Daniel Webster." Or you may have read his magnificent long poem of the Civil War, "John Brown's Body." Winner of the Pulitzer Prize in 1929, it has refused to die. In 1953 Raymond Massey headed an all-star cast as they toured the country with a triumphant reading-aloud version of it.

Note how much of America Benét manages to summon up merely by setting these rough jewels of American place names in the coronet of his singing verse.

I have fallen in love with American names,
The sharp gaunt names that never get fat,

The snakeskin-titles of mining claims,
The plumed war-bonnet of Medicine Hat,
Tucson and Deadwood and Lost Mule Flat.

Seine and Piave are silver spoons,
But the spoonbowl-metal is thin and worn,
There are English counties like hunting-tunes
Played on the keys of a postboy's horn,
But I will remember where I was born.

I will remember Carquinez Straits,
Little French Lick and Lundy's Lane,
The Yankee ships and the Yankee dates
And the bullet-towns of Calamity Jane.
I will remember Skunktown Plain.

I will fall in love with a Salem tree
And a rawhide quirt from Santa Cruz,
I will get me a bottle of Boston sea
And a blue-gum nigger to sing me blues.
I am tired of loving a foreign muse.

Rue des Martyrs and Bleeding-Heart-Yard,
Senlis, Pisa, and Blindman's Oast,
It is a magic ghost you guard;
But I am sick for a newer ghost—
Harrisburg, Spartanburg, Painted Post.

Henry and John were never so,
And Henry and John were always right?
Granted, but when it was time to go
And the tea and the laurels had stood all night,
Did they never watch for Nantucket Light?

I shall not rest quiet in Montparnasse.
I shall not lie easy in Winchelsea.

You may bury my body in Sussex grass,
You may bury my tongue at Champmédy.
I shall not be there. I shall rise and pass.
Bury my heart at Wounded Knee.

# THE HALLS OF MONTEZUMA

## by William H. Prescott

*"From the halls of Montezuma
To the shores of Tripoli . . ."*

No American can hear those lines of the Marine Hymn without a thrill. But how many of us know anything about the fabled halls of Montezuma or what connections they have with the Marines?

Tradition has it that the Marine Corps Hymn was first sung directly after the Mexican War of 1846. An old Spanish folk song is believed to have provided the tune.

And the opening lines referred to "the halls of Montezuma" in Mexico City where, on September 14, 1847, the Marines had taken over guard, thus signalizing the end of the Mexican War.

What were those halls and their master like? The best account is to be found in William Hickling Prescott's *Conquest of Mexico*—a classic history of the fall of Montezuma, King of the Aztec nation, before Cortez's armored cavaliers in 1519.

Montezuma encouraged a taste for architectural magnificence in his nobles and contributed his own share toward the embellishment of the city. Not content with the spacious residence of his father, Montezuma erected another on a yet more magnificent scale.

This pile of buildings spreads over an extent of ground so vast that, as one of the Conquerors assures us, its terraced roof might have afforded ample room for thirty knights to run their courses in a regular tourney. I have already noticed its interior decorations, its fanciful draperies, its roofs inlaid with cedar and other odoriferous woods, its numerous and spacious apartments, which Cortez does not hesitate to declare superior to anything of the kind in Spain.

Adjoining the principal edifice was an armory, filled with the weapons and military dresses worn by the Aztecs, all kept in the most perfect order, ready for instant use. The emperor was himself very expert in the management of the *maquahuitl*, or Indian sword, and took great delight in witnessing athletic exercises and the mimic representation of war by his young nobility. Another building was used as a granary and others as warehouses for the different articles of food and apparel.

There was also an immense aviary, in which birds of splendid plumage were assembled from all parts of the empire. Here was the scarlet cardinal, the golden pheasant, the endless parrot tribe with their rainbow hues (the royal green predominant), and that miniature miracle of nature, the hummingbird, which delights to revel among the honeysuckle bowers of Mexico. Three hundred attendants had charge of this aviary and in the moulting season were careful to collect the beautiful plumage, which, with its many-colored tints, furnished the materials for the Aztec painter.

A separate building was reserved for the fierce birds of prey: the voracious vulture tribes and eagles of enormous size, whose home was in the snowy solitudes of the Andes. No less than five hundred turkeys, the cheapest meat in Mexico, were allowed for their daily consumption.

Adjoining this aviary was a menagerie of wild animals, gathered from the mountain forests and remote swamps. The collection was still further swelled by a great number of reptiles and serpents remarkable for their size and venemous qualities, among which the Spaniards beheld the rattlesnake, which they called "the fiery little animal with the castanets in his tail."

The serpents were confined in long cages lined with down or feathers, or in troughs of mud and water. The beasts and birds of prey were provided with apartments large enough to allow of their moving about and secured by a strong lattice-work, through which light and air were freely admitted.

Extensive gardens were spread out around the buildings. They were filled with fragrant shrubs and flowers and with various medicinal plants, the virtues of which were perfectly understood by the Aztecs. Fountains of pure water sparkled amidst this labyrinth of sweet-scented groves and shrubs. Light and fanciful pavilions, overlooking pools of limpid water, provided shelter for the monarch and his mistresses in the sultry heat of the Mexican summer.

But the most luxurious residence of the Aztec monarch was the royal hill of Chapultepec, consecrated by the ashes of his ancestors. It stood west of the capital, surrounded by the waters of the Tezcuco River. On its lofty crest of red-purple rock there now stands the magnificent, though desolate, castle, erected by the young viceroy Galvez, at the close of the seventeenth century. The view from its windows is one of the finest in Mexico, and Montezuma's gardens stretched for miles around the base of the hill. Even today they are still shaded by gigantic cypresses, more than fifty feet in circumference, which were centuries old at the time of the Conquest.

The domestic establishment of Montezuma was on the same scale of barbaric splendor as everything else about him. He could boast as many wives as were found in the harem of an Eastern sultan. These were lodged in apartments, provided with every accommodation for personal comfort and cleanliness. They passed their hours in weaving and embroidery and especially in the graceful featherwork, for which materials were furnished by the royal aviaries.

They conducted themselves with strict decorum, under the supervision of aged females, who acted in the capacity of duennas. The palace was supplied with numerous baths, and Montezuma himself set the example of frequent ablutions. He bathed at least once and changed his dress four times every day. He never put on the same dress for a second time but gave it away to his attendants. Not even his contemporary—Elizabeth I—could afford such costly habits.

His meals the emperor took alone. The well-matted floor of a large saloon was covered with hundreds of dishes, kept hot over the flame. The royal bill of fare included game from the distant forests and fish which, the day before, had been swimming in the Gulf of Mexico.

The meats were served by the attendant nobles and maidens selected for their personal grace and beauty. A screen of richly gilt and carved wood was drawn around the emperor so as to conceal him from vulgar eyes while he ate. He was seated on a cushion, and his dinner was served on a low table covered with a delicate cotton cloth.

The dishes were of the finest ware of Cholula, and the entire table service was never allowed to appear a second time but was given away to the attendants. The dining room was lighted by torches made of a resinous wood, which sent forth a sweet odor as they burned.

The emperor never took any other beverage than the *chocolatl*, a drink of chocolate flavored with vanilla and other spices and reduced to a froth of the consistency of honey, which gradually dissolved in the mouth. This beverage was served in golden goblets, with spoons of the same metal or of finely wrought tortoise shell. The emperor consumed no less than fifty pitchers of it a day.

The dessert of the Aztec emperor was an assortment of fruits gathered fresh from the luscious trees of the tropics, plucked from the green groves of the *tierra caliente*, and transmitted by means of couriers to the capital.

After the royal appetite was appeased, water was handed to him by female attendants in a silver basin; pipes were brought, made of a varnished and richly gilt wood, from which Montezuma inhaled the fumes of an intoxicating weed, "called *tobacco*," mingled with liquid amber. While smoking, he enjoyed the exhibitions of his mountebanks and jugglers, of whom a regular corps was attached to the palace. No people, not even those of China or Hindustan, surpassed the Aztecs in feats of agility.

When he had sufficiently refreshed his spirits with these various diversions, the emperor composed himself to sleep, for in his siesta he was as regular as a Spaniard. On awakening, he gave audience to ambassadors from foreign states, or his own tributary cities, or to such caciques as had suits to prefer to him.

They were introduced by the young nobles in attendance, and, whatever might be their rank, unless of the blood royal, they were obliged to submit to the humiliation of shrouding their rich dresses with the coarse mantle of *nequen* (sackcloth) and entering barefooted, with downcast eyes, into the presence.

The emperor addressed brief remarks to the suitors, and the parties retired with the same reverential obeisance, taking care to keep their faces turned toward the monarch.

Well might Cortez exclaim that no court, whether of the Grand Seigneur or any other infidel, ever displayed so pompous and elaborate a ceremonial!

The maintenance of this court of several thousands of individuals involved heavy expenditures and required complicated accounts. But everything in Montezuma's household was conducted with perfect order; all the various receipts and disbursements were set down in the picture writing of the country. The arithmetical characters were even more refined than the ones used for letters; and a separate apartment was filled with hierogliphical ledgers—representing the palace accounts.

Such was the picture of Montezuma's domestic establishment and way of living, as Cortez and his Spanish followers saw it.

# THE TREASURER'S REPORT

## by Robert Benchley

Robert Benchley made his reputation as a platform humorist with "The Treasurer's Report." No one can do it as he did, but that hasn't prevented hundreds or maybe thousands from trying. Even when read aloud by a rank amateur, it remains, after the passage of so many years, terribly funny. It's hard, of course, to find people who aren't familiar with it, but if your children are young enough, it may be new to them. At any rate, no collection of "readaloudables" would be quite complete without this treasured classic.

### Author's Note

About eight years ago (eight, to be exact) I was made a member of a committee to plan a little Sunday-night entertainment for some newspapermen who wanted to act. The committee was supposed to meet at a certain time, each member with some suggestions for sketches or song numbers. (In order to get out of this morass of pussyfooting which I have got myself into, I will come right out and say that the "certain time" at which the committee was to meet was 8 P.M. on Sunday night.) At 7:15 P.M. I suddenly realized that I had no suggestions to offer for the entertainment.

As all the other members of the committee were conscientious workers, I felt considerably abashed. But as they were also charming and indulgent fellows, I knew that they would take my dereliction in good part if I could only take their minds off the business of the meeting and possibly put them in good humor with a comical story or a card trick. So, on the way up in the taxi, I decided to make believe, when they called on me for my contribution, that I had misunderstood the purpose of the committee meeting and had come prepared to account for the year's expenditures. These I jotted down on the back of an old shirt.

As is always the case with such elaborate trickery, my plan to escape censure by diverting the minds of the committee fell flat. They listened to my temporizing report and voted me a droll chap, but then they said, "And now what are your suggestions for the entertainment?" As I had to confess that I had none, it was agreed that, *faute de mieux,* I should elaborate the report I had just offered and perhaps acquire some skill in its delivery and give that as my share of the Sunday-night entertainment. At this moment my entire life changed its course.

I guess that no one ever got so sick of a thing as I, and all my friends, have grown of this Treasurer's Report. I did it every night and two matinees a week for nine months in the Third Music Box Revue. Following that, I did it for ten weeks in vaudeville around the country, I did it at banquets and teas, at friend's houses and in my own house, and finally went to Hollywood and made a talking movie of it. In fact, I have inflicted it on the public in every conceivable way except over the radio and dropping it from airplanes. But I have never written it. I have been able to throw myself into a sort of trance while delivering it, so that the horrible monotony of the thing made no impression on my nerve cells, but to sit down and put the threadbare words on paper has always seemed just a little too much to bear.

I am writing it out now more as a release than anything else. Perhaps, in accordance with Freudian theories, if I rid myself of this thing which has been skulking in the back of my mind for eight years, I shall be a normal man again. No one has to read it. I hope that no one does, for it doesn't read at all well. All I want to do is get it on paper and out of the way. I feel better already, just from having told all this. And please let's never bring the matter up again.

*The report is delivered by an assistant treasurer who has been called in to pinch-hit for the regular treasurer who is ill. He is not a very good public speaker, this assistant, but after a few minutes of confusion is caught up by the spell of his own oratory and is hard to stop.*

I shall take but a very few moments of your time this evening, for I realize that you would much rather be listening to this interesting entertainment than to a dry financial statement . . . but I *am* reminded of a story—which you have probably all of you heard.

It seems that there were these two Irishmen walking down the street when they came to a—oh, I should have said in the first place that the parrot which was hanging out in *front* of the store—or rather belonging to one of these two fellows— the *first* Irishman, that is—was—well, *any*way, this parrot—

*(After a slight cogitation, he realizes that, for all practical purposes, the story is as good as lost; so he abandons it entirely and, stepping forward, drops his facile, storytelling manner and assumes a quite spurious businesslike air.)*

Now, in connection with reading this report, there are one or two points which Dr. Murnie wanted brought up in connection with it, and he has asked me to bring them up in connec—to bring them up.

In the first place, there is the question of the work which we are trying to do up there at our little place at Silver Lake, a work which we feel not only fills a very definite need in the community but also fills a very definite need—er—in the community. I don't think that many members of the society realize just how big the work is that we are trying to do up there. For instance, I don't think that it is generally known that most of our boys are between the age of fourteen. We feel that, by taking the boy at this age, we can get closer to his real nature—for a boy *has* a very real nature, you may be sure—and bring him into closer touch not only with the school, the parents, and with each other, but also with the town in which they live, the country to whose flag they pay allegiance, and to the —ah—(*trailing off*) town in which they live.

Now the fourth point which Dr. Murnie wanted brought up was that in connection with the installation of the new furnace last fall. There seems to have been considerable talk going around about this not having been done quite as economically as it might—have—been—done, when, as a matter of fact, the whole thing *was* done just as economically as possible—in fact, even *more* so. I have here a report of the Furnace Committee, showing just how the whole thing was handled from start to finish.

(*Reads from report, with considerable initial difficulty with the stiff covers.*)

Bids were submitted by the following firms of furnace contractors, with a clause stating that if we did not engage a firm to do the work for us we should pay them nothing for submitting the bids. This clause alone saved us a great deal of money. The following firms, then, submitted bids:

Merkle, Wybigant Co., the Eureka Dust Bin and Shaker Co., the Elite Furnace Shop, and Harris, Birnbauer and Harris. The bids of Merkle, Wybigant being the lowest, Harris, Birnbauer were selected to do the job.

*(Here a page is evidently missing from the report, and a hurried search is carried on through all the pages, without result.)*

Well, that pretty well clears up that end of the work.

Those of you who contributed so generously last year to the floating hospital have probably wondered what became of the money. I was speaking on this subject only last week at our uptown branch, and after the meeting, a dear little old lady, dressed in lavender, came up on the plaform and, laying her hand on my arm, said, "Mr. So-and-So (calling me by name), Mr. So-and-So, what the hell did you do with all the money we gave you last year?" Well, I just laughed and pushed her off the platform, but it has occurred to the committee that perhaps some of you, like that little old lady, would be interested in knowing the disposition of the funds.

Now, Mr. Rossiter, unfortunately our treasurer—or rather Mr. Rossiter, our *treasurer, unfortunately* is confined at his home tonight with a bad head cold and I have been asked *(he hears someone whispering at him from the wings, but decides to ignore it)*—and I have been asked if I would *(the whisperer will not be denied, so he goes over to the entrance and receives a brief message, returning beaming and laughing to himself)*. Well, the joke seems to be on *me!* Mr. Rossiter has *pneumonia!*

Following, then, is a summary of the Treasurer's Report:

*(Reads, in a very businesslike manner.)*

During the year 1929—and by that is meant 1928—the Choral Society received the following in donations:

B. L. G. ............................................. $500
G. K. M. .............................................  500

| | |
|---|--:|
| Lottie and Nellie W.— ............... | 500 |
| In memory of a happy summer at Rye Beach ........................... | 10 |
| Proceeds of a sale of coats and hats left in the boathouse .................... | 14.55 |
| And then the Junior League gave a performance of *Pinafore* for the benefit of the fund, which, unfortunately, resulted in a deficit of ..................... | $300 |
| Then, from dues and charges .......... | 2,354.75 |
| And, following the installation of the new furnace, a saving in coal amounting to $374.75—which made Dr. Murnie very happy, you may be sure. | |
| Making a total of receipts amounting to . | $3,645.75 |

This is all, of course, reckoned as of June.

In the matter of expenditures, the club has not been so fortunate. There was the unsettled condition of business, and the late spring, to contend with, resulting in the following—er—rather discouraging figures, I am afraid.

| | |
|---|--:|
| Expenditures ........................ | $23,574.85 |
| Then there was a loss, owing to—several things—of ........................ | 3,326.70 |
| Carfare ............................. | $ 4,452.25 |
| And then, Mrs. Rawlins' expense account, when she went down to see the work they are doing in Baltimore, came to $256.50, but I am sure that you will all agree that it was worth it to find out—er—what they are doing in Baltimore. | |
| And then, under the general head of Odds and Ends ........................ | 2,537.50 |

Making a total disbursement of (*hurriedly*) .............................. $416,546.75

or a net deficit of—ah—several thousand dollars.

Now, these figures bring us down only to October. In October my sister was married, and the house was all torn up, and
in the general confusion we lost track of the figures for May
and August. All those wishing the *approximate* figures for
May and August, however, may obtain them from me in the
vestry after the dinner, where I will be with pledge cards for
those of you who wish to subscribe over and above your an-
nual dues, and I hope that each and every one of you here tonight will look deep into his heart and (*archly*) into his
pocketbook, and see if he can not find it there to help us to
put this thing over with a bang (*accompanied by a wholly in-
effectual gesture representing a bang*) and to help and make
this just the biggest and best year the Armenians have ever
had. . . . I thank you.

(*Exits, bumping into proscenium.*)

# THE SPELL

## by Arthur Gordon

> Some stories, once read, never leave the memory. Arthur
> Gordon's "The Spell" is a little like that. If you read
> this aloud, do so after nightfall—and send the children
> to bed first.

Excuse me, sir, I see that you are smoking—could you possibly
spare a cigarette? We are not allowed to have them here. A
wise rule, no doubt, in the majority of cases. Lunatics should
never be trusted with fire.

But believe me, sir, I don't belong in this place with all
these crazy people. Really, I don't! I'm as sane as anyone, as
sane as you are. But there you sit in your parked car, free to
come and go as you please. And here am I behind these bars
. . .

Oh, please don't go away! Don't drive off just because I am
talking to you. I won't cause you any embarrassment. Not the
slightest. I won't even ask you again for a cigarette.

I suppose you're waiting for someone. Your wife? A friend,
perhaps? One of the doctors who work here in the asylum?
It doesn't matter. If I see anyone coming, I'll stop talking.
I'll go away from the window. But until then, please stay. You
don't know what it means to be able to talk to somebody on

the outside. Somebody who will listen, somebody who might even believe . . .

No, that's too much to expect, of course. But tell me, sir, do I sound like a madman? My mind is as good as it ever was; truly, it is. I can solve a problem in trigonometry for you or recite one of Shakespeare's sonnets. But when I try to tell the truth, they won't believe me.

Sir, you're a gentleman, that's obvious. You have the sympathy and the tolerance, the willingness to hear a man out. I can recognize those qualities for a very good reason. You see, I'm a gentleman myself.

Oh, you wouldn't think so from looking at me, I know. And you wouldn't think so if you read my medical file. It says that I am David Greenlea, merchant seaman, a hopeless paranoiac suffering from insane delusions. But, sir, I swear to you I'm not David Greenlea and I'm not insane!

Let me tell you, sir, just how it happened. And let me beg of you not to judge me by the way I look. This broken nose, these gnarled hands—they're not mine, I tell you, they're not mine! They belong to David Greenlea, that's true. But I'm not David Greenlea, I'm not. I'm not.

I'm Edgar Greenlea, vice-president of the Overseas Shipping Company, with a house on Edgewater Drive and a wife and two fine children . . . oh, you must believe me!

But wait. I'm going too fast. I can see the disbelief in your eyes. And the pity. Yes, the pity. I don't blame you, sir, really I don't. But hear me out, I beg of you. It will only take a minute or two. And it will cost you nothing. Just a cigarette, perhaps, if you're so inclined.

It happened almost a year ago. I was in my office, as usual. I was in my own body, too, not this tattooed monstrosity that you're looking at. Oh, I know that does sound insane, but let me explain, please! Just listen . . .

One of our ships, the Eastern Star, had docked only that morning. About noon they brought me word that David Greenlea had come ashore, was drinking himself blind in a water-front tavern. David Greenlea, my first cousin, a wretched ne'er-do-well, always drunk or fighting, always in trouble. I had got him his berth on the *Eastern Star*. Without my influence he would have lost it a dozen times. But there was no gratitude on his part, sir. None at all. Indeed, he hated me because I was successful, respected, everything he wanted to be—and was not.

Malevolent as he was, I felt responsible for him as a member of the family. And so I went down to that tavern. I found him, drunk and disgusting. I took him into a back room and ordered coffee. We were alone there . . .

Sir, could you possibly let me have a cigarette? Look, I'll stretch my arm through the bars as far as it will go. If you could just put one in my fingers, I'd be so grateful. Really, you don't know how agonizing it is to watch another man smoke when you . . . oh, thank you, sir, you are most kind!

So I made David drink the coffee. I got him fairly sober, but he kept reviling me. He accused me of secretly loathing him, despising him. I said that I didn't despise him, I only pitied him. When I said that, he gave me a strange look, half drunken and half cunning. Then he smiled. I tell you, sir, I have seen that smile a thousand times since in my dreams.

"Let me show you a trick, Cousin Edgar," he said, "a trick I learned from a singsong girl in Hong Kong. A little magic, black or white, depending on where you sit."

He took something out of his pocket and put it on the table, and I saw that it was a cone of cheap incense. "First there must be pity," he said, smiling that evil smile, "if the spell is to work. Then there must be a burnt offering, and finally there must be the words."

I thought he was raving, but I decided to humor him. So I . . . pardon me, sir, could I trouble you for a light? You needn't give me a match, just hold the flame where I can reach it with the tip of the cigarette. Thank you, sir. Ah, that's good . . .

So I said to my cousin David, "What words?"

He had the incense lighted now, and the smoke was rising. He looked at me through it, just as I am looking at you. Then he said the words. Come closer. I'll whisper them to you. Just a little closer. There!

It works! It works! By the ancient and terrible gods, the spell still works! I thought it would, I hoped it would! Oh, I am sorry, sir, to leave you in there. But I had to get out, I had to! And this was the only way. I had to change places with you, don't you see? I had to exchange bodies with you, just the way David did with me!

Oh, please don't scream like that and shake the bars. The attendants will come and put you in a straitjacket. Because to them you'll just be David Greenlea, merchant seaman, hopeless paranoiac. And no matter what you say, they don't believe you. You'll have to bide your time, just as I did. You'll have to wait until someone pities you, and then there must be a burnt offering, remember, and the words. Don't forget the words.

Now I must be going, for I have much to do. Ah, yes, much to do. My cousin David will not be expecting me, not looking like this. What a surprise for David!

I'll take your car, sir, because you won't be needing it any more. Thank you for everything, especially the burnt offering —I mean, the cigarette. Good-by, sir. Good-by.

# F. D. R. AND
# THE GREAT SPROUT CRISIS

## by Mrs. Kermit Roosevelt

Admirers and non-admirers of F.D.R. will probably agree on two of his qualities. He had a sense of humor, though not a very subtle one. And on occasion he could put up a pretty good bluff. Both these qualities are illustrated in a story that during the last few years has become part of the F.D.R. folklore—and is remembered in certain diplomatic circles as "The Sprout Incident."

Quite a serious affair, all flowing from the question as to whether or not Lady Churchill's countrymen know how to cook Brussels sprouts.

Now the fact is that F.D.R. doesn't seem to have known or cared much about really good food. But the amusing story here printed shows him, I think, on firm gastronomical ground. It isn't only that our British cousins know only one way to handle Brussels sprouts, which is to treat them to a Turkish bath. It's that they believe the bigger the vegetable the better. Their cricket-ball sprouts are simply not in a class with the small, nutty, compact French *choux de Bruxelles*. The Brussels sprout, it has been noted, has neither a head, like the cabbage, nor a heart, like the cauliflower. Yet the French can take this brainless, heartless vegetable and cook it so that it tastes delicious. Jean Conil in his authoritative *Haute Cuisine* lists eleven ways of treating the lowly sprout. If Mr. Roosevelt had known them he might have made Ambassador Winant's job easier.

"The Sprout Incident" is told in a privately printed book by Mrs. Kermit Roosevelt who, via Oyster Bay, is a distant cousin by marriage of the late President. It gives us a pleasant view of Mr. Roosevelt's lighter side.

Like Lincoln, he knew the value of a joke in times of stress.

There had been cocktails and immense quantities of Mr. Stalin's caviar served in the President's study on the evening of March 2, 1945. We had dined quietly in the West corridor of the White House. We had heard wondrous accounts of travel and adventure, laughed at official dilemmas, listened to details of the Yalta Conference.

As we reluctantly rose to say good night, I asked for news of Ambassador Winant. "Oh," said the President, "sit down again. Didn't I tell you Gil is very angry with me?" I sat down on the sofa beside him, aware from the twinkle in his eye that F.D.R. was preparing to amuse himself and me.

To repeat exact wording is difficult. To recapture the flavor of one of F.D.R.'s anecdotes is all but impossible. I have tried faithfully to produce the substance of his story, using the first person and eliminating quotation marks.

The President began: Last summer in Quebec, Mrs. Churchill asked me when I was going to England.

Parenthetically, I do want to go to England and, by the way, expect to go after the San Francisco Conference ends— perhaps while it is still going on.

I explained to Mrs. Churchill, "I love England—I love the English as I hope you and Winnie and the British people all know. I like London—I like English country—I don't even mind your English climate. But there is one reason I do not want to go to England. I do not like the way you cook your vegetables."

Mrs. Churchill expressed surprise and pain. "Take Brussels sprouts, for instance," I said. "Why," I asked, "do you boil them? But if you must boil them, why do you leave the water in them when they are served? Why don't you throw away that gray, saltless, tepid water before sending the Brussels sprouts to the table?"

Mrs. Churchill was indignant. An argument ensued.

Mrs. Churchill is charming—but determined—so, with sudden inspiration, I proposed a compromise. "I'll come to England if you will promise never to boil my sprouts."

"Not boil your Brussels sprouts!" she exclaimed. "How else would you cook Brussels sprouts?"

"Why," I responded, "there are dozens of ways—hundreds of ways to cook sprouts. You can make soup of them, and salad— and soufflé. They can be roasted, baked, fried, and sautéed. Perhaps the broiled Brussels sprout, however, is the best."

Mrs. Churchill was incredulous—and so was I, myself! nevertheless, I continued rashly, delighted with my own imaginative power, "The sprout, when properly prepared, arouses enthusiasm in even the most fastidious epicure because of its extraordinary flavor, which is lost in boiling—accentuated in the broiling. Unless you have tasted broiled Brussels sprouts, you can have no conception of the true delicacy of the sprout."

Mrs. Churchill was interested. "How," she inquired, "do you broil Brussels sprouts?" I was getting in deeper and deeper but dismissed the subject airily by saying, "Of course, I am no cook—never have cared for cooking itself. Ask somebody else. All Americans love broiled Brussels sprouts—it's a favorite dish."

Mrs. Churchill never forgets. Returning to 10 Downing Street, she sent for her great friend, the American ambassador. "How do you broil Brussels sprouts?" she asked Mr. Winant. "How do I broil Brussels sprouts?" inquired the startled ambassador. "Why, I've never heard of broiled Brussels sprouts. Who ever heard of broiled Brussels sprouts?"

Mrs. Churchill is renowned for her serenity, but she was obviously annoyed. "You have never heard of broiled Brussels sprouts?" she repeated almost angrily. "Why, Mr. Winant, how amazing. Your President tells me it is a common and favorite dish in America."

Mr. Winant is very quick. He is a good ambassador and a loyal friend. He gathered himself together and explained that he was the last person in the world to consult about food. "You see," he went on humbly, "I really don't know what I'm eating. I don't notice how things are prepared or cooked—nor even what they are. Of course, now I think about it, the broiled Brussels sprout is almost our national dish. I shall bring back the recipe to you from America."

The next time I saw John Winant  he was preternaturally grave. His demeanor and expression indicated an international crisis. "Mr. President," he said, "I must beg for an immediate leave of absence."

"A leave now, at this time?" I exclaimed in consternation. "Why, Gil, what is the trouble—what has happened?" "Well, Mr. President," he pronounced solemnly, "if a knowledge of cooking is part of diplomatic training, and if you are going to put me on a spot with the Prime Minister's wife, I must take a course of cooking at the Cordon Bleu—or resign as ambassador to Great Britain."

I had a really bad time placating him. I offered to create a new cabinet post, appoint a Secretary for Brussels sprouts, or set up another government agency. Gil was against any such idea. He insisted on a more tactful approach. He thought we should devise a method of simultaneously educating the British and ourselves in cooking and appreciating the sprout.

Gil outlined his vision of English-speaking peoples throughout the world pledging themselves to permanent friendship over plates piled high with the once despised Brussels sprouts, the sprout cooked to perfection in many different ways—tender, fragrant, succulent, and served always and forever without water!

The President asked: "Don't you love it?" using that familiar phrase of his with which he so often ended a favorite story. He chuckled as he paused reflectively, then added, "Gil may think he is on a spot with Mrs. Churchill, but what about me? I'm in a pretty awkward predicament myself."

"I can do something for you," I interrupted, suddenly fired with enthusiasm. "You don't have to create a new government agency. I will collect recipes, past, present, and future, for Brussels sprouts."

F.D.R. did not allow me to forget—hence, recipes were gathered from all parts of the United States.

During the following weeks the President inquired many times regarding the progress of the necessary research. On March 24, as I was ending my visit at the White House, he specifically urged that work be hastened in order that he might, himself, present this little book of recipes to Mrs. Churchill on his impending trip to England.

That early-spring morning in 1945 was the last time I saw the President.

The trip to England was never made. I published the recipes as in trust from Franklin D. Roosevelt to Lady Churchill.

# OUR LADY'S JUGGLER

## by Anatole France

This traditional legend has often been retold, but its classical form was given it by the French writer Anatole France in a rendering which has become familiar through much anthologizing. It's a little leisurely for these hurried days, but, if the proper quiet mood is created, it makes an effective "readaloudable." One would hardly suspect from its almost childlike piety that the author was somewhat given to free thought.

## I

In the days of King Louis there was a poor juggler in France, a native of Compiègne, Barnaby by name, who went about from town to town performing feats of skill and strength.

On fair days he would unfold an old worn-out carpet in the public square, and when by means of a jovial address, which he had learned of a very ancient juggler, and which he never varied in the least, he had drawn together the children and loafers, he assumed extraordinary attitudes and balanced a tin plate on the tip of his nose. At first the crowd would feign indifference.

But when, supporting himself on his hands face downward, he threw into the air six copper balls, which glittered in the sunshine, and caught them again with his feet, or when throwing himself backward until his heels and the nape of the neck met, giving his body the form of a perfect wheel, he would juggle in this posture with a dozen knives, a murmur of admiration would escape the spectators and pieces of money rain down upon the carpet.

Nevertheless, like the majority of those who live by their wits, Barnaby of Compiègne had a great struggle to make a living.

Earning his bread in the sweat of his brow, he bore rather more than his share of the penalties consequent upon the misdoings of our father Adam.

Again, he was unable to work as constantly as he would have been willing to do. The warmth of the sun and the broad daylight were as necessary to enable him to display his brilliant parts as to the trees if flower and fruit should be expected of them. In wintertime he was nothing more than a tree stripped of its leaves, and as it were dead. The frozen ground was hard to the juggler, and, like the grasshopper of which Marie de France tells us, the inclement season caused him to suffer both cold and hunger. But as he was simple-natured he bore his ills patiently.

He had never meditated on the origin of wealth, nor upon the inequality of human conditions. He believed firmly that if this life should prove hard, the life to come could not fail to redress the balance, and this hope upheld him. He did not resemble those thievish and miscreant Merry Andrews who sell their souls to the devil. He never blasphemed God's name; he lived uprightly, and although he had no wife of his own, he did not covet his neighbor's, since woman is ever the enemy of the strong man, as it appears by the history of Samson recorded in the Scriptures.

In truth, his was not a nature much disposed to carnal delights, and it was a greater deprivation to him to forsake the tankard than the Hebe who bore it. For while not wanting in

ANATOLE FRANCE

sobriety, he was fond of a drink when the weather waxed hot. He was a worthy man who feared God and was very devoted to the Blessed Virgin.

Never did he fail on entering a church to fall upon his knees before the image of the Mother of God and offer up this prayer to her:

"Blessed Lady, keep watch over my life until it shall please God that I die, and when I am dead, ensure to me the possession of the joys of paradise."

## II

Now on a certain evening after a dreary wet day, as Barnaby pursued his road, sad and bent, carrying under his arm his balls and knives wrapped up in his old carpet, on the watch for some barn where, though he might not sup, he might sleep, he perceived on the road, going in the same direction as himself, a monk, whom he saluted courteously. And as they walked at the same rate they fell into conversation with one another.

"Fellow traveler," said the monk, "how comes it about that you are clothed all in green? Is it perhaps in order to take the part of a jester in some mystery play?"

"Not at all, good father," replied Barnaby. "Such as you see me, I am called Barnaby, and for my calling I am a juggler. There would be no pleasanter calling in the world if it would always provide one with daily bread."

"Friend Barnaby," returned the monk, "be careful what you say. There is no calling more pleasant than the monastic life. Those who lead it are occupied with the praises of God, the Blessed Virgin, and the saints; and, indeed, the religious life is one ceaseless hymn to the Lord."

Barnaby replied, "Good father, I own that I spoke like an ignorant man. Your calling cannot be in any respect compared to mine, and although there may be some merit in dancing with a penny balanced on a stick on the tip of one's nose, it is not a merit which comes within hail of your own. Gladly would I, like you, good father, sing my office day by day, and especially the office of the most Holy Virgin, to whom I have vowed a singular devotion. In order to embrace the monastic life I would willingly abandon the art by which from Soissons to Beauvais I am well known in upward of six hundred towns and villages."

The monk was touched by the juggler's simplicity, and as he was not lacking in discernment, he at once recognized in Barnaby one of those men of whom it is said in the Scriptures: Peace on earth to men of good will. And for this reason he replied, "Friend Barnaby, come with me, and I will have you admitted into the monastery of which I am prior. He who guided St. Mary of Egypt in the desert set me upon your path to lead you into the way of salvation."

It was in this manner, then, that Barnaby became a monk. In the monastery into which he was received the religious vied with one another in the worship of the Blessed Virgin, and in her honor each employed all the knowledge and all the skill which God had given him.

The prior on his part wrote books dealing, according to the rules of scholarship, with the virtues of the Mother of God.

Brother Maurice, with a deft hand, copied out these treatises upon sheets of vellum.

Brother Alexander adorned the leaves with delicate miniature paintings. Here were displayed the Queen of Heaven seated upon Solomon's throne, and while four lions were on guard at her feet, around the nimbus which encircled her head hovered seven doves, which are the seven gifts of the Holy Spirit, the gifts, namely, of Fear, Piety, Knowledge, Strength, Counsel, Understanding, and Wisdom. For her companions she had six virgins with hair of gold, namely, Humility, Prudence, Seclusion, Submission, Virginity, and Obedience.

At her feet were two little naked figures, perfectly white, in an attitude of supplication. These were souls imploring her all-powerful intercession for their soul's health, and we may be sure not imploring in vain.

Upon another page, facing this, Brother Alexander represented Eve, so that the Fall and the Redemption could be perceived at one and the same time—Eve the Wife abased, and Mary the Virgin exalted.

Furthermore, to the marvel of the beholder, this book contained presentments of the Well of Living Waters, the Fountain, the Lily, the Moon, the Sun, and the Garden enclosed of which the Song of Songs tells us, the Gate of Heaven and the City of God, and all these things were symbols of the Blessed Virgin.

Brother Marbode was likewise one of the most loving children of Mary.

He spent all his days carving images in stone, so that his beard, his eyebrows, and his hair were white with dust, and his eyes continually swollen and weeping; but his strength and cheerfulness were not diminished, although he was now well gone in years, and it was clear that the Queen of Paradise still cherished her servant in his old age. Marbode represented her seated upon a throne, her brow encircled with an orb-shaped nimbus set with pearls. And he took care that the folds of her dress should cover the feet of her, concerning whom the prophet declared: My beloved is as a garden enclosed.

Sometimes, too, he depicted her in the semblance of a child full of grace and appearing to say, "Thou art my God, even from my mother's womb."

In the priory, moreover, were poets who composed hymns in Latin, both in prose and verse, in honor of the Blessed Virgin Mary, and among the company was even a brother from Picardy who sang the miracles of Our Lady in rhymed verse and in the vulgar tongue.

### III

Being a witness of this emulation in praise and the glorious harvest of their labors, Barnaby mourned his own ignorance and simplicity.

"Alas!" he sighed, as he took his solitary walk in the little shelterless garden of the monastery, "wretched wight that I am, to be unable, like my brothers, worthily to praise the Holy Mother of God, to whom I have vowed my whole heart's affection. Alas! alas! I am but a rough man and unskilled in the arts, and I can render you in service, Blessed Lady, neither edifying sermons, nor treatises set out in order according to rule, nor ingenious paintings, nor statues truthfully sculptured, nor verses whose march is measured to the beat of feet. No gift have I, alas!"

After this fashion he groaned and gave himself up to sorrow. But one evening, when the monks were spending their hour of liberty in conversation, he heard one of them tell the tale of a religious man who could repeat nothing other than the Ave Maria. This poor man was despised for his ignorance; but after his death there issued forth from his mouth five roses in honor of the five letters of the name Mary (Marie), and thus his sanctity was made manifest.

While he listened to this narrative Barnaby marveled yet once again at the loving-kindness of the Virgin; but the lesson of that blessed death did not avail to console him, for his heart overflowed with zeal, and he longed to advance the glory of his Lady, who is in heaven.

How to compass this he sought but could find no way, and day by day he became the more cast down, when one morning he awakened filled full with joy, hastened to the chapel, and remained there alone for more than an hour. After dinner he returned to the chapel once more.

And, starting from that moment, he repaired daily to the chapel at such hours as it was deserted and spent within it a good part of the time which the other monks devoted to the liberal and mechanical arts. His sadness vanished, nor did he any longer groan.

A demeanor so strange awakened the curiosity of the monks.

These began to ask one another for what purpose Brother Barnaby could be indulging so persistently in retreat.

The prior, whose duty it is to let nothing escape him in the behavior of his children in religion, resolved to keep a watch over Barnaby during his withdrawals to the chapel. One day, then, when he was shut up there after his custom, the prior, accompanied by two of the older monks, went to discover through the chinks in the door what was going on within the chapel.

They saw Barnaby before the altar of the Blessed Virgin, head downward, with his feet in the air, and he was juggling with six balls of copper and a dozen knives. In honor of the Holy Mother of God he was performing those feats which aforetime had won him most renown. Not recognizing that the simple fellow was thus placing at the service of the Blessed Virgin his knowledge and skill, the two old monks exclaimed against the sacrilege.

The prior was aware how stainless was Barnaby's soul, but he concluded that he had been seized with madness. They were all three preparing to lead him swiftly from the chapel, when they saw the Blessed Virgin descend the steps of the altar and advance to wipe away with a fold of her azure robe the sweat which was dropping from her juggler's forehead.

Then the prior, falling upon his face upon the pavement, uttered these words, "Blessed are the simple-hearted, for they shall see God."

"Amen!" responded the old brethren, and kissed the ground.

# THE WHISTLE

## by Benjamin Franklin

Most of us answer our mail. Few of us write letters. "The letter which merely answers another letter," it's been said, "is no letter at all."

A good letter transmits a private image of the writer. At its best it is informal literature.

That is the case with Ben Franklin's story, "The Whistle," written on November 10, 1779, to one of his friends, Madame Brillon. Madame Brillon was one of the many aristocratic ladies Franklin charmed when he was our minister to the French Court. "People have the audacity," she wrote him when she was in her thirties and he in his seventies, "to criticize my pleasant habit of sitting on your knee, and yours of asking me what I always refuse." Franklin once played chess with Madame Brillon while she was seated in her (covered) bath.

"Apples of King John," or "applejohns," incidentally, were a variety of apple that lasted up to two years without spoiling. They got their name from the fact that they ripened around St. John's Day in May.

"The Whistle," as Carl Van Doren remarks in his classic biography of Franklin, was "a distinct small work of art," and Franklin knew it. We cannot all write letters as charming as Franklin's. But how few of us ever even try!

Passy, France, Nov. 10, 1779

Madame:

I am charmed with your description of Paradise and with your plan of living there, and I approve much of your conclusion that in the meantime we should draw all the good we can from this world. In my opinion, we might all draw more good from it than we do, and suffer less evils, if we would take care not to give too much for whistles. Most unhappy people are become so by neglect of that caution.

You ask what I mean? You love stories and will excuse my telling one of myself.

When I was a child of seven years old my friends on a holiday filled my pocket with coppers. I went directly to a shop where they sold toys for children, and being charmed with the sound of a whistle that I met by the way in the hands of another boy, I voluntarily offered and gave all my money for one. I then came home and went whistling all over the house, much pleased with my whistle, but disturbing all the family. My brothers and sisters and cousins, understanding the bargain I had made, told me I had given four times as much for it as it was worth, put me in mind what good things I might have bought with the rest of the money, and laughed at me so much for my folly that I cried with vexation; and the reflection gave me more chagrin than the whistle gave me pleasure.

This, however, was afterward of use to me, the impression continuing on my mind, so that often when I was tempted to buy some unnecessary thing I said to myself, don't give too much for the whistle; and I saved my money.

As I grew up, came into the world, and observed the actions of men, I thought I met with many, very many, who gave too much for the whistle.

When I saw one, too ambitious to court favor, sacrificing his time in attendance on levees, his repose, his liberty, his virtue, and perhaps his friends, to attain it, I have said to myself, this man gives too much for his whistle.

When I saw another, fond of popularity, constantly employing himself in political bustles, neglecting his own affairs and ruining them, he pays, indeed, said I, too much for his whistle.

If I knew a miser who gave up any kind of a comfortable living, all the pleasure of doing good to others, all the esteem of his fellow citizens and the joys of benevolent friendship for the sake of accumulating wealth, poor man, said I, you pay too much for your whistle.

When I met with a man of pleasure sacrificing every laudable improvement of the mind or of his fortune to mere corporal sensations, and ruining his health in their pursuit, mistaken man, said I, you are providing pain for yourself instead of pleasure; you give too much for your whistle.

If I see one fond of appearance or fine clothes, fine houses, fine furniture, fine equipages, all above his fortune, for which he contracts debts and ends his career in a prison, alas! say I, he had paid dear, very dear, for his whistle!

When I see a beautiful, sweet-tempered girl married to an ill-natured brute of a husband, what a pity, say I, that she should pay so much for a whistle!

In short, I conceive that a great part of the miseries of mankind are brought upon them by the false estimates they have made of the value of things, and by their giving too much for their whistles.

Yet I ought to have charity for these unhappy people when I consider that with all this wisdom of which I am boasting there are certain things in the world so tempting; for example, the apples of King John, which happily are not to be bought; for if they were put up to sale by auction, I might very easily be led to ruin myself in the purchase, and find that I had once more given too much for the whistle.

BENJ. FRANKLIN

# LINCOLN PARDONS
# A SLEEPING SENTINEL

# by L. E. Chittenden

The Lincoln legend is a strange thing—strange because it *is* a legend, almost like those of Ulysses or King Arthur. A legend may be true, but it's different from a fact. You learn the fact, but the legend is something you seem to have known all your life.

I cannot remember ever *not* having known that Abraham Lincoln once saved from the death penalty a young Union sentinel who had fallen asleep at his post. But I don't recall having been taught it or having read it anywhere. It was just part of the Lincoln legend we all grew up with.

Then I found out that the sentinel story is true. Apparently it goes back to a forgotten book called *Recollections of President Lincoln and His Administration*, published in 1891 and written by L. E. Chittenden, a Vermont lawyer and politician who served under Lincoln as registrar of the United States Treasury.

Chittenden was not a practiced writer. But he had here a naturally moving incident, full of suspense and with a marvelous conclusion. By telling it straight, without any moralizing, he achieved an effect beyond the reach of art.

This story, I think, shows us the Lincoln who was more than a great President.

When I reached my office in the Treasury one dark September morning in 1861, I found a party of soldiers, none of whom I personally knew. They were from the Third Vermont Regiment and were waiting to see me about the case of William Scott, eighteen, Company K.

Scott had volunteered to take the place of a sick comrade who had been detailed for guard duty and had passed the night as a sentinel on guard. The next day he was himself detailed for the same duty. That night the relief guard found him asleep on his post. He was tried by a court-martial, found guilty, and sentenced to death within twenty-four hours.

Scott's comrades called a meeting and appointed a committee with power to use all the resources of the regiment in his behalf. They resolved to call on me because I was a Vermonter. The captain assumed all the blame. Scott's mother had opposed the boy's enlistment on the ground of his inexperience and had only consented when the captain promised to look after him as if he were his own son. This he had failed to do.

He must have been asleep himself, he said, because he paid no attention to the boy when he said that he had been on duty the night before and feared he could not keep awake on the second successive night. Instead of sending someone or going himself in Scott's place, as he should have, he had let him go to his death. He alone was guilty. "If anyone ought to be shot, I am the fellow, and everybody at home would have the right to say so. There must be some way to save him, Judge! He is as good a boy as there is in the army, and he ain't to blame. You will help us, now, won't you?" he said.

The other members of the committee told me that Scott had always wanted to be a good soldier. What else did he enlist for? They could shoot him, and perhaps they ought to, but he could not have tried harder; and if he were given another chance, he could no more help going to sleep than he could fly.

I was touched by the earnest manner with which the men offered to devote all their resources—even their farms—to the aid of their comrade. But the more I reflected upon what to do, the more hopeless the case appeared. Thought was useless. I must act upon impulse, or I should not act at all.

"Come," I said, "there is only one man on earth who can save your comrade. Fortunately, he is the best man on the continent. We will go to President Lincoln."

I went swiftly out of the Treasury over to the White House and up the stairway to the little office where the President was writing. The boys followed.

"What is this?" asked President Lincoln. "An expedition to kidnap somebody or to get another brigadier appointed or furlough to go home to vote? I cannot do it, gentlemen. Brigadiers are thicker than drum majors, and I couldn't get a furlough for myself if I asked it from the War Department."

There was hope in the tone in which he spoke. I went straight to my point. "Mr. President," I said, "these men want nothing for themselves. They are Green Mountain boys of the Third Vermont, who have come to stay as long as you need good soldiers. They don't want promotion until they earn it. But they do want something that you alone can give them—the life of a comrade."

"What has he done?" asked the President. "You Vermonters are not a bad lot, generally. Has he committed murder or mutiny, or another felony?"

"Tell him," I whispered to the captain.

"I cannot! I cannot! I should stammer like a fool! You can do it better!"

"Captain," I said, pushing him forward, "Scott's life depends on you. You must tell the President the story. I only know it from hearsay."

He started like the man by the Sea of Galilee who had an impediment in his speech, but very soon the string of his tongue was loosened, and he spoke plain. As the words burst from his lips they stirred my own blood. He gave a graphic account of the whole story and ended by saying: "He is as brave a boy as there is in your army, sir. Our mountains breed no cowards. They are the homes of thirty thousand men who voted for Abraham Lincoln. They will not be able to understand that the best thing to be done with William Scott was to shoot him like a traitor and bury him like a dog! Oh, Mr. Lincoln, can you?"

"No, I can't!" exclaimed the President. It was one of the moments when his face took on that melancholy expression which, later in his life, became so infinitely touching.

Then in a flash there was a total change. He smiled and finally broke into a hearty laugh as he asked me: "Do your Green Mountain boys fight as well as they talk?"

Then his face softened again as he said: "But what can I do? As you know, I have not much influence with the departments."

"I have not thought the matter out," I said. "But it seems to me that if you would sign an order suspending Scott's execution until his friends can have his case examined, I might carry it to the War Department through regular channels."

"No!" said the President. "You do not know these officers of the regular army. They sincerely think that it is a good example occasionally to shoot a soldier. I can see it, where a soldier deserts or commits a crime, but I cannot in such a case as Scott's. I do not think an honest, brave soldier, conscious of no crime but sleeping when he was weary, ought to be shot or hung. The country has better uses for him. I will have to attend to the matter myself. I will do so today." I remarked that he was undertaking a burden that we had no right to impose, that it was asking too much of the President in behalf of a private soldier.

"Scott's life is as valuable to him as that of any person in the land," he said. "You remember the remark of a Scotsman about the head of a nobleman who was decapitated? 'It was a small matter of the head, but it was valuable to him, poor fellow, for it was the only one he had.' "

Later in the day the President started in the direction of the camp. . . .

Within a day or two the newspapers reported that a soldier sentenced to be shot for sleeping on his post had been pardoned by the President and returned to his regiment.

It was a long time before Scott would speak of his interview with Mr. Lincoln. But one night, after he had received a long letter from home, he opened his heart and told the following story.

"The President arrived at our camp and I was scared at first, for I had never before talked with a great man. But Mr. Lincoln was so easy with me, so gentle that I soon forgot my fright. He asked me all about the people at home, the neighbors, the farm, and where I went to school, and who my schoolmates were. Then he asked me about Mother and how she looked. He said how thankful I ought to be that my mother still lived and how, if he was in my place, he would try to make her a proud mother and never cause her a sorrow or a tear.

"He said nothing yet about that dreadful next morning. I thought it must be that he was so kindhearted that he didn't like to speak of it. But why did he say so much about my mother and my not causing her a sorrow or a tear when I knew that I must die the next morning? So I decided to ask him whether he could fix it so that the firing party would not be from my regiment. For the hardest of all would be to die by the hands of my comrades.

"Just as I was going to ask him this favor, he stood up, and he says to me, 'My boy, stand up here, and look me in the face.' I did as he bade me. 'My boy,' he said, 'you are not going to be shot tomorrow. I believe you when you tell me that you could not keep awake. I am going to trust you and send you back to your regiment. But I have been put to a great deal of trouble on your account. I have had to come up here from Washington where I have a great deal to do; and what I want to know is, how are you going to pay my bill?'

"There was a big lump in my throat. I had expected to die and had kind of got used to thinking that way. To have it all changed in a minute! But I managed to say: 'I am grateful, Mr. Lincoln! I hope as grateful as ever a man can be. But it comes upon me sudden and unexpected-like. I didn't lay out for it at all. But there is some way to pay you, and I will find it after a little. There is the bounty in the savings bank. I guess we could borrow some money on the mortgage of the farm,'— and if he could wait until payday, I was sure the boys would help—if it wasn't more than five or six hundred dollars.

" 'But it's a great deal more than that,' he said. Then I said I didn't just see how, but I was sure I would find some way out—if I lived.

"Then Mr. Lincoln put his hands on my shoulders and looked into my face and said: 'My boy, my bill is a very large one. Your friends cannot pay it, nor your bounty, nor the farm, nor all your comrades! There is only one man in all the world who can pay it, and his name is William Scott! If from this day on William Scott does his duty, so that, if he suddenly comes to die, he can look me in the face as he does now and say, "I have kept my promise, and I have done my duty as a soldier," then my debt will be paid. Will you make that promise and try to keep it?'

"I said I would make the promise and with God's help I would keep it. I wanted to tell him how hard I would try to do all he wanted, but the words would not come, so I had to let it all go unsaid. He went away, out of my sight forever."

# HARPIST ON HORSEBACK

## by Hilda Cole Espy

Voltaire once said, "If God did not exist, it would be necessary to invent him." If children did not exist, it would be impossible to invent them—for who could ever think them up? In Mrs. Espy's true story, Cassie, who fell in love with a harp, is no more baffling than your children or mine. To be a parent is to be permanently mystified.

I like this story not only because it's funny and comes out of the author's own experience but also because it's about a successful nonconformist. The harp is such a peculiar instrument that maybe harpists more or less have to be nonconformists.

This is the first story about a harp I've read, outside of the Bible. And yet harps are so universal that we're told that they exist in other worlds than our own, and so ancient that remains of harps have been found in Egyptian tombs almost 4,000 years old.

When we think of the harp we usually think of Ireland. In 1947, it was reported, somebody had fitted up an Irish harp with waterproof nylon strings and had played it under water. Cassie Espy might try that next, perhaps riding a sea horse.

Cassie was eight the first time she mentioned that she wanted to play the harp. Now and then she still jumped off her bed to

see if she could fly like Peter Pan. Her bedroom floor being un-
carpeted, we usually knew when she had once again met with
disillusionment.

Her three older sisters were turning young-ladyish and making sense at that time. But Cassie was a character who, whether
she could fly or not, still managed to spend most of her time
in never-never land. Her rainy-day drawings were of frowzy
little mermaids and frowzy little fairies who bore a strong
resemblance to the artist. Cassie seldom combed her reddish-
brown hair or tied her shoelaces or washed her neck.

In those days she was a genius at the irrelevant question. I
recall her asking one lovely sunny May day, "Mommy, do you
think it'll rain next Halloween?" She had many "ideers," as
she called them, and they were all so fantastic that it took
heroic restraint to deal with them patiently. While her big
sisters might ask on a Saturday morning if they could walk
downtown and buy some bobby pins, Cassie would ask if she
could catch the next train to New York, some fifty miles from
our village of Mount Kisco, and buy a horse.

One Saturday morning we were sitting around the kitchen
table. Mona, Freddy, and Joanna were discussing what they'd
like to be when they grew up. Mona thought she'd like to be
a vet; Freddy planned to design clothes, and Joanna decided
to get married and have a lot of children. Cassie had been
swiveling her head around thoughtfully.

"Mommy," she chirped, "do you think I could combine
riding horseback with playing the harp?"

We all fastened mirthfully disparaging gazes upon her.
"Let's not be weird," I teased. "Let's have no member of this
family cantering about while playing the harp . . ."

Cassie glared. Then her eyes filled with tears.

"That's not what I meant!" she shouted. I didn't mean I'd
play it *on* the horse!"

And she went running upstairs to her room, letting out loud
boohoos. When I followed to make up with her, she cried,

"You think everything I say is funny! I wanna play the harp and I'm *gonna* play the harp!" She darted her disheveled head at me like a small snake.

I patted her bony little shoulder. This "ideer," like the "ideer" of buying a horse, would pass, I knew. (I thought I knew!)

In the next six months Cassie gave up attempting to fly like Peter Pan and stopped saying that she was going to marry Mel Ferrer. But she did not stop predicting that she was going to play the harp. She managed ingeniously to insinuate her yen for the instrument into all family conversations. If Mona complained of poison ivy, Cassie would remark that she was glad *she* didn't get poison ivy, as it might interfere with her playing the harp. Let Joanna mention that she'd like ice skates for Christmas, and Cassie would smile and crowd winsomely up against her father or me and croon, "I know what I'd like for Christmas."

That September, when the three older girls resumed piano lessons, Cassie was offered a chance to join them. She angrily refused. "You know what I want to play," she said.

I felt it was time for a showdown. "All right, we'll go see Mr. Stochek," I said. "We'll find out how to get hold of a harp."

Mr. Stochek sells violins, tubas, harmonicas, oboes, guitars, clarinets in Mount Kisco. He also arranges for a child to take lessons on any instrument he elects.

"Mr. Stochek," I said as we entered the store, "this is Cassie. She wants to take harp lessons."

"Harp lessons?" He made a why-can't-anything-go-right-today sort of face. "Why do you want to take harp lessons?"

Cassie glared at him.

"I just do," she said.

"Want to buy a harp, do you, Mrs. Espy?" he asked me dryly. "Cost you twenty-five hundred dollars."

"Of course not. Even if we had that much money, which we don't, we wouldn't want to *buy* a harp without knowing how much talent Cassie has or how hard she is willing to work."

Mr. Stochek began to shake his head.

"I don't know where you'd ever rent a harp," he said. "Even if you found one to rent, where would you find a harp teacher around here?"

I looked at Cassie. "See?" said my look. "Why don't you learn to play an instrument you could use in the school band?" Mr. Stochek challenged Cassie. "You could march in all the parades," he suggested. "A harp's very, very hard to learn."

He reached into the glass display case where instruments flashed and glowed. "See this here, Cassie? This is an oboe. Listen to this . . ."

He put the instrument to his lips and produced a rich oriental-sounding series of notes. Cassie stared stubbornly, refusing to be charmed.

Mr. Stochek strummed a guitar and sang a few bars of "Davy Crockett." He blew a trumpet. He played "Dark Eyes" on an accordion.

"You like that?" he'd ask Cassie after each performance.

"It's all right," she'd say, with maddening listlessness, "but I don't *want* to play anything until I play the harp."

Mr. Stochek sagged against the counter.

"Thank you," I said.

"You're welcome." His voice was very carefully controlled.

I walked Cassie out on Main Street; her eyes were spilling over with tears, and she had her mouth stuck out like a Ubangi.

"Now listen, Cassie," I said. "If you want to play something, you'll just have to play something that's available, that's all."

The tears rolled on.

"How can you take harp lessons if we can't get hold of a harp?" I screamed.

She marched along silently, tragically.

"Stop drizzling!" I cried. "We tried—what more can we do?"

"I'll pray," declared Cassie. "I'll pray every night."

The following spring I made one of my rare trips to New York to lunch with a friend. Before catching the 3:20 home I decided to walk across 57th Street and window-shop on my way to Grand Central Station. I thought this route was my own idea, but of course Cassie had been constantly in touch with Heaven, and they're all harpists up there except for the horn player, Gabriel. Suddenly I saw a neat black sign: "Lyon and Healy. Harps."

Cassie's face came to mind, the big gray eyes, the face drawn with wistfulness. As in a dream I found my way upstairs to a quiet room, gleaming with huge golden harps. A man was sitting at a desk at the end of an aisle formed by harps.

"I am Mark Hunzinger. What can I do for you?" he inquired cordially.

"I have a little girl, Cassie," I began. "She gets queer ideas. Now she wants to play the harp."

"Tell me about her," he invited. "How long has she had this idea?"

"For a couple of years," I said, twisting my gloves. "She keeps saying she wants to play one. She keeps saying she *hears* harps—in orchestrations and things."

"Well, she's beginning to sound like a real harpist!" pronounced Mr. Hunzinger. He spoke like a doctor diagnosing the mumps.

"Most harpists, like Cassie, have had to overcome a lot of resistance," he said. "It's not the easiest instrument to get hold of, and it's difficult to play. Did *you* ever, by any chance, want to play the harp?"

"Oh no," I said. "It never would have occurred to me."

It seemed important to him to establish that this was Cassie's own burning idea, that she was not the daughter of a frustrated harpist.

"She certainly should have her harp," he decided briskly. "I'll rent you one." He put his hand on a beautiful little harp, crowned like a queen. "This would be the right size for Cassie."

I gulped.

"Don't you think perhaps we'd better think about it?" I asked. Renting the harp was expensive. Somehow I felt I hadn't communicated to Mr. Hunzinger what Cassie was really like, wanting to fly off her bed and marry Mel Ferrer.

"This is a difficult instrument and the sooner she starts the better," he said. "You can pick it up Friday, on the loading platform at Steinway Hall. And meantime, you call Lucile Lawrence, in Larchmont. She teaches the harp. I'll tell Miss Lawrence all about Cassie, and I think she'll try to arrange to teach her."

Homeward bound on a later train, it seemed to me that my life was already strewn with abandoned fancies of the children: unfinished knitting, puppies who were now dogs, kittens who were now cats, drum majors' batons, and oil painting sets . . . and now it seemed I had a great big harp on my hands.

My husband and I drove the station wagon into New York on Friday night to pick up the harp. In its large wooden case it occupied the entire car except for the front seat; it required the combined muscles of my husband and Mr. Hunzinger to wedge it into place. "She couldn't play the flute. Oh no," I said crossly.

Cassie was waiting up for us at home. She held the door open gravely while we grunted and heaved the heavy harp case into the living room. She did not jump up and down and clap her hands, as she usually did when she was pleased. She stood quietly while we lifted the harp out of the case. Then she ran one finger up and down the strings. A strange and beautiful sound went vibrating through the house. She gave a sudden, radiant smile.

"It's just what I thought it would be like," she said.

That Sunday we drove Cassie to Larchmont for her first lesson with Miss Lawrence—one of the many, many Sundays we were to spend this way, an hour to Larchmont, an hour or more for the lesson itself, an hour back.

Propped up on a telephone book on a bench behind Miss Lawrence's enormous concert grand harp, Cassie looked very small. I found myself afraid for her; I didn't want her to meet frustration.

Miss Lawrence showed her how to balance the harp and explained how a harpist, on playing a chord, closes his hand and raises it, as if he had captured the sound in his palm.

"Nijinsky, the dancer, worked all one summer in Maine with Salzedo, the harpist, to develop these motions, Cassie," she said. "An audience tends to watch a harpist. So it is important how we look."

Cassie scuffled and hitched reflectively. Why, I'll bet she starts tucking in her blouse, I thought. (She did. As she improved on the harp, she improved in neatness.)

I listened to Miss Lawrence outline the ground she expected Cassie to cover by next week: the notes of the scales, the functions of the seven pedals. "And, Cassie," she added, "would you write me a piece?"

"All right," said Cassie, who had never read a note of music in her life, let alone write it!

She doesn't know Cassie, I thought apprehensively. Cassie, the most disorganized member of the family, who had always preferred fantastic dreams to grappling with realities within actual reach! But Miss Lawrence *did* know Cassie; it was I who did not know Cassie—the harpist.

She learned her notes and she learned her pedals and she composed her piece, too, and Miss Lawrence made an arrangement of it for her. It was the first thing she played after "Yankee Doodle." (There is nothing quite like "Yankee Doodle" played smartly on a big harp by a small girl.)

But I still had reservations about Cassie's future on the instrument. I wasn't a musician, but I had friends who were musicians, and I knew how hard they had to work. I watched and waited. And meantime learned a few things, like how to string a harp, and how to tune a harp.

When we planned our vacation on Cape Cod, I thought Cassie might be relieved to leave the harp behind, escape from practicing. But she wanted to take it with her.

"You see, I have more time to practice in the summer," she said.

Miss Lawrence backed her up, and we arranged to transport the harp to Cape Cod.

When we returned to school that fall, Cassie had to make a decision she'll have to make over and over and over again as time goes on. Did she care enough about practicing the harp to forego many of the activities in which her friends were engaging?

"I'd sorta like to go in for cheer leading," she said to me wistfully, "but I can't go out for cheer leading because then I wouldn't have enough time for my harp."

I was on the point of thinking that Cassie would never again make my head spin with an impossible "ideer" when, one Saturday morning, I heard her ask her father to drive her to Sunnyfield Farm. They give horseback riding lessons there.

"Now just a minute!" I whirled from the sink. "We can't afford riding lessons as well as harp lessons, Cassie!"

"I know that." She nodded. "I just want to *look* at the horses . . ."

On her return she happily reported that George, the riding master, had let her help him groom the horses.

"Some Saturdays, when the horses aren't all being ridden, he'll let me ride after I groom them," she said. "Wasn't that nice of George?"

My eyes narrowed. For suddenly I remembered her question, "Do you think I could combine horseback riding with playing the harp?"

I thought of calling George and warning him. But then I decided, George can learn his own lessons. I'm too busy figuring out how to buy the harp!

Most Sundays we drove Cassie to Larchmont for her lesson.

It was never dull to listen to Miss Lawrence teaching because she somehow taught much more than the harp.

"You must look at good pictures, Cassie," she told our daughter, "and read good books. This will help you play the harp well."

"You must use *everything*, Cassie," Miss Lawrence would say. "You must listen with your ears as well as think with your mind and see with your eyes that read the music."

How true! Most of us don't use everything but lean too hard on one faculty or another . . . our great big brains, or our great big hearts . . .

In the fall of Cassie's thirteenth year, a little more than two years after her first trip to Miss Lawrence's, she joined the Westchester Youth Symphony in White Plains.

She got her audition music (preludes from the opera *Carmen*) in the mail two days before she was due to play for Norman Leydon, the conductor. On Saturday morning her father and I lifted the harp into the station wagon and drove Cassie to the County Center Building at White Plains, for her audition.

She made the orchestra and stayed for rehearsal. And now, every Saturday morning, we load the harp into the station wagon at 9:15 so that Cassie can be set up and on the stage at White Plains by 9:45. The orchestra rehearses until 12:30, and by one o'clock we're back in Mount Kisco again.

I've said it before and I'll say it again: Cassie had better marry a moving man. A moving man who is fond of horses.

# AN UNDESIRED RENDEZVOUS

## by Ernest K. Gann

Ernest Gann's *Fate Is the Hunter* may come to be a classic account of the passenger transport phase of aviation. The experience of near-fatality in the air has perhaps never been so tensely and professionally described as in the extract that follows. You, the reader, seem virtually to be in the cockpit.

It is a summer night at precisely nine twenty-six, at precisely five thousand and fifty feet, at precisely one hundred and seventy-one miles per hour. The chief participants are easily identified as Beattie and myself. Both airmen possess Airline Transport ratings numbered 42453 and 36631 respectively. Both men are fully qualified on the equipment and route—see chief pilot's report of recent date. Company and government physical examinations, also of recent date. Eyes 20-20 or better; pulse before and after reclining, satisfactory. Schneider test of both men, 18, the highest possible. Outside influences which might lead to emotional disturbances—none. Condition of aircraft and engine, satisfactory. Records show no history of major mechanical or structural deficiencies or repairs. Last routine check, date of incident. Signed off in logbook by company crew chief Buffalo with confirming signature attached thereto. Weather good. Visibility approximately twenty miles.

Position reports checked against flight plan and found routine. Proper Air Traffic Control clearance received from New York shortly after reporting over Wilkes-Barre. Witnesses. Farmer located approximately on airway claims he observed subject flight first blink landing lights and then . . .

Beattie reaches to the floor beside his seat and takes up the logbook. It is two pieces of metal hinged together and painted a dark blue, with the number of the aircraft stenciled on the outside. The forms are inside. It is the uninspiring duty of every co-pilot to complete these forms. Some do so begrudgingly; others approach the task with the grubby exactitude of postal clerks writing a money order. Our pay is calculated from the times recorded in these logbooks, and the formula for computation is so absurdly involved that a mistake of only a few minutes can result in the loss of several dollars. Therefore all pilots take an inordinate interest in the time figures, whereas if the flight is routine they hardly notice those recording engine temperatures, pressures, and fuel consumed.

Beattie turns up the small spotlight behind his head and focuses it on the logbook. He sighs audibly and begins to fill in the vacant squares with symbols and numerals.

I can feel the passengers moving about in the cabin, almost count their individual trips to the washroom in the tail. They have been looking at their watches and know we must soon be on the ground. Their movements come to me through the adjustments required on the stabilizer. I am obliged to move the wheel, controlling it frequently, and thus counterbalancing their weight. The stewardess will come forward in a few minutes. Her name is Katherine and she will smell better than we do and she will ask how soon we are going to land. When she is told, she will stand for a moment in the darkness between the baggage and mail bins and adjust her girdle. Then she will return to the cabin. Or because Beattie is a bachelor, she may linger without explanation.

I reach into my left-hand shirt pocket and take out a celluloid disk about the size of a small saucer. Actually it is a slide rule by means of which I can quickly calculate the time required to descend from five thousand feet to approach altitude at New York. I can easily compute the time in my head. The slide rule is merely habit, and a good one, for it is always a reminder that the days of happy guesswork are gone.

Our altitude is still five thousand and fifty feet. The time now: nine twenty-eight.

Two things displease me. The extra fifty feet above five thousand is sloppy flying, and there is too much light in the cockpit.

I glance at Beattie, then ask him to turn down his light. As he complies, my eyes return to the flight instruments and my hand caresses the stabilizer wheel. I rotate it forward an inch or so, then pull back the two red-topped throttles a like amount. At once a subtle change occurs within the cockpit. The constant muffled roar of our slip stream takes on a more urgent tone. The rate-of-climb needle sags. The air speed increases to one hundred and eighty and the altimeter starts its slow unwinding. For the moment both Beattie and myself are entirely absorbed in the instruments, for their silent passing of information has a remarkable, nearly hypnotic way of capturing any pilot's eyes. The momentary result is an unblinking stare, as if we would question their honesty for the ten thousandth time. This is as it should be. When things are going well, as now, our faces are those of men in harmony with the exactness of machinery. We are attentive, yet lulled by the security so gently transmitted from the luminous dials and needles. We are the masters in sure command of all those mechanical contrivances which comprise the unit of this one flying machine. We do not trouble our sense of authority in brooding on those rare enough occasions when we were more the frightened servants than the masters; when the machine rebelled with the instruments to rob us of all dignity and make us feel like the sorcerer's apprentice.

The altimeter needle indicates precisely five thousand feet. We have lost only the sloppy fifty feet, and I hold the exact five thousand for perhaps thirty seconds while my eyes travel upward to the windshield glass. This trifling hesitation before continuing the descent is not to rest my eyes. It is only because my seat is somewhat too far back. Now my sole desire is to adjust it according to long-established personal taste, thereby innocently deceiving myself that from such a particular position of the seat, and from no other, can I make a good and proper landing.

I bend down, seeking the lever which controls the fore and aft movements of the seat. I ease the seat forward one notch and hear the lever click. As I straighten, Beattie snaps the metal logbook closed with a gesture of finality.

My hand seeks the stabilizer wheel again. My eyes alternate between the rate-of-climb needle and the black windshield. A few seconds pass. Beattie is preoccupied with stuffing a pencil into his shirt pocket. He also looks ahead, but not in anticipation of seeing anything—facing the windshield is simply the most easy and natural position. There is just enough light within the cockpit to reflect faintly Beattie's image in the glass. Compelled only by his scrupulous regard for personal appearance, he bends forward and starts to adjust his tie. This humble gesture is almost the very last the human body identified as Beattie will ever be called upon to make.

For his next movement is a parting of the lips, followed by a horrible, inarticulate sucking sound, audible even above the engines. His actual cry of instantaneous shock is still unfinished when my own attention is drawn to the windshield. My every sense is appalled. There is not time-space for true fear to build, but the primeval urges are instantly uncovered. My stunned brain demands a challenging scream, yet I am unable to make any sound. My body, along with my soul, has stopped dead, severed of all vitality within.

My hands freeze on the control wheel. In the blackness

ahead there is a sudden, hideous apparition; the mass is no more than a thickening of the night, but it supports a green wing-tip light and, just below it, two flickering tongues of engine exhaust flame.

The whole frightful assembly slides swiftly across our field of vision. It is so close it seems I could reach out and touch it. It is too late for any reaction. Almost before our minds can appreciate its significance, the spectacle is gone from ahead. Beattie, his face pressed against the glass, follows its disappearance off to our right. His whole body swivels quickly with its ghostly progress.

The entire drama begins and ends in two seconds. Beattie and I are sole members of the audience, for it is obvious that those in the other airplane never saw us. Yet, except for a miraculous separation of no more than fifty feet, they would also be quite dead. Only a new audience on the ground would have heard the explosion. And watched the descent of two bundles of flaming metal.

It is over. The peril was instantly there and then almost as instantly not there. We peeped behind the curtain, saw what some dead men have seen, and survived with it engraved forever on our memories.

Now we are not even afraid. That will come when there is time for contemplation. I have not moved, nor is there even a quickening in my breathing.

Slowly Beattie turns in his seat and our eyes meet. A smile touches the corner of his mouth, but it is a melancholy smile and for the moment it seems the perfect comment on what had been our utter helplessness. Those fifty additional sloppy feet held only a few minutes previously—so insignificant then—are now revealed as the pinion of our lives. To have maintained those fifty feet one second more would have matched our altitude exactly with the stranger's. Then who chose the moment to descend? Why just then? It was certainly not our own premeditated decision.

I pick up the microphone slowly, my movements now devoid of flourish.

"New York from Flight Five . . ."

"Go ahead, Flight Five."

"Have you any reported traffic?" I want desperately to accuse him—any handy victim will do until I can vent my fury on Air Traffic Control. Yet even as I wait I realize they cannot be aware of every outlaw ship in the sky. The reply is a foregone conclusion or we would have been warned.

"No reported traffic. . . . Five."

"Okay. Five."

I replace the microphone carefully and fumble in my pants pocket for a cigarette. When I bring it out, the package is squashed. They are always squashed, which they would not be if I ever learned to carry them elsewhere. In such poor thoughts my mind seeks momentary refuge, convincing itself, or trying to, that what I have just seen really was not seen. I should much prefer the innocence of our passengers, who almost performed the interesting feat of instantly perishing while in the act of combing their hair or dabbing a drop of perfume behind an ear.

Since the choked, half-born sounds which were more plaintive than defiant, Beattie and I have not had any audible exchange. Lighting my cigarette with a hand that has no good reason to be so steady, I prospect through several things I might say to my companion in fortune.

Tradition calls for me to be outwardly calm and collected, which is not overly difficult, doubtless because the actual exposure to imminent death was of such short duration. Peace within is not so easily re-established. That one second's difference, its selection, the reason for it, must haunt the rest of my living days, whatever their number. Years may pass before I shall relive that instant, but it must come to me again and again, always jeering at logic, always mysterious and incomprehensible. Why should that second of time have been given to

Beattie and myself and to our eleven passengers, whoever they might be, and to Katherine the stewardess? I can only assume that the occupants of the outlaw plane were not deliberately bent upon a combination of suicide and mass murder. They too were spared by a particle of time.

And then, what of the uneasiness Beattie and I had both known before the near catastrophe? There had been no basis for it, yet it would not be denied. Strangely, now that the moment has passed, the feeling no longer persists.

To my personal God I mutter two words of gratitude. My thank you is given almost begrudgingly, for it is still extremely difficult to appreciate our salvation. I can only think that the moment was an evil one, and so long as the issue does not constitute a mere reprieve, I am content to believe it must be good.

After a decent time, as if he is reluctant to break the silence between us, Beattie asks for a cigarette.

"I didn't know you smoked."

"I don't. I just think I might like to try one . . . now."

# MR. THEODORE CASTWELL

## by G. E. M. Skues

> The late G. E. M. Skues was an eminent English dry-fly fisherman. But, though this is a fishing story, its delicious moral (which you won't encounter till you read the last words) applies to many of our human activities. It's a good example of a story ending with a twist that is more than a mere trick.

Mr. Theodore Castwell, having devoted a long, strenuous, and not unenjoyable life to hunting to their doom innumerable salmon, trout, and grayling in many quarters of the globe, and having gained much credit among his fellows for his many ingenious improvements in rods, flies, and tackle employed for that end, in the fullness of time died and was taken to his own place.

St. Peter looked up from a draft balance sheet at the entry of the attendant angel.

"A gentleman giving the name of Castwell. Says he is a fisherman, your Holiness, and has 'Fly-Fishers' Club, London' on his card."

"Hm-hm," says St. Peter. "Fetch me the ledger with his account."

St. Peter perused it.

"Hm-hm," said St. Peter. "Show him in."

Mr. Castwell entered cheerfully and offered a cordial right hand to St. Peter.

"As a brother of the angle—" he began.

"Hm-hm," said St. Peter. "I have been looking at your account from below."

"I am sure I shall not appeal to you in vain for special consideration in connection with the quarters to be assigned to me here."

"Hm-hm," said St. Peter.

"Well, I've seen worse accounts," said St. Peter. "What sort of quarters would you like?"

"Do you think you could manage something in the way of a country cottage of the Test Valley type, with modern conveniences and, say, three quarters of a mile of one of those pleasant chalk streams, clear as crystal, which proceed from out the throne, attached?"

"Why, yes," said St. Peter. "I think we can manage that for you. Then what about your gear? You must have left your fly rods and tackle down below. I see you prefer a light split cane of nine foot or so, with appropriate fittings. I will indent upon the Works Department for what you require, including a supply of flies. I think you will approve of our dresser's productions. Then you will want a keeper to attend you."

"Thanks awfully, your Holiness," said Mr. Castwell. "That will be first-rate. To tell you the truth, from the Revelations I read, I was inclined to fear that I might be just a teeny-weeny bit bored in heaven."

"In h-hm-hm," said St. Peter, checking himself.

It was not long before Mr. Castwell found himself alongside an enchantingly beautiful clear chalk stream, some fifteen yards wide, swarming with fine trout feeding greedily; and presently the attendant angel assigned to him had handed him the daintiest, most exquisite, light split-cane rod conceivable—perfectly balanced with the reel and line—with a beautifully damped tapered cast of incredible fineness and strength, and a box of flies of such marvelous typing as to be almost mistakable for the natural insects they were to simulate.

Mr. Castwell scooped up a natural fly from the water, matched it perfectly from the fly box, and knelt down to cast to a riser putting up just under a tussock ten yards or so above him. The fly lit like gossamer, six inches above the last ring, and next moment the rod was making the curve of beauty. Presently, after an exciting battle, the keeper netted out a beauty of about two and a half pounds.

"Heavens," cried Mr. Castwell. "This is something like."

"I am sure his Holiness will be pleased to hear it," said the keeper.

Mr. Castwell prepared to move upstream to the next riser when he noticed that another trout had taken up the position of that which he had just landed and was rising, "Just look at that," he said, dropping instantaneously to his knee and drawing off some line. A moment later an accurate fly fell just above the neb of the fish, and instantly Mr. Castwell engaged in battle with another lusty fish. All went well, and presently the landing net received its two and a half pounds.

"A very pretty brace," said Mr. Castwell, preparing to move on to the next string of busy nebs which he had observed putting up around the bend. As he approached the tussock, however, he became aware that the place from which he had just extracted so satisfactory a brace was already occupied by another busy feeder.

"Well, I'm damned," said Mr. Castwell. "Do you see that?"

"Yes, sir," said the keeper.

The chance of extracting three successive trout from the same spot was too attractive to be foregone, and once more Mr. Castwell knelt down and delivered a perfect cast to the spot. Instantly it was accepted and battle was joined. All held, and presently a third gleaming trout joined his brethren in the creel.

Mr. Castwell turned joyfully to approach the next riser round the bend. Judge, however, his surprise to find that once more the pit beneath the tussock was occupied by a rising trout, apparently of much the same size as the others.

"Heavens," exclaimed Mr. Castwell. "Was there ever anything like it?"

"No, sir," said the keeper.

"Look here," said he to the keeper, "I think I really must give this chap a miss and pass on to the next."

"Sorry, it can't be done, sir. His Holiness would not like it."

"Well, if that's really so," said Mr. Castwell, and knelt rather reluctantly to his task.

Several hours later he was still casting to the same tussock.

"How long is this confounded rise going to last?" inquired Mr. Castwell. "I suppose it will stop soon."

"No, sir," said the keeper.

"What, isn't there a slack hour in the afternoon?"

"No afternoon, sir."

"What? Then what about the evening rise?"

"No evening rise, sir," said the keeper.

"Well, I shall knock off now. I must have had about thirty brace from that corner."

"Beg pardon, sir, but his Holiness would not like that."

"What?" said Mr. Castwell. "Mayn't I even stop at night?"

"No night here, sir," said the keeper.

"Then do you mean that I have got to go on catching these damned two-and-a-half pounders at this corner forever and ever?"

The keeper nodded.

"Hell!" said Mr. Castwell.

"Yes," said his keeper.

# SHE DID NOT KNOW
# HOW TO BE FAMOUS*

## by Clifton Fadiman

As we all know, Madame Curie and her husband Pierre
discovered radium. Marie Curie therefore is one of the
long line of great scientists who step by step ushered us
into the terrible and magnificent Atomic Age in which
we live.

Some years ago there appeared *Madame Curie*, written by her daughter Eve. It has since become a classic
biography and was made into a motion picture. At the
time I wrote an account of the book, from which I have
adapted the miniature biography here printed and
which I hope will interest you. It has been reprinted,
more frequently than anything I have ever written, but
that is not because it is particularly admirable in itself.
It is because almost any story of the life of this wonderful woman who did not know how to be famous has the
power to move the human heart.

As we need food to nourish our bodies so do we need
heroes and heroines to nourish our spirits. The problem
is always to find the right objects of admiration. I think
Madame Curie is such a one.

The lives of Marie and Pierre Curie are two of the most beautiful lives that have ever been lived. It is appropriate that this
man and this woman, with characters of shining purity, should

* Originally appeared in *The New Yorker*

have built their careers around a physical element recognizable by its essential radiance.

I am looking at a photograph of Marie taken in 1929, when she was sixty-two. The face is lined. From underneath the white and casually arranged hair arcs an abnormally spacious brow. She is dressed in a simple black dress that looks like a laboratory smock. The face is that of a truly beautiful woman, the beauty lying in the bones and in the brain that sends its clear signals through the deep, penetrating eyes.

The story of Marie Curie is not merely that of a poor Polish governess who struggled against adversity and became a triumphant success. The story of Marie Curie lies precisely in the fact that she was happiest during her struggles and least happy when the world acclaimed her. Hers is a success story with an ironic twist. Einstein said, "Marie Curie is, of all celebrated beings, the only one whom fame has not corrupted." "She did not know how to be famous," says Eve Curie. In one deliberate sentence of her introduction, she strikes to the heart of the secret:

"I hope that the reader may constantly feel, across the ephemeral movement of one existence, what in Marie Curie was even more rare than her work or her life: the immovable structure of a character; the stubborn effort of an intelligence; the free immolation of a human being that could give all and take nothing, could even receive nothing; and above all the quality of a soul in which neither fame nor adversity could change the exceptional purity."

Recall that unbelievably dramatic life. She is born Manya Sklodowska, youngest child of a Warsaw physicist and a sensitive, tubercular mother. The childhood is unhappy, torn by the death of mother and eldest sister, rendered overserious by poverty, given a certain tenseness by the fact that she is a member of a subject race, the Poles. She grows up, becomes the conventional intellectual rebel of her time, like "all the little Polish girls who had gone mad for culture." She is intelligent, but nothing yet reveals that "immovable structure" of which her daughter speaks.

She becomes a governess, a bit of a bluestocking touched with Tolstoyan sentimentality. Now "the eternal student" begins to rise up in her. The little child who at five stood in rapt awe before her father's case containing the "phys-ics ap-pa-ra-tus" reawakens in the girl of eighteen. Her duties as a governess do not prevent her from studying. She has no money, not even for stamps so that she may write to her brother.

But "I am learning chemistry from a book." Back in Warsaw, she is allowed to perform elementary chemical experiments in a real laboratory, and at last, after inconceivable setbacks and economies, after years of weary waiting, she goes to Paris to study at the Sorbonne.

On 40 rubles a month Manya (now Marie) Sklodowska lives, studies, learns. Solitude, near-starvation, an unheated garret—none of these things matters, as long as at least a part of her day is spent in the laboratory. Now even the miserable 40 rubles cease. She is about to return in despair to Warsaw when she is given a 600-ruble scholarship. A few years afterward, with the first money she earns as a scientist, she returns the amount of the scholarship so that some other poor student may be assisted by it.

In 1894 she meets Pierre Curie, already a physicist of note, a mind "both powerful and noble." In an atmosphere of garrets and laboratories these two, very grave and serious, conduct their love affair. They marry. On her wedding day, to the generous friend who wishes to give her a bridal dress, she writes, "I have no dress except the one I wear every day. If you are going to be kind enough to give me one, please let it be practical and dark so that I can put it on afterward to go to the laboratory."

It is a perfect marriage, the marriage not merely of two people who love each other but, what is incomparably more interesting and important, of two great physicists who can help each other. It is Marie, attracted by the uranium researches of Henri Becquerel, who starts herself and her husband on the long, tedious, glorious path at the end of which lies radium.

They know that radium and polonium (named by Marie to commemorate her beloved native land) exist, but they must prove it. From 1898 to 1902, in a dilapidated, leaking, freezing shed, with primitive apparatus, with little or no help, unaided by the scientific bureaucracy or by the state, these two gentle fanatics work in an absorption that is like a dream. The government is too busy spending money on armament to buy them the few tons of pitchblende they need. Somehow they get their pitchblende, paying for its transportation themselves out of their insufficient salaries.

With "her terrible patience," Marie, doing the work of four strong men, pounds away at her chemical masses. Somewhere in this inert brown stuff lies radium. Marie loses fifteen pounds during these five years. At last they isolate the element.

All this time they have been bringing up a family. The family includes two daughters destined for fame second only to their parents'—writer Eve and scientist Irene. They have had sorrows, family illnesses. Pierre's mother has died of the very disease against which radium is soon to prove a possible weapon. But all this time no provision is made for these selfless geniuses. The world, apparently, cares nothing. "With great merit and even greater modesty," says Montaigne, "one can remain unknown for a long time."

Now the full implications of their work begin to appear. The immovable atom moves; matter is touched with a mysterious life; physics revises its nineteenth-century conceptions of the indestructibility of matter and the conservation of energy. The Curies are triumphant. And their first major decision is to refrain from patenting their radium-extraction process. They give it freely to the world. This gesture alone—or rather the inevitable expression of their characters—is enough to lend their lives a depth that can never attach to a career of mere success, however brilliant.

In 1903 the Curies, with Becquerel, receive the Nobel Prize for physics. The world pursues them. Now they must flee the world. "In science we must be interested in things, not in persons," says Marie, who was never to be interested in herself.

One evening, at the height of their fame, as they are about to leave for a banquet, Pierre looks at his wife, with her ash-gray eyes, her ash-blond hair, her exquisite wrists and ankles, and he murmurs, "It's a pity. Evening dress becomes you." Then, with a sigh, he adds, "But there it is, we haven't got time."

They are offered decorations, ribbons, rosettes. But no laboratory. Then on April 19, 1906, tragedy. Pierre's head is crushed by a van in a street accident, and Marie becomes "a pitiful and incurably lonely woman." She refuses a pension (always the state makes its generous offers too late). She proceeds with the education of her daughters. She takes over Pierre's teaching post and, in a dry, monotonous voice, without making any reference to her predecessor, resumes the lectures at the exact point at which Pierre had left off before he died.

The rest of her life is the story of her marriage with radium. For her laboratory, for science, she will do anything, even try to be "famous." In 1911 she receives a second Nobel Prize, this time for chemistry. During the First World War she equips, with superhuman energy, a fleet of radiological cars so that the wounded may be helped by X rays.

Later she comes to America to receive a gram of radium from the hand of President Harding. Then, applauded by all America, she goes back to France, and all America turns to the next celebrity.

Almost blind, her hands and arms scarred, pitted, and burned by thirty years of radium emanations, she works almost to the day of her death, caused in part by that very element she had released for the use of mankind.

# THE PEARL OF LOVE

## by H. G. Wells

> This strange, ironical fable is one of Wells's very early
> stories and is not at all the sort of writing characteristic
> of him. As he indicates in his introductory paragraphs,
> you will have to extract your own meaning from it.
> Whatever its moral, it is extremely well told and holds
> one's interest from first word to last.

The pearl is lovelier than the most brilliant of crystalline
stones, the moralist declares, because it is made through the
suffering of a living creature. About that I can say nothing, because I feel none of the fascination of pearls. Their cloudy
luster moves me not at all. Nor can I decide for myself upon
that agelong dispute whether "The Pearl of Love" is the cruel-
est of stories or only a gracious fable of the immortality of
beauty.

Both the story and the controversy will be familiar to students of medieval Persian prose. The story is a short one,
though the commentary upon it is a respectable part of the literature of that period. They have treated it as a poetic inven-
tion and they have treated it as an allegory meaning this, that,
or the other thing. Theologians have had their copious way
with it, dealing with it particularly as concerning the restora-
tion of the body after death, and it has been greatly used as a

parable by those who write about esthetics. And many have held it to be the statement of a fact, simply and baldly true.

The story is laid in North India, which is the most fruitful soil for sublime love stories of all the lands in the world. It was in a country of sunshine and lakes and rich forests and hills and fertile valleys; and far away the great mountains hung in the sky, peaks, crests, and ridges of inaccessible and eternal snow. There was a young prince, lord of all the land; and he found a maiden of indescribable beauty and delightfulness and he made her his queen and laid his heart at her feet. Love was theirs, full of joys and sweetness, full of hope, exquisite, brave and marvelous love, beyond anything you have ever dreamed of love. It was theirs for a year and a part of a year; and then suddenly, because of some venomous sting that came to her in a thicket, she died.

She died and for a while the prince was utterly prostrated. He was silent and motionless with grief. They feared he might kill himself, and he had neither sons nor brothers to succeed him. For two days and nights he lay upon his face, fasting, across the foot of the couch which bore her calm and lovely body. Then he arose and ate, and went about very quietly like one who has taken a great resolution. He caused her body to be put in a coffin of lead mixed with silver, and for that he had an outer coffin made of the most precious and scented woods wrought with gold, and about that there was to be a sarcophagus of alabaster, inlaid with precious stones. And while these things were being done he spent his time for the most part by the pools and in the garden houses and pavilions and groves and in those chambers in the palace where they two had been most together, brooding upon her loveliness. He did not rend his garments nor defile himself with ashes and sackcloth as the custom was, for his love was too great for such extravagances. At last he came forth again among his councilors and before the people and told them what he had a mind to do.

He said he could never more touch woman, he could never

more think of them, and so he would find a seemly youth to
adopt for his heir and train him to his task, and that he would
do his princely duties as became him; but that for the rest of
it, he would give himself with all his power and all his strength
and all his wealth, all that he could command, to make a monument worthy of his incomparable, dear, lost mistress. A building it should be of perfect grace and beauty, more marvelous
than any other building had ever been or could ever be, so that
to the end of time it should be a wonder, and men would
treasure it and speak of it and desire to see it and come from
all the lands of the earth to visit and recall the name and the
memory of his queen. And this building he said was to be
called the Pearl of Love.

And this his councilors and people permitted him to do, and
so he did.

Year followed year, and all the years he devoted himself to
building and adorning the Pearl of Love. A great foundation
was hewn out of the living rock in a place whence one seemed
to be looking at the snowy wilderness of the great mountain
across the valley of the world. Villages and hills there were, a
winding river, and very far away three great cities. Here they
put the sarcophagus of alabaster beneath a pavilion of cunning
workmanship; and about it there were set pillars of strange and
lovely stone and wrought and fretted walls, and a great casket
of masonry bearing a dome and pinnacles and cupolas, as exquisite as a jewel. At first the design of the Pearl of Love was
less bold and subtle than it became later. At first it was smaller
and more wrought and encrusted; there were many pierced
screens and delicate clusters of rosy-hued pillars, and the sarcophagus lay like a child that sleeps among flowers. The first
dome was covered with green tiles, framed and held together
by silver, but this was taken away again because it seemed
close, because it did not soar grandly enough for the broaden-
ing imagination of the prince.

For by this time he was no longer the graceful youth who

had loved the girl queen. He was now a man, grave and intent, wholly set upon the building of the Pearl of Love. With every year of effort he had learned new possibilities in arch and wall and buttress; he had acquired greater power over the material he had to use and he had learned of a hundred stones and hues and effects that he could never have thought of in the beginning. His sense of color had grown finer and colder; he cared no more for the enameled gold-lined brightness that had pleased him first, the brightness of an illuminated missal; he sought now for blue colorings like the sky and for the subtle hues of great distances, for recondite shadows and sudden broad floods of purple opalescence and for grandeur and space. He wearied altogether of carvings and pictures and inlaid ornamentation and all the little careful work of men. "Those were pretty things," he said of his earlier decorations, and had them put aside into subordinate buildings where they would not hamper his main design. Greater and greater grew his artistry. With awe and amazement people saw the Pearl of Love sweeping up from its first beginnings to a superhuman breadth and height and magnificence. They did not know clearly what they had expected, but never had they expected so sublime a thing as this. "Wonderful are the miracles," they whispered, "that love can do," and all the women in the world, whatever other loves they had, loved the prince for the splendor of his devotion.

Through the middle of the building ran a great aisle, a vista, that the prince came to care for more and more. From the inner entrance of the building he looked along the length of an immense pillared gallery and across the central area from which the rose-hued columns had long since vanished, over the top of the pavilion under which lay the sarcophagus, through a marvelously designed opening, to the snowy wilderness of the great mountain, the lord of all mountains, two hundred miles away. The pillars and arches and buttresses and galleries soared and floated on either side, perfect yet unobtrusive, like great archangels waiting in the shadows about the presence of God.

When men saw that austere beauty for the first time they were exalted, and then they shivered and their hearts bowed down. Very often would the prince come to stand there and look at that vista, deeply moved and not yet fully satisfied. The Pearl of Love had still something for him to do, he felt, before his task was done. Always he would order some little alteration to be made or some recent alteration to be put back again. And one day he said that the sarcophagus would be clearer and simpler without the pavilion; and after regarding it very steadfastly for a long time, he had the pavilion dismantled and removed.

The next day he came and said nothing, and the next day and the next. Then for two days he stayed away altogether. Then he returned, bringing with him an architect and two master craftsmen and a small retinue.

All looked, standing together silently in a little group, amid the serene vastness of their achievement. No trace of toil remained in its perfection. It was as if the God of nature's beauty had taken over their offspring to himself.

Only one thing there was to mar the absolute harmony. There was a certain disproportion about the sarcophagus. It had never been enlarged, and indeed how could it have been enlarged since the early days? It challenged the eye; it nicked the streaming lines. In that sarcophagus was the casket of lead and silver, and in the casket of lead and silver was the queen, the dear immortal cause of all this beauty. But now that sarcophagus seemed no more than a little dark oblong that lay incongruously in the great vista of the Pearl of Love. It was as if someone had dropped a small valise upon the crystal sea of heaven.

Long the prince mused, but no one knew the thoughts that passed through his mind.

At last he spoke. He pointed.

"Take that thing away," he said.

# THE DAY GRANT SALUTED LEE

## by General Horace Porter

General Robert E. Lee was great, as a Southerner, as an American, as a human being. Today his career is studied and his name venerated in the schoolrooms of Vermont as well as in those of Virginia. For our national instinct refuses to see in Lee only the leader of a lost cause. The nobility of his character has made his memory part of the spiritual resources of the whole country. If you're interested in him, I warmly recommend Douglas Southall Freeman's magnificent four-volume biography, *Robert E. Lee.*

The Confederate surrender at Appomattox Courthouse on April 9, 1865, in the small brick "McLean House" has somehow never become a symbol of either "victory" or "defeat." In it Grant does not triumph. By it Lee's glory is not lessened.

One of the few actual eyewitnesses of that sad and moving scene was twenty-seven-year-old Horace Porter. For over a year he had been Grant's aide-de-camp, finally rising to the rank of brigadier general. Porter later became a railroad official and also from time to time set down his memories of the war. He died in 1921 at eighty-four.

The following account of the surrender is drawn from his *Campaigning with Grant,* published in 1897. Its simplicity and quiet factual tone make it very moving.

It catches the characters of the forty-two-year-old
Grant and the fifty-eight-year-old Lee. It makes us feel
the emotion that flowed through the little "room on the
left" of the McLean House. It marks the moment in
which it was at last silently recognized on both sides
that these United States were to be forever one and in-
divisible.

And somehow, in this account by a Union officer who
had fought against him, Robert E. Lee wins not only
our sympathy but our admiration.

About one o'clock the little village of Appomattox Courthouse, with its half-dozen houses, came in sight, and soon we
were entering its single street. The enemy was seen with his
columns and wagon trains covering the low ground. Our cav-
alry were occupying the high ground to the south and west of
the enemy, heading him off completely.

We saw a group of Union officers who had dismounted and
were standing at the edge of the town, and at their head we
soon recognized General Sheridan. As our party came up
Grant greeted the officers and asked, "Is Lee over there?"
pointing up the road.

"Yes, he is in that brick house, waiting to surrender to you,"
answered Sheridan.

"Well, then, we'll go over," said Grant.

The general-in-chief now rode on, accompanied by Sheridan,
Ord, and others. The house had a comfortable wooden porch
with seven steps leading up to it. We entered the grounds and
dismounted. In the yard was a fine, large gray horse, General
Lee's favorite animal, called "Traveler."

General Grant mounted the steps and entered the house. As
he stepped into the hall, Colonel Babcock opened the door of
the room on the left, in which he had been sitting with General Lee, awaiting General Grant's arrival. The general passed
in, and as Lee arose and stepped forward Grant extended his

hand, saying, "General Lee," and the two shook hands cordially.

The contrast between the two commanders was singularly striking. General Grant, then nearly forty-three years of age, was five feet eight inches in height with shoulders slightly stooped. His hair and full beard were nut-brown, without a trace of gray. He had on his single-breasted blouse of dark-blue flannel, unbuttoned in front and showing a waistcoat underneath. He had no sword or sash, and a pair of shoulder straps was all there was to designate his rank.

Lee, on the other hand, was six feet and one inch in height and erect for one of his age, for he was Grant's senior by sixteen years. His hair and full beard were a silver-gray. He wore a new uniform of Confederate gray and a handsome sword and sash.

Grant began the conversation by saying, "I met you once before, General Lee, while we were serving in Mexico."

"Yes," replied General Lee, "I know I met you on that occasion and I have often thought of it."

After some further mention of Mexico, General Lee said, "I suppose, General Grant, that the object of our present meeting is fully understood. I asked to see you to ascertain upon what terms you would receive the surrender of my army. I presume we have both carefully considered the proper steps to be taken, and I would suggest that you commit to writing the terms you have proposed, so that they may be formally acted upon."

"Very well," replied Grant. "I will write them out." And calling for his manifold order book, he opened it, laid it on a small oval table, and proceeded to write the terms. He wrote very rapidly and did not pause until he had finished the sentence ending with "officers appointed by me to receive them."

Then he looked toward Lee, and his eyes seemed to be resting on the handsome sword that hung at that officer's side. He said afterward that this set him to thinking that it would

be an unnecessary humiliation to require the officers to surrender their swords and a great hardship to deprive them of
their personal baggage and horses. After a short pause he
wrote the sentence: "This will not embrace the side arms of
the officers, nor their horses or baggage."

When he had finished the letter he called Colonel Parker
and looked it over with him, and directed him as they went
along to interline six or seven words and to strike out the word
"their," which had been repeated. When this had been done
the general took the manifold writer in his right hand, extended his arm toward Lee, and started to rise from his chair
to hand the book to him. As I was standing equally distant
from them, I stepped forward, took the book, and passed it to
General Lee.

Lee pushed aside some books and two brass candlesticks
which were on the table, then took the book and laid it down
before him, while he drew from his pocket a pair of steel-
rimmed spectacles and wiped the glasses carefully with his
handkerchief. He crossed his legs, adjusted the spectacles very
slowly and deliberately, took up the draft of the terms, and
proceeded to read them attentively. They consisted of two
pages.

When Lee came to the sentence about the officers' side
arms, private horses and baggage, he showed for the first time
during the reading of the letter a slight change of countenance
and was evidently touched by this act of generosity. It was
doubtless the condition mentioned to which he particularly
alluded when he looked toward General Grant, as he finished
reading, and said with some degree of warmth in his manner,
"This will have a very happy effect upon my army."

General Grant then said, "Unless you have some suggestions
to make in regard to the form in which I have stated the terms,
I will have a copy of the letter made in ink and sign it."

"There is one thing I should like to mention," Lee replied,
after a short pause. "The cavalrymen and artillerists own their

own horses in our army. Its organization in this respect differs from that of the United States. I should like to understand whether these men will be permitted to retain their horses."

Grant said very promptly, "Well, the subject is quite new to me. I take it that most of the men in the ranks are small farmers and it is doubtful whether they will be able to put in a crop to carry themselves and their families through the next winter without the aid of the horses they are now riding, and I will arrange it in this way: I will instruct the officers I shall appoint to receive the paroles to let all men who claim to own a horse or a mule take the animals home with them to work their little farms."

Lee now looked greatly relieved, and though anything but a demonstrative man, he gave every evidence of his appreciation of this concession, and said, "This will have the best possible effect upon the men. It will be very gratifying and will do much toward conciliating our people."

A little before four o'clock General Lee shook hands with General Grant, bowed to the other officers, and left the room. One after another we followed and passed out to the porch. Lee signaled to his orderly to bring up his horse, and while the animal was being bridled the general stood on the lowest step and gazed sadly in the direction of the valley beyond, where his army lay—now an army of prisoners. He thrice smote the palm of his left hand slowly with his right fist in an absent sort of way, seemed not to see the group of Union officers in the yard who rose respectfully at his approach, and appeared unaware of everything about him. All appreciated the sadness that overwhelmed him, and he had the personal sympathy of everyone who beheld him at this supreme moment of trial. The approach of his horse seemed to recall him from his reverie, and he at once mounted. General Grant now stepped down from the porch, moving toward him, and saluted him by raising his hat. He was followed in this act of courtesy by all our officers present. Lee raised his hat respectfully and rode off at a slow trot to break the sad news to the brave fellows whom he had so long commanded.

General Grant and his staff then started for the headquarters camp, which, in the meantime, had been pitched nearby. The news of the surrender had reached the Union lines, and the firing of salutes began at several points; but the general sent an order at once to have them stopped, using these words: "The war is over; the rebels are our countrymen again; and the best sign of rejoicing after the victory will be to abstain from all demonstrations in the field."

# THE OPEN WINDOW

## by Saki

This ghost story is one of the best I know. You might try reading it aloud on Halloween.

It's by the brilliantly malicious English writer, Hector Munro, who wrote under the name of "Saki" and was killed in the First World War.

I could fill a dozen pages with witty epigrams by Saki, but here's just one you may have heard without knowing who wrote it: "The cook was a good cook, as cooks go; and as cooks go, she went."

About ghost stories: of course, no real ghost can compete with the ones we conjure up out of our own imaginations. I don't want to spoil Saki's delicious ghost story by saying any more at this point. However, you might note that Vera's name is the feminine of the Latin *verus*, meaning "true."

"My aunt will be down presently, Mr. Nuttel," said a very self-possessed young lady of fifteen. "In the meantime you must try and put up with me."

Framton Nuttel endeavored to say the correct something which should duly flatter the niece of the moment without unduly discounting the aunt that was to come. Privately he doubted more than ever whether these formal visits on a succession of total strangers would do much toward helping the nerve cure which he was supposed to be undergoing.

"I know how it will be," his sister had said when he was preparing to migrate to this rural retreat. "You will bury yourself down there and not speak to a living soul, and your nerves will be worse than ever from moping. I shall just give you letters of introduction to all the people I know there. Some of them, as far as I can remember, were quite nice."

Framton wondered whether Mrs. Sappleton, the lady to whom he was presenting one of the letters of introduction, came into the nice division.

"Do you know many of the people round here?" asked the niece, when she judged that they had had sufficient silent communion.

"Hardly a soul," said Framton. "My sister was staying here, at the rectory, you know, some four years ago, and she gave me letters of introduction to some of the people here."

He made the last statement in a tone of distinct regret.

"Then you know practically nothing about my aunt?" pursued the self-possessed young lady.

"Only her name and address," admitted the caller. He was wondering whether Mrs. Sappleton was in the married or widowed state. An indefinable something about the room seemed to suggest masculine habitation.

"Her great tragedy happened just three years ago," said the child. "That would be since your sister's time."

"Her tragedy?" asked Framton. Somehow in this restful country spot tragedies seemed out of place.

"You may wonder why we keep that window wide open on an October afternoon," said the niece, indicating a large French window that opened onto a lawn.

"It is quite warm for the time of the year," said Framton. "But has that window got anything to do with the tragedy?"

"Out through that window, three years ago to a day, her husband and her two young brothers went off for their day's shooting. They never came back. In crossing the moor to their favorite snipe-shooting ground they were all three engulfed in a treacherous piece of bog.

"It had been that dreadful wet summer, you know, and places that were safe in other years gave way suddenly without warning. Their bodies were never recovered. That was the dreadful part of it." Here the child's voice lost its self-possessed note and became falteringly human. "Poor Aunt always thinks that they will come back some day, they and the little brown spaniel that was lost with them, and walk in at that window just as they used to do. That is why the window is kept open every evening till it is quite dusk.

"Poor dear Aunt, she has often told me how they went out, her husband with his white waterproof coat over his arm, and Ronnie, her youngest brother, singing, 'Bertie, why do you bound?' Do you know, sometimes on still, quiet evenings like this I almost get a creepy feeling that they will all walk in through that window—"

She broke off with a little shudder. It was a relief to Framton when the aunt bustled into the room.

"I hope Vera has been amusing you?" she said.

"She has been very interesting," said Framton.

"I hope you don't mind the open window," said Mrs. Sappleton briskly. "My husband and brothers will be home directly from shooting, and they always come in this way. They've been out for snipe in the marshes today, so they'll make a fine mess over my poor carpets. So like you menfolk, isn't it?"

She rattled on cheerfully about the shooting and the scarcity of birds and the prospects for duck in the winter. To Framton it was all purely horrible. He made a desperate but only partially successful effort to turn the talk on to a less ghastly topic. He was conscious that his hostess was giving him only a fragment of her attention, and her eyes were constantly straying past him to the open window and the lawn beyond. It was certainly an unfortunate coincidence that he should have paid his visit on this tragic anniversary.

"The doctors agree in ordering me complete rest, an absence of mental excitement and avoidance of anything in the nature of violent physical exercise," announced Framton, who labored under the tolerantly widespread delusion that total strangers and chance acquaintances are hungry for the least detail of one's ailments and infirmities, their cause and cure. "On the matter of diet they are not so much in agreement," he continued.

"No?" said Mrs. Sappleton, in a voice which only replaced a yawn at the last moment. Then she suddenly brightened into alert attention—but not to what Framton was saying.

"Here they are at last!" she cried. "Just in time for tea, and don't they look as if they were muddy up to the eyes!"

Framton shivered slightly and turned toward the niece with a look intended to convey sympathetic comprehension. The child was staring out through the open window with dazed horror in her eyes. In a chill shock of nameless fear Framton swung round in his seat and looked in the same direction.

In the deepening twilight three figures were walking across the lawn toward the window; they all carried guns under their arms, and one of them was additionally burdened with a white coat hung over his shoulders. A tired brown spaniel kept close at their heels. Noiselessly they neared the house, and then a hoarse young voice chanted out of the dusk, "*I said, Bertie, why do you bound?*"

Framton grabbed wildly at his stick and hat. The hall door, the gravel drive, and the front gate were dimly noted stages in his headlong retreat. A cyclist coming along the road had to run into the hedge to avoid collision.

"Here we are, my dears," said the bearer of the white mackintosh, coming in through the window. "Fairly muddy, but most of it's dry. Who was that who bolted out as we came up?"

"A most extraordinary man, a Mr. Nuttel," said Mrs. Sappleton. "Could only talk about his illnesses, and dashed off without a word of good-by or apology when you arrived. One would think he had seen a ghost."

"I expect it was the spaniel," said the niece calmly. "He told

me he had a horror of dogs. He was once hunted into a cemetery somewhere on the banks of the Ganges by a pack of pariah
dogs and had to spend the night in a newly dug grave with the
creatures snarling and grinning and foaming just above him.
Enough to make anyone lose their nerve."

Romance at short notice was her specialty.

# ARMINIA EVANS AVERY

## by George R. Leighton

> I reprinted this moving story many years ago in an an-
> thology I put together called *Reading I've Liked* and
> received so many appreciative letters that I am con-
> vinced most readers receive from it the same charge of
> emotion I experienced when I first read it. As with
> Riis' "I Admire the Human Race" (see page 109), it's
> particularly suitable for reading aloud when you or those
> near to you feel discouraged or uncertain about things
> in general.

On an afternoon in March 1938 Arminia Evans Avery lay
asleep in Tunkhannock, a little Pennsylvania town on the
Susquehanna River, not far north of Wilkes-Barre. She was
ninety-four years old and she was dying a slow, deliberate
death of old age. During the preceding days her descendants
had been coming by ones and twos to take their farewell. Now
beside her bed were her grandson and her one great-grandson,
awaiting their turn.

She was intensely old. In maturity she had been a slender
woman with delicate features. Now her head was barely more
than a skull, all the bones showing plainly and her closed eyes
sunk deep in their sockets. Her white hair was cut short; one
hand, little more than bone, rested upon the patchwork com-

fortable. Her breath came in long, slow breaths, so slow that sometimes it seemed that breathing had stopped altogether. Then it would come, evidence that the machinery that had operated so faithfully all those ninety-four years was still obedient to the demands made upon it.

"Is she dead yet?" said the little boy.

"No," said his father. "She's asleep. She will wake up pretty soon."

The man and the little boy watched.

This woman's preacher father had ridden circuit through this Pennsylvania wilderness region where Indians still lived, helping the settlers build log churches. This woman's mother had told her of a day when money was scarcely seen, when a little silver was hoarded to pay taxes and buy tea. This woman's Welsh grandfather, a soldier in the British Army sent to subdue the rebellious colonists, was buried over on the other side of Miller Mountain. Nothing was known of him except that he could write his name and was thought to have been a yeoman. The bones of another forebear were in the Wyoming monument, along with the others killed in the massacre. All were immigrants from the old country, settling in a wilderness.

When this woman at sixteen went to the seminary, she went down the river road to Kingston in a stagecoach. She was at school there when the news came of the firing on Sumter, and she had said goodbye to Southern boys, going home to fight. She had seen the war spirit die away and in her own village had heard the cursing against the draft. In 1864 she had married a young man who ran a gristmill down by the river and had seen him die of a mysterious "consumption." As a widow she kept a dame school in the village, and so little was known of contagion that her own small daughter, ill of scarlet fever, was left in bed near the schoolroom.

Her own brother, a wilderness boy, had gone to New York in the sixties and become an iron broker. She had married again and had seen the village tannery bought by "the Trust" and closed down; she had seen her husband's foundry and machine shop slowly fade out and her sons become interested in automobiles. She had seen the old stagecoach river road turned into a concrete highway for trucks that never stopped in the village but went straight through to Buffalo. She had seen the farm families over the river die out one by one and the farms go to ruin. She had seen Polish coal miners come up from Wilkes-Barre and Pittston and buy the run-down farms and make them bloom again. She had seen almost a hundred years of America and now she was dying.

Slowly her eyelids lifted and the old woman lay quiet, looking straight up at the ceiling.

"Has the funeral been arranged?" she said, seeing no one.

Her daughter heard, looked in the door, and then went away again.

Then, with deliberation so slow that it was difficult to follow the movement, the old woman began to turn her head. Little by little it moved until, after a lapse of minutes, her eyes, gray and clear and steady, rested upon the man and the little boy. There was no recognition. But as the two watched they could see the recognition coming, just as deliberately as had been the turning of the head. At last it came. She knew.

"I am glad that you have come," she said.

She looked at the little boy for a while.

"A fine boy," she said.

She looked at the man.

"How is everything?"

"All right."

There was a considerable pause while she thought.

"Are you finding out a good deal about the country?"

"A good deal," the man said.

"You have found out some things about the people in those towns but not all. Shenandoah you tell about. They have trouble now, but they do not have a lot of the trouble you tell about because the people who had those troubles are all dead and it was long ago."

The old woman closed her eyes.

"Can I go now?" the little boy asked.

"Yes," his father said.

After a while the old woman opened her eyes again and, without effort, since her head was turned, looked directly at her grandson.

"I would like to ask you a question," he said.

"All right."

"Why was it that you never gave anyone—your children, your friends, anyone—your confidence? Did you have some secret?"

The old woman's eyes were fixed upon her grandson.

"The secret is that there was never any secret . . . I didn't give anybody any confidences because there weren't any to give."

She was silent again, and it was almost as though under the skull and the transparent skin the machinery of her mind could be seen at work—thinking—so slowly that one could all but see each thought being put together, every nail and screw in each thought, slowly and surely being driven home. Finally:

"For a long time when I was young it was very difficult for me to talk to people. I could not get through. It troubled me a great deal because I was fond of people, I could not live without them. I was uneasy and could not feel at home . . . in the world. Then, one day, I knew. I knew that in some way I could not understand people knew how I felt and that I did not need to worry or work over it any more. That is all there is to the secret and that is why there were no confidences. Confidences are made by people who are afraid, but I was no longer afraid and so there was nothing to tell."

She stopped talking in order to think again.

"The world," she said, "is in dreadful torment now." The clock on her dresser could be heard ticking. "I hear a great deal of criticism of the President. Do you?"

Her grandson nodded.

"Do you know anyone," she said, "who could do any better?"

"No."

"Neither do I," she said.

The old woman's daughter came into the room.

"Are you tired from talking, Mother?" she asked.

"If I don't talk now," said the old woman, "I never will."

She looked at her grandson again.

"Do you believe—you know, Hitler, Russia, people here without food or hope—do you believe that the world is coming to an end?"

"Almost," the man said, "but not quite."

A look of confidence, born out of some knowledge that the man could not fathom, spread over the old woman's face. Her body was almost done, but thought and spirit remained.

"It isn't coming to an end. It's such a little while since men got up off the ground. So many ways are useless now. They shut down the tannery. They don't come down the river road to market any more."

With the slowest of motions she raised her hand, so soon to be just a member of a skeleton, and laid it against her face.

"We get so used to doing things one way . . . and you can only change a little at a time. We have got to believe we can find new ways because that is what we always do, and until we do believe it, people are afraid. That's what makes this awful trouble, being afraid."

She closed her eyes again and then spoke without opening them.

"All over the world there are people afraid . . . millions of people crying in the dark. They are frightened . . . they tear each other to pieces."

When she opened her eyes again her grandson could see in them complete repose.

"It will never work that way," she said. "But when the strain gets so people can't stand it any more, somehow light will come and we shall see many things that have been here all the time."

She was very tired now, but from somewhere in her she found a breath of effort left.

"You have to work with what you've got and that's all there is to work with. You can't start out anywhere except from the place you come from. People can't do it any other way here in the United States either. It's all plain, but we don't see it yet. The people in all those towns, they are frightened and sometimes murderous, just because in one way or another they're crying in the dark. And that's all, I guess."

Just before suppertime she died.

# EVERY DAY IS MONDAY

## by Ogden Nash

Somehow Monday is not popular; it will never be chosen as Miss Day-of-the-Week.

The only man I know who has written a poem—or a reasonable facsimile of a poem—about Monday is Ogden Nash. I once nominated Mr. Nash for the Pulitzer Prize, but the judges weren't listening. I think Mr. Nash not only the best writer of light verse now living, but a sort of poet laureate of our age of small frictions. He writes, in a suitably bumpy manner, about those troubles we all share, such as the common cold. And Mondays.

It doesn't seem possible that he has been making us laugh for over thirty years. Yet it's a fact, one of the brighter facts of life. When his first book came out, the London *Times Literary Supplement* disposed of it with dignified severity: "Neat ideas marred by careless rhyming." Here's to another thirty years and more of careless rhyming. May Mr. Nash's verse long be heard in the land.

Monday is the day that everything starts all over again,
Monday is the day when just as you are beginning to feel
    peaceful you have to get up and get dressed and put on
    your old gray bonnet and drive down to Dover again.

It is the day when life becomes grotesque again,

Because it is the day when you have to face your desk again;

It is a day with no fun about it,

Because it is the first of a series of days filled with one task or
another that something has to be done about it.

When the telephone rings on Saturday or Sunday you are
pleased because it probably means something pleasing
and you take the call with agility,

But when it rings on any other day it just usually means some
additional responsibility,

And if in doubt,

Why, the best thing to do is to answer it in a foreign accent
or if you are a foreigner answer it in a native accent and
say you are out.

Oh, there is not a weekday moment that can't wring a sigh
from you,

Because you are always being confronted with people who
want to sell you something, or if they don't want to sell
you something, there is something they want to buy from
you,

And every shining hour swaggers arrogantly up to you demand-
ing to be improved,

And apparently not only to improve it, but also to shine it, is
what you are behooved.

Oh, for a remedy, oh, for a panacea, oh, for a something, oh
yes, oh, for a coma or swoon,

Yes, indeed, oh, for a coma that would last from nine A.M. on
Monday until Friday afternoon.

# THE CAMPERS
# AT KITTY HAWK

## by John Dos Passos

I like to think about beginnings—it keeps the tarnish
off my sense of wonder.

Almost five hundred years ago Leonardo da Vinci
began fooling around with flying machines. He never
got anywhere. But, being one of the dozen or so supreme geniuses of the world, he felt sure someone would
get somewhere, some day: "There shall be wings. If the
accomplishment be not for me, it is for some other. It
shall be done."

It was done at Kitty Hawk in 1903. On the desolate
sand dunes of North Carolina our Air Age was born. As
the rickety crate of the Wright brothers wavered into
the air, the future rose invisibly with it.

The great flight has often been described. But to my
mind no more moving account exists than the one that
follows, "The Campers at Kitty Hawk," by the distinguished American novelist John Dos Passos. Many
years ago I reprinted it in my anthology, *Reading I've
Liked*. It's still reading I like. Don't be troubled by the
fact that part of it is written like poetry—this was a de-
vice Dos Passos used to capture the quivering-alive essence of a happening.

The selection comes from Dos Passos's novel, *The*

268 JOHN DOS PASSOS

*Big Money,* part of his trilogy, *U.S.A.,* a landmark of our fiction. It's a first-rate "readaloudable"—particularly if there's a small boy in the family.

On December 17, 1903, Bishop Wright of the United Brethren, onetime editor of the "Religious Telescope," received in his frame house on Hawthorn Street in Dayton, Ohio, a telegram from his boys Wilbur and Orville, who'd gotten it into their heads to spend their vacations in a little camp out on the dunes of the North Carolina coast tinkering with a homemade glider they'd knocked together themselves. The telegram read:

SUCCESS STOP FOUR FLIGHTS THURSDAY MORNING ALL AGAINST TWENTYONE MILE WIND STOP STARTED FROM LEVEL WITH ENGINEPOWER ALONE STOP AVERAGE SPEED THROUGH AIR THIRTYONE MILES LONGEST FIFTYSEVEN SECONDS STOP INFORM PRESS STOP HOME CHRISTMAS

The figures were a little wrong because the telegraph operator misread Orville's hasty penciled scrawl.
    but the fact remains
    that a couple of young bicycle mechanics from Dayton, Ohio, had designed, constructed, and flown
    for the first time ever a practical airplane.

    Orville Wright wrote:

*After running the motor a few minutes to heat it up I released the wire that held the machine to the track and the machine started forward into the wind. Wilbur ran at the side of the machine holding the wing to balance it on the track. Unlike the start on the 14th made in a calm the machine facing a 27-mile wind started very slowly. . . . Wilbur was*

*able to stay with it until it lifted from the track after a 40-foot
run. One of the life-saving men snapped the camera for us
taking a picture just as it reached the end of the track and
the machine had risen to a height of about two feet. . . .
The course of the flight up and down was extremely erratic,
partly due to the irregularities of the air, partly to lack of
experience in handling this machine. A sudden dart when
a little over 120 feet from the point at which it rose in the air
ended the flight. . . . This flight lasted only 12 seconds but
it was nevertheless the first in the history of the world in which
a machine carrying a man had raised itself by its own power
into the air in full flight, had sailed forward without reduction
of speed and had finally landed at a point as high as that
from which it started.*

A little later in the day the machine was caught in a gust
of wind and turned over and smashed, almost killing the coast-
guardsman who tried to hold it down;

    it was too bad
    but the Wright brothers were too happy to care,
    they'd proved that the damn thing flew.

And Orville wrote:

*When these points had been definitely established we at
once packed our goods and returned home, knowing that the
age of the flying machine had come at last.*

They were home for Christmas in Dayton, Ohio, where
they'd been born in the seventies of a family who had been
settled west of the Alleghenies since eighteen fourteen, in
Dayton, Ohio, where they'd been to grammarschool and high-
school and joined their father's church and played baseball
and hockey and worked out on the parallel bars and the flying
swing and sold newspapers and built themselves a printing
press out of odds and ends from the junkheap and flown kites

and tinkered with mechanical contraptions and gone around town as boys doing odd jobs to turn an honest penny.

The folks claimed it was the bishop's bringing home a helicopter, a fiftycent mechanical toy made of two fans worked by elastic bands that was supposed to hover in the air, that had got his two youngest boys hipped on the subject of flight

so that they stayed home instead of marrying the way the other boys did, and puttered all day about the house picking up a living with jobprinting,

bicyclerepair work,

sitting up late nights reading books on aerodynamics.

Still they were sincere churchmembers, their bicycle business was prosperous, a man could rely on their word. They were popular in Dayton.

In those days flyingmachines were the big laugh of all the crackerbarrel philosophers. Langley's and Chanute's unsuccessful experiments had been jeered down with an I-told-you-so that rang from coast to coast. The Wrights' big problem was to find a place secluded enough to carry on their experiments without being the horselaugh of the countryside. Then they had no money to spend;

they were practical mechanics; when they needed anything they built it themselves.

They hit on Kitty Hawk,

on the great dunes and sandy banks that stretch south toward Hatteras seaward of Albemarle Sound,

a vast stretch of seabeach

empty except for a coastguard station, a few fishermen's shacks and the swarms of mosquitoes and the ticks and chiggers in the crabgrass behind the dunes

and overhead the gulls and swooping terns, in the evening fishhawks and cranes flapping across the salt-marshes, occasionally eagles

that the Wright brothers followed soaring with their eyes
as Leonardo watched them centuries before
straining his sharp eyes to apprehend
the laws of flight.

Four miles across the loose sand from the scattering of
shacks, the Wright brothers built themselves a camp and a
shed for their gliders. It was a long way to pack their groceries,
their tools, anything they happened to need; in the summer it
was hot as blazes, the mosquitoes were hell;

but they were alone there

and they'd figured out that the loose sand was as soft as
anything they could find to fall in.

There with a glider made of two planes and a tail in which
they lay flat on their bellies and controlled the warp of the
planes by shimmying their hips, taking off again and again all
day from a big dune named Kill Devil Hill,

they learned to fly.

Once they'd managed to hover for a few seconds
and soar ever so slightly on a rising air current .
they decided the time had come
to put a motor in their biplane.

Back in the shop in Dayton, Ohio, they built an airtun-
nel, which is their first great contribution to the science of
flying, and tried out model planes in it.

They couldn't interest any builders of gasoline engines so
they had to build their own motor.

It worked; after that Christmas of 1903 the Wright
brothers weren't doing it for fun any more; they gave up their
bicycle business, got the use of a big old cowpasture belonging to the local banker for practice flights, spent all the time
when they weren't working on their machine in promotion,
worrying about patents, infringements, spies, trying to interest
government officials, to make sense out of the smooth involved heartbreaking remarks of lawyers.

In two years they had a plane that would cover twenty-

four miles at a stretch round and round the cowpasture.
People on the interurban car used to crane their necks out of
the windows when they passed along the edge of the field,
startled by the clattering pop pop of the old Wright motor
and the sight of the white biplane like a pair of ironing boards
one on top of the other chugging along a good fifty feet in the
air. The cows soon got used to it.

    As the flights got longer
    the Wright brothers got backers,
    engaged in lawsuits,
    lay in their beds at night sleepless with the whine of phan-
tom millions, worse than the mosquitoes at Kitty Hawk.

    In nineteen seven they went to Paris,
    allowed themselves to be togged out in dress suits and
silk hats,
    learned to tip waiters,
    talked with government experts, got used to gold braid
and postponements and Vandyke beards and the outspread
palms of politicos. For amusement
    they played diabolo in the Tuileries gardens.

    They gave publicized flights at Fort Myers, where they
had their first fatal crackup, St. Petersburg, Paris, Berlin; at
Pau they were all the rage,
    such an attraction that the hotel-keeper
    wouldn't charge them for their room.
    Alfonso of Spain shook hands with them and was photo-
graphed sitting in the machine,
    King Edward watched a flight,
    the Crown Prince insisted on being taken up,
    the rain of medals began.

    They were congratulated by the Czar

and the King of Italy and the amateurs of sport, and the
society climbers and the papal titles,
        and decorated by a society for universal peace.

Aeronautics became the sport of the day.
The Wrights don't seem to have been very much impressed by the upholstery and the braid and the gold medals
and the parades of plush horses,
        they remained practical mechanics
        and insisted on doing all their own work themselves,
        even to filling the gasolinetank.
        In nineteen eleven they were back on the dunes
        at Kitty Hawk with a new glider.
Orville stayed up in the air for nine and a half minutes,
which remained a long time the record for motorless flight.
        The same year Wilbur died of typhoid fever in Dayton.
        In the rush of new names: Farman, Blériot, Curtiss, Fer-
ber, Esnault-Peltrie, Delagrange;
        in the snorting impact of bombs and the whine and rattle
of shrapnel, and the sudden stutter of machineguns after the
motor's been shut off overhead,
        and we flatten into the mud
        and make ourselves small cowering in the corners of
ruined walls,
        the Wright brothers passed out of the headlines
        but not even headlines or the bitter smear of newsprint or
the choke of smokescreen and gas or chatter of brokers on the
stockmarket or barking of phantom millions or oratory of
brasshats laying wreaths on new monuments
        can blur the memory
        of the chilly December day
        two shivering bicycle mechanics from Dayton, Ohio,
        first felt their homemade contraption
        whittled out of hickory sticks,
        gummed together with Arnstein's bicycle cement,

stretched with muslin they'd sewn on their sister's sewing-machine in their own backyard on Hawthorn Street in Dayton, Ohio,

    soar into the air
    above the dunes and the wide beach
    at Kitty Hawk.

# HIGH PASTURE

## by Sandy Stuart

Just as you don't have to be a fisherman to enjoy "Mr. Theodore Castwell" (see page 234), you don't have to be a racing fan or a lover of horses to be both amused and moved by this charming anecdote about an equine paradise. The surprise ending here is, I feel, legitimate, which is not the case with much magazine fiction. And it's not a bad story to read aloud during the Christmas season.

It was quiet as I came over the knoll—so quiet that you could hear all the nice noises. There was no road or path, and yet I was sure I knew the way. It was strange, that feeling of confidence. I wasn't used to it, even after this much time. The turf was kind to my hoofs, and although the journey was all uphill, I still had the soundness of wind and limb that I'd had when I was a colt.

When Pegasus finally made up his mind this morning and told me offhandedly that I could go to the High Pasture, I nickered like a mare. I knew that it was only because my name was Man o' War that I had been chosen for the elite company that grazed in the High Pasture. I had heard all about them. Even on earth men had erected statues to their honor and to the honor of the great men whom they had carried.

275

I rounded a copse, and there was the Pasture before me.
They must have known I was coming, because all of them
were standing together and looking toward me. A small donkey
stood off to one side of the group, and he, too, was looking at
me. The horses were magnificent. I had always been amused
at the word *steed*, but the beauty and stature of these animals
set them apart. They *were* steeds: Robert E. Lee's Traveller,
Wellington's Copenhagen. . . . That beautiful black with the
white star on his forehead, that must be Bucephalus. And all
the rest—I felt a little dizzy as I walked among them.

A stately chestnut charger came up to me and said in a soft,
sure voice, "You're Man o' War, aren't you? We were told that
you were going to join us. It's been a long time since we've had
a new companion."

I knew that he was Ronald and had carried Lord Cardigan
in the Charge of the Light Brigade at Balaklava. When I told
him that I knew him by reputation, he said: "That's gratifying,
old fellow. Just make yourself at home, and later I'll be around
to introduce you to the rest of the chaps. That lower part
down there is a fine place for a roll."

I took the hint, and Ronald went back to grazing. I wasn't
hungry, but when I started to graze after my roll, I found that
each mouthful tasted like the first bite when you eat after a
day's work.

The following morning I joined the group, and Ronald took
me around to introduce me. There was quite a lot of formality,
as was fitting in such company, and I knew that I would have
to get used to answering to Man o' War instead of my nickname. The pride they all took in the great generals and warriors
they had carried made me feel that a race horse with only a
jockey for a rider was there on sufferance.

Later on Cincinnati—he had been given to General Grant
by the citizens of that city—came over to me and said, "Man
o' War, you and I should get better acquainted, because we're
the youngest ones here. I came in 1874, and I know how I felt
when everyone started to argue about who had carried the

greatest warrior. I never say much, because I'm the youngest, but everyone knows that General Grant was made President in honor of his greatness as a soldier."

I said that yes, everyone knew that they had honored General Grant as a great man, and I felt proud that I, too, was an American.

"Here comes Marengo," said Cincinnati, as a light brown stallion limped toward us. "He limps only when he thinks that someone is watching him. He probably wants to brag about being shot in the hip when Napoleon was riding him at Waterloo. I'll see you later, Man o' War," he finished as he cantered away.

Sure enough, Marengo did tell me all about Napoleon, but it was new to me and I enjoyed hearing everything about it.

Late that lovely afternoon Phil Sheridan's horse Winchester came out to where I was grazing and talked to me for a while. "You know," he said after we had exhausted all the small talk, "I think that Pegasus must have sent you up here for a purpose. You're the only neutral one besides the donkey." He nodded over toward the brook where the little donkey stood in the shade. "And nobody ever talks to him."

"Who is he, Win—chester?" I had almost called him by a nickname.

"I really don't know, nor do any of the rest," he answered. "He's just here, and I guess he has been for a long time. Don't pay any attention to him."

But I was curious, so I excused myself on the pretext of being thirsty and went down to the brook to get a drink. I didn't go right off to where the little donkey was browsing, because I didn't want to offend the grand ones. I took my drink and gradually sauntered over to where the little fellow stood.

When I got close enough to speak, he raised his long ears, looked up at me, and in a kindly voice said, "Hello, Big Red."

I was so surprised and pleased at hearing someone use my nickname that for a moment I was tongue-tied.

I finally stammered, "You—you know me?"

278SANDY STUART

"Oh yes," he answered. "All of us knew that you were coming."

"Who are you?" I asked, though I knew it wasn't polite to be so abrupt.

"My name is Wistful, but you can call me Wisty if you like —you're the first one who ever asked me that. But you'll lose your social standing with your warrior friends if they see you talking to me."

Reluctantly I went back to the group; and as I approached, I heard Bucephalus saying to General Washington's charger, "After all, Nelson, Genghis Khan once said that horses were the equal of man, even more so than women."

"Better than that," answered Nelson. "There's Lee's comment, inspired by Traveller, 'There's many a war horse who is more entitled to immortality than the man who rides him.' "

I could see the beginning of an argument, so I went down to the rolling place for some exercise. It felt so good just to stretch my legs that I took a sprint around the Pasture. It was only a breeze, and it didn't wind me a bit, so I went right back to grazing.

I should have known that anything unusual would attract attention, but I was used to a daily workout, so I didn't realize that it would be considered out of the ordinary. When I looked up, all the horses were standing together, looking my way and talking excitedly. I was afraid that I had offended their dignity, but I found out that it was something else entirely.

The very next morning everybody started to take workouts— everybody, that is, except Marengo, who chose to remember his wound. I had started something, but on reflection I was glad I had; because if they used up all their energy that way, they might be too busy to argue about war. Although I was left alone most of the time, I felt that I was fulfilling my mission and that Pegasus would be pleased.

Being alone so much, and the rest of the horses being so

busy, gave me an opportunity to go down to the brook and have an occasional visit with Wisty. He really wasn't wise enough to tell me anything I didn't already know; but somehow, after Wisty said it, you were more sure of it yourself. I always felt better after one of these visits. Perhaps it was because the donkey was the only one in the Pasture who wasn't vain about what he was.

The days were long and pleasant, and often I would take a romp too. The other horses began to show the results of their exercise. Their coats were sleek; their eyes shone; and they held their heads even more erect. They didn't get into such lengthy arguments, but they were quicker to snap each other up. Bucephalus, especially, was on edge because he didn't have much chance to talk about himself. I guess that's why he came and told me some intimate things. I had just returned from the brook and a chat with Wisty when Bucephalus came out to meet me.

"Man o' War," he said, "I used to be an ardent follower of yours when you were on earth, and I often said that you could have been a great war horse if you had had the opportunity. I was thinking to myself today that it didn't seem fair that I should know all about you and that you should know so little about me. So I decided to tell you something about myself."

I felt that it would do him good to let off a little steam, so I didn't interrupt him.

"At first," Bucephalus went on, "I didn't belong to Alexander. When I was a colt, I was given to Alexander's father, Philip of Macedon, by some friends of his. I was young then, and unruly, so Philip was going to have me destroyed, but young Alexander, who was thirteen, was impressed with my fire and spirit and begged his father to give me to him.

"Alexander saw that I was afraid of my own shadow, so he kept my head turned toward the sun, and, holding the reins, he stroked and caressed me until he had won my confidence.

One day he leaped on my back, and I gradually accepted him. I served him faithfully all the rest of my days, and when I died, he had me buried on the banks of the River Hydaspes, where he had fought his most glorious battle. A great city rose and was named Bucephala in my honor—a monument to the aid given by horses to men in the business of making war."

We had turned and were walking back toward the brook, and as we approached Wisty, he nodded to us and moved away. Bucephalus ignored him completely. I looked at Bucephalus and saw that he was really happiest when he was talking about the great conqueror, Alexander.

Some time later Lexington, who had carried General Sherman through Georgia, came up to me and said, "Man o' War, we're going to have a race. We've all been training, and we feel that the best way to settle our differences, once and for all, is to let the best man win."

I started to interrupt, but Lexington cut me off with, "Oh, we know that you were considered the fastest horse of your time, but then, you were much older than the rest of us when you got here—thirty-one, wasn't it? The winner will be conceded to be the greatest war horse of all time, and the rest of us will pay him the homage due him. Of course, at your age we don't expect you to win, but you can enter if you want to."

I told him that I would consider it an honor to compete against them, and we set the time for the following afternoon.

The day dawned bright and clear, and most of us loafed through the morning. I had made up my mind that I was going to lose, just staying off the pace until the leaders had crossed the wire. You could feel the tenseness as we got ready to line up at the barrier. Marengo was acting as starter, and the distance was twice around the Pasture, or about a mile and a half —my favorite distance.

Two false starts, and then we got off in a bunch. There was a scramble for the pole position, but I stayed out of it, easily keeping abreast of the pack on the outside. As we rounded the first turn, I began to feel the old thrill—the erratic hollow rhythm of the hoofbeats, the smell of saliva from the straining front runners, the hot breath on my flank of the horse behind me. It was just like Churchill Downs again, with little Clarence Kummer on my back. I could hear him rate me into the half, "Easy, Red, easy! This is just a breeze for us. Let those goats run themselves into the ground, and then we'll make our move."

I forgot everything except Clarence's voice. It was my life. At the three-quarter pole the field was strung out. Winchester was out in front by one length; Ronald was second on the rail and tiring rapidly. I stayed away on the outside, running fifth, because I knew that pace would make someone falter, and I didn't want to pass a staggering horse. Bucephalus and Copenhagen started to make their bid and passed me on the inside. Ronald started to show his tongue as Copenhagen caught him. Sure enough, Winchester faltered and went off badly to the outside, and I had to run wide to avoid him. And then we came to the head of the stretch.

"Here it is, Red," I could hear Clarence's voice. "Take your head." And I did. I flattened my ears, stretched out my neck so I could feel the wind under my mane, and then I poured on the coal.

I won by six lengths; Copenhagen placed, and Bucephalus showed.

I could have kicked myself. Everybody sulked and was touchy. Me, because I had spoiled whatever chance I had of making a permanent peace—the rest because they just didn't know how to lose. They started to give me the silent treatment. If they spoke to me at all now, it was with only cold formality.

We were right back where we started, only worse—all of them bragging about past glories. Copenhagen, who beat the rest of them, was almost insufferable, boasting about his rare luck of first opening his eyes on the field of battle. Wasn't Marshal Lord Grosvenor riding his mare in the battle of

Copenhagen, he bragged, when she dropped her foal? But in worse taste, he even bragged about the epitaph on his marble tombstone at Stratsfieldsaye: *"Here lies Copenhagen, the charger ridden by the Duke of Wellington the entire day at the battle of Waterloo. Born 1808—Died 1836. God's humbler instrument, though meaner clay, should share the glory of that day."*

Later on, down at the brook, they all got into it at once. It was bedlam: Marengo telling about his skeleton in the place of honor at the United Service Institute at Whitehall, London; Traveller, about following Lee's coffin in the funeral cortège. They were all shouting at the same time. In fact, they were on the verge of coming to blows. I was just as glad I was out of it.

Finally, in desperation, Bucephalus turned to Wisty, who was standing off to one side, and shouted, "You settle it, Donkey. Who was the greatest warrior?"

Wistful raised his head and said, "I have no opinion, sir."

"Everybody has an opinion," roared Bucephalus. "Who are you, anyway, who has no opinion?"

"I have no opinion about the greatest warrior," said the donkey. "You see, I'm the one who gave up my manger for the Prince of Peace."

# THE LOTTERY TICKET

## by Anton Chekhov

Anton Chekhov was born in 1860, in southern Russia, and died in 1904. He is generally considered one of the world's greatest writers of short stories, as well as one of the finest of modern dramatists. His stories have no "plot," in the usual sense of the word; but they give us an immediate warm (and often sorrowful) feeling of real life. This, one of his most famous stories, is of course merely a development of the ancient adage about counting chickens before they're hatched. But see how much Chekhov gets out of the well-worn theme.

Ivan Dmitritch, a middle-class man who lived with his family on an income of twelve hundred a year and was very well satisfied with his lot, sat down on the sofa after supper and began reading the newspaper.

"I forgot to look at the newspaper today," his wife said to him as she cleared the table. "Look and see whether the list of drawings is there."

"Yes, it is," said Ivan Dmitritch, "but hasn't your ticket lapsed?"

"No, I took the interest on Tuesday."

"What is the number?"

"Series 9,499, number 26."

"All right . . . we will look . . . 9,499 and 26."

Ivan Dmitritch had no faith in lottery luck and would not, as a rule, have consented to look at the lists of winning numbers, but now, as he had nothing else to do and as the newspaper was before his eyes, he passed his finger downward along the column of numbers. And immediately, as though in mockery of his skepticism, no further than the second line from the top, his eye was caught by the figure 9,499! Unable to believe his eyes, he hurriedly dropped the paper on his knees without looking to see the number of the ticket, and, just as though someone had given him a douche of cold water, he felt an agreeable chill in the pit of the stomach, tingling and terrible and sweet!

"Masha, 9,499 is there!" he said in a hollow voice.

His wife looked at his astonished and panic-stricken face and realized that he was not joking.

"9,499?" she asked, turning pale and dropping the folded tablecloth on the table.

"Yes, yes . . . it really is there!"

"And the number of the ticket?"

"Oh yes! There's the number of the ticket too. But stay . . . wait! No, I say! Anyway, the number of our series is there! Anyway, you understand. . . ."

Looking at his wife, Ivan Dmitritch gave a broad, senseless smile, like a baby when a bright object is shown it. His wife smiled too; it was as pleasant to her as to him that he only mentioned the series and did not try to find out the number of the winning ticket. To torment and tantalize oneself with hopes of possible fortune is so sweet, so thrilling!

"It is our series," said Ivan Dmitritch, after a long silence. "So there is a probability that we have won. It's only a probability, but there it is!"

"Well, now look!"

"Wait a little. We have plenty of time to be disappointed.

It's on the second line from the top, so the prize is seventy-five thousand. That's not money but power, capital! And in a minute I shall look at the list, and there—26! Eh? I say, what if we really have won?"

The husband and wife began laughing and staring at one another in silence. The possibility of winning bewildered them; they could not have said, could not have dreamed, what they both needed that seventy-five thousand for, what they would buy, where they would go. They thought only of the figures 9,499 and 75,000 and pictured them in their imagination, while somehow they could not think of the happiness itself which was so possible.

Ivan Dmitritch, holding the paper in his hand, walked several times from corner to corner and only when he had recovered from the first impression began dreaming a little.

"And if we have won," he said, "why, it will be a new life, it will be a transformation! The ticket is yours, but if it were mine I should, first of all, of course, spend twenty-five thousand on real property in the shape of an estate; ten thousand on immediate expenses, new furnishing . . . traveling . . . paying debts, and so on. . . . The other forty thousand I would put in the bank and get interest on it."

"Yes, an estate, that would be nice," said his wife, sitting down and dropping her hands in her lap.

"Somewhere in the Tula or Oryol provinces. . . . In the first place we shouldn't need a summer villa, and besides, it would always bring in an income."

And pictures came crowding on his imagination, each more gracious and poetical than the last. And in all these pictures he saw himself well-fed, serene, healthy, felt warm, even hot! Here, after eating a summer soup, cold as ice, he lay on his back on the burning sand close to a stream or in the garden under a lime tree. . . . It is hot. . . . His little boy and girl are crawling about near him, digging in the sand or catching ladybirds in the grass. He dozes sweetly, thinking of nothing,

and feeling all over that he need not go to the office today, tomorrow, or the day after. Or, tired of lying still, he goes to the
hayfield, or to the forest for mushrooms, or watches the peasants catching fish with a net. When the sun sets he takes a
towel and soap and saunters to the bathing shed, where he un-
dresses at his leisure, slowly rubs his bare chest with his hands,
and goes into the water. And in the water, near the opaque
soapy circles, little fish flit to and fro and green water weeds
nod their heads. After bathing there is tea with cream and milk
rolls. . . . In the evening a walk or *vint* with the neighbors.

"Yes, it would be nice to buy an estate," said his wife, also
dreaming, and from her face it was evident that she was enchanted by her thoughts.

Ivan Dmitritch pictured to himself autumn with its rains, its
cold evenings, and its St. Martin's summer. At that season he
would have to take longer walks about the garden and beside
the river, so as to get thoroughly chilled, and then drink a big
glass of vodka and eat a salted mushroom or a soused cucum-
ber, and then—drink another. . . . The children would come
running from the kitchen garden, bringing a carrot and a
radish smelling of fresh earth. . . . And then, he would lie
stretched full length on the sofa, and in leisurely fashion turn
over the pages of some illustrated magazine, or, covering his
face with it and unbuttoning his waistcoat, give himself up to
slumber.

The St. Martin's summer is followed by cloudy, gloomy
weather. It rains day and night; the bare trees weep; the wind
is damp and cold. The dogs, the horses, the fowls—all are wet,
depressed, downcast. There is nowhere to walk: one can't go
out for days together; one has to pace up and down the room,
looking despondently at the gray window. It is dreary!

Ivan Dmitritch stopped and looked at his wife.

"I should go abroad, you know, Masha," he said.

And he began thinking how nice it would be in late autumn
to go abroad somewhere to the South of France . . . to Italy
. . . to India!

"I should certainly go abroad too," his wife said. "But look at the number of the ticket!"

"Wait, wait! . . ."

He walked about the room and went on thinking. It occurred to him: what if his wife really did go abroad? It is pleasant to travel alone, or in the society of light, careless women who live in the present, and not such as think and talk all the journey about nothing but their children, sigh, and tremble with dismay over every farthing. Ivan Dmitritch imagined his wife in the train with a multitude of parcels, baskets, and bags; she would be sighing over something, complaining that the train made her head ache, that she had spent so much money. . . . At the stations he would continually be having to run for boiling water, bread and butter. . . . She wouldn't have dinner because of its being too dear. . . .

"She would begrudge me every farthing," he thought, with a glance at his wife. "The lottery ticket is hers, not mine! Besides, what is the use of her going abroad? What does she want there? She would shut herself up in the hotel and not let me out of her sight. . . . I know!"

And for the first time in his life his mind dwelt on the fact that his wife had grown elderly and plain, and that she was saturated through and through with the smell of cooking, while he was still young, fresh, and healthy, and might well have got married again.

"Of course, all that is silly nonsense," he thought, "but . . . why should she go abroad? What would she make of it? And yet she would go, of course. . . . I can fancy . . . In reality it is all one to her, whether it is Naples or Klin. She would only be in my way. I should be dependent upon her. I can fancy how, like a regular woman, she will lock the money up as soon as she gets it. . . . She will hide it from me. . . . She will look after her relations and grudge me every farthing."

Ivan Dmitritch thought of her relations. All those wretched brothers and sisters and aunts and uncles would come crawling about as soon as they heard of the winning ticket, would begin

ANTON CHEKHOV

whining like beggars, and fawning upon them with oily, hypo-
critical smiles. Wretched, detestable people! If they were
given anything, they would ask for more, while if they were
refused, they would swear at them, slander them, and wish
them every kind of misfortune.

Ivan Dmitritch remembered his own relations, and their
faces, at which he looked impartially in the past, struck him
now as repulsive and hateful.

"They are such reptiles!" he thought.

And his wife's face, too, struck him as repulsive and hateful.
Anger surged up in his heart against her, and he thought
malignantly:

"She knows nothing about money, and so she is stingy. If
she won it she would give me a hundred roubles and put the
rest away under lock and key."

And he looked at his wife, not with a smile now, but with
hatred. She glanced at him, too, and also with hatred and
anger. She had her own daydreams, her own plans, her own reflections; she understood perfectly well what her husband's
dreams were. She knew who would be the first to try and grab
her winnings.

"It's very nice making daydreams at other people's expense!"
is what her eyes expressed. "No, don't you dare!"

Her husband understood her look; hatred began stirring
again in his breast, and in order to annoy his wife he glanced
quickly, to spite her, at the fourth page on the newspaper and
read out triumphantly:

"Series 9,499, number 46! Not 26!"

Hatred and hope both disappeared at once, and it began
immediately to seem to Ivan Dmitritch and his wife that their
rooms were dark and small and low-pitched, that the supper
they had been eating was not doing them good, but lying heavy
on their stomachs, that the evenings were long and weari-
some. . . .

"What the devil's the meaning of it?" said Ivan Dmitritch,

beginning to be ill-humored. "Wherever one steps there are bits of paper under one's feet, crumbs, husks. The rooms are never swept! One is simply forced to go out. Damnation take my soul entirely! I shall go and hang myself on the first aspen tree!"

# THE STANDARD OF LIVING

## by Dorothy Parker

Here is a story which should start family discussion between young people and their elders. Dorothy Parker wrote it in 1941. Youngsters (twenty to twenty-five years old) say it's cynical. Older heads (forty plus) say it is touching and recalls their own depression days. Somerset Maugham says of its two little window-shopping stenographers, "They have all the charm, the impertinence, the pathos, and the absurdity of youth." See what happens in your family. If you have a teen-age daughter, let her be the reader-aloud. And if you'd like to read more Dorothy Parker, get Viking's *The Portable Dorothy Parker.*

Annabel and Midge came out of the tearoom with the arrogant slow gait of the leisured, for their Saturday afternoon stretched ahead of them.

They had been best friends almost from the day that Midge had found a job as stenographer with the firm that employed Annabel. By now Annabel, two years longer in the stenographic department, had worked up to the wages of $18.50 a week; Midge was still at $16. Each girl lived at home with her family and paid half her salary to its support.

The girls sat side by side at their desks; they lunched together every noon; together they set out for home at the end of the day's work. Many of their evenings and most of their Sundays were passed in each other's company. Often they were joined by two young men, but there was no steadiness to any such quartet. The two young men would give place, unlamented, to two other young men, and lament would have been inappropriate, really, since the newcomers were scarcely distinguishable from their predecessors. Invariably the girls spent the fine idle hours of their hot-weather Saturday afternoons together.

They looked alike, though the resemblance did not lie in their features. It was in the shape of their bodies, their movements, their style, and their adornments. Annabel and Midge did, and completely, all that young office workers are besought not to do. They painted their lips and their nails; they darkened their lashes and lightened their hair, and scent seemed to shimmer from them. They wore thin, bright dresses, tight over their breasts and high on their legs, and tilted slippers, fancifully strapped. They looked proud and cheap and charming.

Now, as they walked across to Fifth Avenue with their skirts swirled by the hot wind, they received audible admiration. Young men grouped lethargically about newsstands awarded them murmurs, exclamations, even—the ultimate tribute—whistles. Annabel and Midge passed without the condescension of hurrying their pace; they held their heads higher and set their feet with exquisite precision, as if they stepped over the necks of peasants.

Always the girls went to walk on Fifth Avenue on their free afternoons. The game could be played anywhere, and, indeed, was, but the great shop windows stimulated the two players to their best form.

Annabel had invented the game, or rather she had evolved it from an old one. Basically it was no more than the ancient sport of what-would-you-do-if-you-had-a-million-dollars. But Annabel had drawn a new set of rules for it, had narrowed it,

292                                    DOROTHY PARKER

pointed it, made it stricter. Like all games, it was the more absorbing for being more difficult.

Annabel's version went like this: You must suppose that
somebody dies and leaves you a million dollars, cool. But there
is a condition to the bequest—you must spend every nickel of
the money on yourself.

There lay the hazard of the game. If, when playing it, you
forgot and listed among your expenditures the rental of a new
apartment for your family, for example, you lost your turn to
the other player. It was astonishing how many—and some of
them among the experts, too—would forfeit all their innings by
such slips.

It was essential, of course, that it be played in passionate
seriousness. Each purchase must be carefully considered and,
if necessary, supported by argument. There was no zest to
playing wildly.

But Annabel and Midge were surely born to be comrades, for
Midge played the game like a master from the moment she
learned it. It was she who added the touches that made the
whole thing cozier. According to Midge's innovations, the ec-
centric who died and left you the money was not anybody you
loved, or, for the matter of that, anybody you even knew. It
was somebody who had seen you somewhere and had thought,
"That girl ought to have lots of nice things. I'm going to leave
her a million dollars when I die."

And the death was to be neither untimely nor painful. Your
benefactor, full of years and comfortably ready to depart, was
to slip softly away during sleep and go right to heaven.

These embroideries permitted Annabel and Midge to play
their game in the luxury of peaceful consciences.

Midge played with a seriousness that was not only proper
but extreme. The single strain on the girls' friendship had followed an announcement once made by Annabel that the first
thing she would buy with her million dollars would be a silver-
fox coat. It was as if she had struck Midge across the mouth.

When Midge recovered her breath, she cried that she couldn't imagine how Annabel could do such a thing—silver-fox coats were common! Annabel defended her taste with the retort that they were not common, either. Midge then said that they were so. She added that everybody had a silver-fox coat. She went on to declare that she herself wouldn't be caught dead in silver fox.

For the next few days, though the girls saw each other as constantly, their conversation was careful and infrequent, and they did not once play their game. Then one morning, as soon as Annabel entered the office, she came to Midge and said that she had changed her mind. She would not buy a silver-fox coat with any part of her million dollars. Immediately on receiving the legacy she would select a coat of mink.

Midge smiled and her eyes shown. "I think," she said, "you're absolutely right." Now, as they walked along Fifth Avenue, they played the game anew. It was one of those days with which September is repeatedly cursed: hot and glaring, with slivers of dust in the wind. People drooped and shambled, but the girls carried themselves tall and walked a straight line, as befitted young heiresses on their afternoon promenade. There was no longer need for them to start the game at its formal opening. Annabel went direct to the heart of it.

"All right," she said. "So you've got this million dollars. So what would be the first thing you'd do?"

"Well, the first thing I'd do," Midge said, "I'd get a mink coat." But she said it mechanically, as if she were giving the memorized answer to an expected question.

"Yes," Annabel said, "I think you ought to. The terribly dark kind of mink." But she, too, spoke as if by rote. It was too hot; fur, no matter how dark and sleek and supple, was horrid to the thoughts.

They stepped along in silence for a while. Then Midge's eye was caught by a shop window. Cool, lovely gleamings were there set off by chaste and elegant darkness.

"No," Midge said, "I take it back. I wouldn't get a mink coat the first thing. I'd get a string of pearls. Real pearls."

Annabel's eyes turned to follow Midge's.

"Yes," she said, slowly. "I think that's a kind of a good idea. You can wear pearls with anything."

Together they went over to the shop window and stood pressed against it. It contained but one object—a double row of great, even pearls clasped by a deep emerald around a little pink velvet throat.

"What do you suppose they cost?" Annabel said.

"Gee, I don't know," Midge said. "Plenty, I guess."

"Like a thousand dollars?" Annabel said.

"Oh, I guess like more," Midge said. "On account of the emerald."

"Well, like ten thousand dollars?" Annabel said.

"Gee, I wouldn't even know," Midge said.

The devil nudged Annabel in the ribs. "Dare you to go in and price them," she said.

"Like fun!" Midge said.

"Dare you," Annabel said.

"Well," Midge said. "But you've got to come too."

They tendered thanks, icily, to the doorman for ushering them into the shop. The girls wore expressions of bitter disdain, as if they stood in a sty.

A clerk came to them and bowed. His neat face showed no astonishment at their appearance.

"Good afternoon," he said. He implied that he would never forget it if they would grant him the favor of accepting his greeting.

"Good afternoon," Annabel and Midge said together and in freezing accents.

"Is there something—?" the clerk said.

"Oh, we're just looking," Annabel said. It was as if she flung the words down from a dais.

The clerk bowed.

"My friend and myself merely happened to be passing," Midge said. "My friend here and myself," she went on, "merely happened to be wondering how much are those pearls you've got in your window."

"Ah, yes," the clerk said. "The double rope. That is two hundred and fifty thousand dollars, madam."

"I see," Midge said.

The clerk bowed. "An exceptionally beautiful necklace," he said. "Would you care to look at it?"

"No, thank you," Annabel said.

"My friend and myself merely happened to be passing," Midge said.

They turned to go. The clerk sprang ahead and opened the door. He bowed as they swept by him.

The girls went on along the avenue, and disdain was still on their faces.

"Honestly!" Annabel said. "Can you imagine a thing like that?"

"Two hundred and fifty thousand dollars!" Midge said. "Why, that's a quarter of a million dollars!"

"He's sure got his nerve!" Annabel said.

They walked on. Slowly the disdain went, slowly and completely as if drained from them, and with it went the regal carriage and tread. Their shoulders dropped and they dragged their feet. They were silent and their eyes were cloudy.

Suddenly Midge straightened her back, flung her head high, and spoke clear and strong.

"Listen, Annabel," she said. "Look. Suppose there was this terribly rich person, see? You don't know this person, but this person has seen you somewhere and wants to do something for you. Well, it's a terribly old person, see? And so this person dies, just like going to sleep, and leaves you ten million dollars. Now, what would be the first thing you'd do?"

# VISION OF AMERICA

## Through the Eyes of Its Presidents

The Fourth of July, 1776, opened a new era in the history of the world. America's growth has been so rapid and so vast that we tend to take ourselves for granted. From time to time we should look back and take stock of ourselves. Here is a gallery of our thirty-four Presidents, with a quotation from the writings or speeches of each man. Their subject is America—the land, the people, the government, the ideal. Back of most of these quotes lies a sense of the destiny of the United States that is permanently bound up with morality, with principle, with the essentials of decency.

### GEORGE WASHINGTON: 1789–1797

"The name of American . . . must always exalt the just pride of patriotism . . . The independence and liberty you possess are the work of joint councils and joint efforts, of common dangers, sufferings and successes."

### JOHN ADAMS: 1797–1801

"I must study politics and war, that my sons may have liberty to study mathematics and philosophy . . . in order to give their children the right to study painting, poetry, music."

THOMAS JEFFERSON: 1801–1809

"The new circumstances under which we are placed call for new words, new phrases, and for the transfer of old words to new objects. An American dialect will therefore be formed."

JAMES MADISON: 1809–1817

"The face of our country everywhere presents the evidence of laudable enterprise . . . In the extension of manufactures . . . we behold a rapid diminution of our dependence on foreign supplies."

JAMES MONROE: 1817–1825

"The emigrants . . . although of different political parties and of different religious sects . . . all flew from persecution, in pursuit of liberty, and they inculcated that sentiment on their descendants."

JOHN QUINCY ADAMS: 1825–1829

"America, in the assembly of nations . . . has invariably . . . held forth the hand of honest friendship . . . She has uniformly spoken among them . . . the language of equal liberty, equal justice and equal rights."

ANDREW JACKSON: 1829–1837

"As long as our Government is administered for the good of the people, and is regulated by their will . . . it will be worth defending."

MARTIN VAN BUREN: 1837–1841

"The effects of distance have been averted by the inventive genius of our people, developed and fostered by the spirit of our institutions."

WILLIAM HENRY HARRISON: 1841–1841

"Of all the great interests that appertain to our country, that of Union . . . is by far the most important, since it is the only true and sure guaranty of all others."

## JOHN TYLER: 1841–1845

"Let it, then, be henceforth proclaimed to the world, that man's conscience was created free; that he is no longer accountable to his fellow man for his religious opinions, being responsible therefor only to his God."

## JAMES K. POLK, 1845–1849

"While the people of other countries are struggling to establish free institutions, under which man may govern himself, we are in the actual enjoyment of them—a rich inheritance from our fathers."

## ZACHARY TAYLOR: 1849–1850

"Sixty years have elapsed since the establishment of this Government . . . and the United States presents to the world the most stable and permanent Government on earth."

## MILLARD FILLMORE: 1850–1853

"The ability to produce every necessary of life renders us independent in war as well as in peace."

## FRANKLIN PIERCE: 1853–1857

"While men inhabiting different parts of this vast continent cannot be expected to hold the same opinions . . . they can unite in a common object and sustain common principles."

## JAMES BUCHANAN: 1857–1861

"We shall best promote the prosperity of the new States and Territories by furnishing them with a hardy and independent race of honest and industrious citizens."

ABRAHAM LINCOLN: 1861–1865
"Fellow citizens, we cannot escape history. We . . . will be remembered in spite of ourselves . . . The fiery trial through which we pass will light us down, in honor or dishonor, to the latest generation."

ANDREW JOHNSON: 1865–1869
"It is the only government suited to our condition; but we have never sought to impose it on others, and we have consistently followed the advice of Washington to recommend it only by its careful preservation."

ULYSSES S. GRANT: 1869–1877
"Our republican institutions were regarded as experiments up to the breaking out of the rebellion . . . Now our people have proven themselves to be the most formidable in war of any nationality."

RUTHERFORD B. HAYES: 1877–1881
"It is vain to hope for the success of a free government without the means of insuring the intelligence of those who are the source of power."

JAMES A. GARFIELD: 1881–1881
"To all our means of culture is added the powerful incentive to personal ambition . . . No post of honor is so high but the poorest may hope to reach it."

CHESTER A. ARTHUR: 1881–1885
"No higher proof could exist of the strength of popular government than the fact that, though the chosen of the people be struck down, his constitutional successor is peacefully installed without shock or strain."

GROVER CLEVELAND: 1885–1889—1893–1897

"Our nation . . . lives in us—in our hearts and minds and consciences . . . The land we live in seems to be strong and active. But how fares the land that lives in us?"

BENJAMIN HARRISON: 1889–1893

"Our growth has not been limited to territory, population and aggregate wealth . . . The facilities for popular education have been vastly enlarged and more greatly diffused."

WILLIAM MCKINLEY: 1897–1901

"The mission of the United States is one of benevolent assimilation, substituting the mild sway of justice and right for arbitrary rule."

THEODORE ROOSEVELT: 1901–1909

"Like all Americans, I like big things: big prairies, big forests and mountains, big wheatfields, railroads . . . and everything else. But no people ever yet benefited by riches if their prosperity corrupted their virtue."

WILLIAM HOWARD TAFT: 1909–1913

"We have taken millions of foreigners into our civilization, but we have amalgamated them, and . . . we have made them all Americans. We have bred to a type."

WOODROW WILSON: 1913–1921

"America . . . consists of all of us; and it can consist of all of us only as our spirits are banded together in a common enterprise. That common enterprise is the enterprise of liberty and justice and right."

WARREN G. HARDING: 1921–1923

"The motor car has become an indispensable instrument in our political, social and industrial life. There is begun a new era . . ."

CALVIN COOLIDGE: 1923–1929

"It would be folly to argue that the people cannot make political mistakes. They can and do make grave mistakes. But compared with the mistakes which have been made by every kind of autocracy they are unimportant."

HERBERT HOOVER: 1929–1933

"We believe in equal opportunity for all, but we know that this includes the opportunity to rise to leadership, to be uncommon! The great human advances have not been brought about by mediocre men and women."

FRANKLIN D. ROOSEVELT: 1933–1945

"This great Nation will endure as it has endured, will revive and will prosper . . . The only thing we have to fear is fear itself—which paralyzes needed efforts to convert retreat into advance."

HARRY S. TRUMAN: 1945–1953

"We want to . . . do the things in peace that we have been able to do in war. If we can put this tremendous machine of ours . . . to work for peace, we can look forward to the greatest age in the history of mankind."

DWIGHT D. EISENHOWER: 1953–1961

"What we call foreign affairs is no longer foreign affairs. It's a local affair. Whatever happens in Indonesia is important to Indiana . . . The world must learn to work together—or finally it will not work at all."

JOHN F. KENNEDY: 1961–

"To those nations who would make themselves our adversary, we offer not a pledge but a request . . . let both sides join in creating a new endeavor—not a new balance of power, but a new world of law, where the strong are just and the weak secure and the peace preserved."

# THE NIGHTMARE CANNON

## by Victor Hugo

*The power of the printed word!*

In our age of TV, movies, and picture magazines we sometimes forget that miracles beyond the reach of Hollywood and Radio City can be performed by these odd little black squiggles on white paper.

I was casting back in my mind for a good example of this miracle, and I suddenly remembered an episode written by one of the greatest word magicians of all, Victor Hugo.

It comes from *Ninety-three*, a novel of the French Revolution. The scene is the deck of the small Royalist man-of-war *Claymore*, whose mission is to carry a mysterious old man, disguised as a peasant, to Britanny, where Royalists and Republicans are fighting bitterly.

As the ship nears the coast, a frightful thing happens —a heavy cannon breaks loose. And so begins this powerful short narrative.

The huge cannon, broken from its moorings, was suddenly transformed into a supernatural beast!

A monster had been bred from a machine! This hulk runs along on its wheels as easily as a billiard ball; it rolls with the rolling, pitches with the pitching, comes and goes, stops, seems

302

to meditate, begins anew, darts like an arrow from one end of the ship to the other, whirls around, evades, rears, hits out, crushes, kills. It is a ram battering a wall at its own pleasure. It weighs ten thousand pounds, and it bounds like a child's ball.

In an instant the crew was on its feet. It was the fault of the chief gunner, who had neglected to fasten the screw-nut of the breeching chain and had not thoroughly chocked the four trucks of the cannon. The lashings were broken, so that the gun was no longer firm on its carriage. As a wave struck the ship's side the cannon, insufficiently secured, had receded and, having broken its chain, began to wander threateningly over the deck.

When the fastening broke, the gunners were in the battery, singly and in groups, clearing the ship for action. The cannon, thrown forward by the pitching, dashed into a group of men, killing four of them at the first blow; then hurled back by the rolling, it cut in two a fifth and struck and dismounted one of the guns of the port battery. The gun-deck was empty in the twinkling of an eye.

The monstrous gun was left to itself. It was its own mistress, and mistress of the ship.

Captain Boisberthelot and Lieutenant la Vieuville, brave men though they were, paused at the top of the ladder, silent, pale, and undecided, looking down on the deck. Someone pushed them aside with his elbow and descended. It was their passenger, the peasant, the man about whom they were talking a moment ago. Having reached the bottom of the ladder, he halted.

The cannon was rolling to and fro on the deck. A dim wavering of lights and shadows was added to this spectacle by the marine lantern swinging below deck. The outlines of the cannon were indistinguishable, because of the rapidity of its motion; sometimes it looked black when the light shone upon it, then again it would cast pale, glimmering reflections in the darkness. It had already shattered four other guns and made two breaches in the ship's side fortunately above the water line.

The captain gave orders to throw down the hatchway all that could check the mad onslaught of this infuriated gun: mattresses, hammocks, spare sails, coils of rope, and bags of the crew. But what availed these rags? No one dared go down to arrange them, and in a few moments they were reduced to lint.

Meanwhile the havoc increased. The mizzenmast was split, and even the mainmast was damaged by the convulsive blows of the cannon. The destruction of the battery still went on. Ten out of the thirty cannon were useless. The old passenger, who had descended to the gun deck, looked like one carved in stone as he stood motionless at the foot of the stairs and glanced sternly over the devastation. It would have been impossible to move a step upon the deck.

Each bound of the liberated cannon seemed to threaten the destruction of the ship. They must either overcome this calamity or perish; some action must be taken. But what? What a combatant was this gun! How was this mad creature to be arrested, this flash of lightning to be seized, this thunderbolt to be crushed?

Suddenly a man appeared, grasping an iron bar. It was the author of the catastrophe, the chief gunner, whose criminal negligence had caused the accident. Having brought about the evil, his intention was to repair it. Holding a handspike in one hand, and in the other a tiller rope with the slip noose in it, he had jumped through the hatchway to the deck below.

Then began a titanic spectacle—a combat between cannon and cannoneer; a contest between mind and matter; a duel between man and the inanimate. The man stood in one corner in an attitude of expectancy, holding in his hands the bar and the rope; calm, livid, and tragic, he stood firmly on his legs, that were like two pillars of steel. He was waiting for the cannon to approach him.

The gunner knew his gun, and he felt as though it must

know him. How often he had put his hand in its mouth. He began to talk to it as he would to a dog. "Come," said he.

Not a breath was drawn freely, except perhaps by the old man, who remained on the gun deck gazing on the two combatants. He himself was in danger of being crushed by the piece; still he did not move.

Beneath them the blind sea had command of the battle. When, in the act of accepting this awful hand-to-hand struggle, the gunner approached to challenge the cannon, it happened that the surging sea held the gun motionless for an instant, as though stupefied. "Come on!" said the man. It seemed to listen.

Suddenly it leaped toward him. The man dodged. Then the struggle began. Now this colossal grasshopper would strike the low overhead of the gun deck, then falling back on its four wheels, like a tiger on all fours, rush upon the man. He—supple, agile, adroit—writhed like a serpent before these lightning movements. The man avoided encounters but he fought. He even attacked the cannon at times, crawling along by the side of the ship and clutching his handspike and the rope; the cannon seemed to understand his movements and fled as though suspecting a trap. The man, nothing daunted, pursued his chase.

Such a struggle must necessarily be brief. Suddenly the cannon seemed to say to itself: Now, then, there must be an end to this. And it stopped. A crisis was felt to be at hand. The cannon as if in suspense seemed to meditate some furious design. All at once it rushed on the gunner, who sprang aside with a laugh, crying out, "Try it again!" as the cannon passed him.

The gun in its fury smashed one of the port cannon; then, by the invisible sling in which it seemed to be held, it was thrown to the starboard, toward the man, who escaped. Three cannon were crushed by its onslaught; then, as though blind and beside itself, it turned from the man and rolled from stern to stem, causing a breach in the timbers of the prow. The gunner took refuge at the foot of the ladder, a short distance from the old man, who stood watching. He held his handspike in readiness. The cannon seemed aware of it, and without taking the trouble to turn, it rushed backward on the man, as swift as the blow of an ax. The gunner, if driven up against the side of the ship, would be lost. A single cry arose from the crew.

The old passenger—who until this moment had stood motionless—sprang forward more swiftly than all those mad swirls. He seized a bale and, at the risk of being crushed, succeeded in throwing it between the wheels of the carronade.

The bale had the effect of a plug. A pebble may block a log; a branch sometimes changes the course of an avalanche. The cannon stumbled, and the gunner, availing himself of the perilous opportunity, thrust his iron bar between the spokes of the back wheels. Pitching forward, the cannon stopped; and the man, using his bar for a lever, rocked it backward and forward. The heavy mass upset, with the resonant sound of a bell that crashes in its fall. The man, reeking with perspiration, threw himself upon it and passed the slipnoose of the tiller rope around the neck of the defeated monster.

The combat was ended. The man had conquered. The ant had overcome the mastodon; the pigmy had imprisoned the thunderbolt.

> The rest of the story is almost as exciting. The old man reveals his authority—he is the commander-in-chief of the Breton counterrevolutionary army. First he decorates for bravery the gunner whose life he has just saved. Then, without any sign of emotion, he orders the gunner to be shot—for his act of carelessness.
>
> —C. F.

# THE LAST DAY
# OF THE ALAMO

## by Lon Tinkle

There are many real-life adventures that still live in the stones and masonry, the pavements, the landscapes which witnessed them. The place where a great and memorable event occurred has a compelling quality, whether you read about it, see a picture of it, or go there and experience its haunting magic firsthand.

Visit San Antonio and your footsteps turn inevitably toward the ruins of the Alamo. One hundred and twenty-four years ago, 182 Texans fought off 5,000 Mexicans for thirteen heroic days and nights. In Texas' fight for independence the Alamo played a decisive role, for its defenders, who fell to the last man, roused the whole territory to the struggle for independence from Mexico. On the battlefield of San Jacinto, five weeks after the fall of the Alamo, Santa Anna's army was annihilated. For the next decade Texas was an independent republic, joining the union in 1845.

In our time, no one has told the bloody, glorious tale of the siege better than the Texas writer, Lon Tinkle, in his fine 13 *Days to Glory*. Our story is an excerpt from his book.

And now . . . it is four o'clock on the afternoon of March 5—twelfth day of the siege—and the Mexican guns have just gone suddenly silent.

A bleak, bitter norther blew up at midafternoon on March 5. By nightfall the winds had chilled bodies through the marrow and frozen the crust of the earth. The raging weather hushed for a time the crack of guns. Where blood had spilled on the earth, it hardened in a hurry.

At the end of this twelfth day of the siege, the Texans were still hoarding their powder against the inevitable final assault. But Santa Anna had silenced the Mexican guns late in the afternoon of the freezing March day for a different reason. He knew that his constant cannonade and the real or feigned skirmishes had exhausted Texan nerves as well as ammunition. Now he wanted to give them a chance to sleep the sleep of exhaustion—and awake to find Mexicans scaling the walls.

Up until this sudden cease-fire the Texans had not suffered a single casualty. It was this fact, reported by Travis in his last message on March 3, that now made the threat of loss more terrible. The hand of doom had been stayed for twelve days. How long before it fell—and how heavily?

The startling hush late in the afternoon seemed like a blessed respite to the Texans—a chance to grab a few hours' sleep in the merciful silence. Huddled against the icy walls at their posts, they yielded to long-denied rest. For Travis the silence was ominous. He could only wonder what explosion would follow it.

At two o'clock that afternoon Santa Anna had summoned his staff. The instructions were precise and full: "The time has come to strike a decisive blow upon the enemy occupying the Fortress of the Alamo. His Excellency, the General-in-Chief, has decided that tomorrow at 4 o'clock A.M. the columns shall be stationed at musket-shot distance from the first entrenchments, ready for the charge, which shall commence, at a signal given with a bugle, from the Northern Battery."

Santa Anna hoped to profit not merely by the surprise of this all-out maneuver but also by its perfect timing. In the pre-dawn light, Mexican infantrymen rushing to scale the walls would have the cover of semi-darkness. But once there, they would be able to see well enough to pursue their advantage against men barely roused from their first deep sleep in a fortnight.

The Texans, meanwhile, with three sentries posted outside the walls, slept fitfully. One man within the fort remained awake, watching the fires. Once again silence and shadow were the realities inside the fortress.

Three startling and separate sounds roused the Texans into wakefulness: First, a blast from a bugle lifted the Mexican infantry to its feet. At once there began a wild rush of humanity. The piercing bugle blast was nothing compared to this second sound—the drumming of thousands of feet on the hard ground. There now poured forth the third, most fearful of all. Santa Anna's regimental band burst forth with the ancient Moorish battle march, the famed *deguello*, signal that no quarter would be given.

The Texan sentries posted outside the Alamo must have been bayoneted almost at once; they gave no outcry. The first alarm came from Travis himself: "Come on, men! The Mexicans are upon us! And we will give them hell!" The Mexicans were there, indeed: 2,500 against the Alamo garrison of 182. A large reserve was in back and ready to intercept fugitives. The giant push was on. Cannon balls began to rain down on the fortress from all sides. Travis, with rifle and sword, and followed by his faithful servant Joe, raced seventy yards to his battle station at the fortress's most vulnerable point. He stood by the twelve-pounder mounted on a platform, covering that single breach in the north wall which the Mexican artillery had been able to make.

Davy Crockett and his Tennessee boys were stationed on the southeast side of the open court, guarding the low stockade wall that ran from the chapel westward to the south wall.

Jim Bonham was atop the chapel, commanding three twelve-pound cannon. From debris within the church, the

Texans had made a ramp to a stockade platform and placed the cannon so they could fire in three directions over the roofless church walls—one south, one east, one north. Bonham could pivot his cannon, but most of the others in the fort had been installed in a way which allowed little maneuverability. Jim Bowie lay on his cot in the chapel. Davy Crockett had provided him with loaded pistols.

Though startled, the small garrison rallied in a breath and met the first assault with success. The cannon fire caught scores of Mexicans racing toward the walls. Accurate rifle fire made Mexican casualties so heavy at the start that the Texans got an unexpected respite while the Mexican infantry was regrouped and a second attack organized.

The Texans knew they would lose to sheer force of numbers if ever the Mexicans got over the outer walls. One hundred and eighty-two men could take a mighty toll of several thousand attackers—in the beginning. But the walls must not be breached.

Now, with staggering casualties, the Mexican generals could risk no delay. Some of the units had already lost nearly half their men. The second charge must follow swiftly on the rout of the first.

Despite the concentration of force on the sector defended by Travis, Texan fire succeeded in repulsing the second attack. No scaling ladder stood in place long enough to permit entry. The Texans picked off top man after top man, tumbling him onto the men below.

It was possible now, in the half-light, to make out the colors of the Mexican uniforms. As for the uniforms of the defenders, they were of every kind—buckskin hunting shirt, blanket coat, remnants of costume from the New Orleans Grays, and the rags and tags of handmade clothing. Besides the coonskin cap, the Texans had headgear of every description. Their commander, however, was dressed in a style worthy of his position. William Barret Travis had ordered himself a uniform: gray swallow-tail coat, pantaloons and forage cap, with facings, stripes, and bands of black. He always carried a sword at his side.

It was this group of volunteers, half in rags, that turned back the second attack too. They endured a third swift attack as well, but this one they could not keep outside the walls.

The weak center of the northern wall, opened two days before by Mexican fire, was the point finally breached by the Mexicans. It was a victory of sheer numbers. Pouring flood-strong through the northeast wall, the Mexican infantry took quick positions behind segments of blasted rock, behind dead bodies, in angles or recesses. Most of the men had to remain in the open, and following the example of the first ones inside the walls, knelt quickly on one knee to fire swiftly at the nearest target. Single combat with rifle and knife became the pattern. The Texans had no bayonets but they did have bowie knives. They still manned one or two cannon stations that kept blasting away. Half the walls of the convent barracks were split apart.

With the enemy inside the inner court of the Alamo, the Texans had only one recourse: to shut themselves inside the barracks rooms, the two-story former convent, or the Alamo chapel. They fought *mano-a-mano* with swords, tomahawks, knives, and bayonets as they leaped from their posts atop the walls and barricaded themselves inside the barracks for a momentary advantage. The doors and few windows of the Alamo buildings were barricaded with sandbags as tall as a man, but to no avail. Once the rooms were opened, they were stormed, one after the other, and taken at the point of bayonet.

The Texan Resistance was a drama in four acts that morning which lasted not much longer than a full-length tragedy on the stage. The first act was the attempt to hold the walls against the Mexicans. The second act occurred in the courtyard area where the battle was joined hand to hand. The last two acts were in a sense indoors—the first in the barracks, the last in the Alamo chapel.

The third act, and the most bitterly fought with the greatest number of casualties among the Texans, was the retreat into the convent barracks. Most of the rooms had interior parapets just inside the doorway, parapets built of two frames of bear or cowhides stretched on poles, with the inner cavity thickly mounded with rammed earth. By means of this construction the outnumbered Texans could fire at the enemy from considerable protection.

Where they were not blasted out of their refuges by cannon fire, the Texans stacked up the enemy dead in great numbers. But here again, individual bravery could not stand for long against greater numbers and superior weapons. Room after room fell to the invader.

Davy Crockett was still outdoors. Travis had assigned him the most difficult spot of all, a stretch of ground between the chapel and the south wall. "Just give me my place to defend," he told Travis, "and me and my Tennessee boys will hold it."

The place was an appropriate one for the man who had always urged that the battle be carried against the Mexicans outside the walls. "I hate to be hemmed in," Davy had protested.

Now, like Travis, Crockett died outdoors, where he wished to be. Later, he and his men were found at their post near the stockade fence. In his hand was "Old Betsy," his favorite rifle. In mute testimony to a man whose marksmanship was legendary, the greatest concentration of Mexican bodies were found around Crockett's body.

The very last act of the Alamo Drama took place in the only building that stands today, the Alamo chapel.

Though in ruins and largely filled with debris, the chapel, with its four-foot-thick walls, was still the strongest building in the mission. Into the chapel now withdrew the remnants of the Texas army. They had an additional reason for defending the church. Their store of powder had been cached in a northern room of the chapel which was the least vulnerable to enemy gunfire. By agreement, the last man alive was to light a torch to the powder.

It was Major Robert Evans who made the decision that the time had come to obliterate the fort. His torch flaring, Major Evans made a dash for the powder magazine.

But the cannon balls had breached the chapel's barred doors, and the Mexicans streamed in before Major Evans chose his moment. Arm raised to hurl the fire into the powder, he was shot down on the run before he could touch off the explosion. He fell face downward on the earthen floor. This was probably the last act of attempted aggression by any living Texan at the Alamo.

Of those who died there little more remains to be said. On the Texan side 182 men were killed; about fifteen women and children were spared. Perhaps most conclusive is the figure given to Dr. Sutherland by Santa Anna's secretary, Ramon Martinez Caro. Caro said: "We brought to San Antonio more than 5,000 men and we lost during the siege 1,544 of the best of them. The Texans fought more like devils than men."

# "YES, YOUR HONESTY!"

## by George and Helen Papashvily

It has been well said (by John Gunther) that ours is the only country deliberately founded on a good idea. Parts of that good idea you'll find reflected in this true story by George and Helen Papashvily.

Mr. Papashvily reached our shores about forty years ago. He came from the wild, primitive country of Georgia in Russia wearing a caracul fur hat and hoping to ply his trade. He made swords. There was no great demand here for swords, but somehow George got along. And he fell in love with America.

Some years ago he told all about this love affair in a little book describing his early American experiences. It's called *Anything Can Happen*. Written in what George calls "broken words," it's one of the funniest and yet most touching books I know by a man about his adopted country.

From it I've picked this episode dealing with George's first encounter with American justice.

Six months in America and already I was a jailbird. Happened this way.

The weeks seemed extra long that first half year I was in New York. No holidays, no feast days, no celebrations to break up the time and then when Saturday came around I had only twelve dollars, at most fourteen dollars in my pay envelope . . .

But no matter how the week went the Sundays were good because then we made all day the holiday and took ourselves in Van Cortlandt Park where there was country and trees and flowers. We could make fires and roast cubed lamb shashliks and walk on the grass and forget the factory. For one day anyway we could enjoy to live like human beings.

From six o'clock on, every Sunday morning, subway was packed full. Russians, Syrians, Greeks, Armenians, all kinds of peoples, carrying their grampas and babies and gallon jugs and folding chairs and charcoal sacks and hammocks and samovars and lunch baskets and rugs. Everyone hurrying to their regular place in the park so they could start tea and lay out the lunch, to make the day last a long, long time.

Well, this particular Sunday when all my trouble began was in the late spring. Bright blue day with a high sky and white lamb clouds. The kind of day that's for adventures.

I had my first American-bought suit on and a purple striped tie with a handkerchief to match and a real Yankee Doodle hat from straw. I felt happy and full of prance.

Five or six other fellows and me were visiting around the park. We went from family to family we knew and drank a glass of wine here, tried a piece of cake there, met an uncle just came from Buffalo, saw a new baby first time out and so on.

While we were walking and making shortcut down a quiet little path to get on other side of the park we came to a beautiful tree foaming over with white blossoms, how they call in English a dogswood.

"Flowers. Flowers," one Russian fellow, name of Cyrille, said. "I gonna pick. Take bouquet to my lady friend." I don't know who he was, this fellow, he joined us some place we stopped.

"Pick! Pick!" Everybody got the idea. "Pick flowers, take a bouquet to all the lady friends."

"Why spoil a tree?" I said. "Use your brains better. If you want to make friends with a nice young lady, ask her to take a walk. Tell her you gonna show her a bouquet bigger than a house, a bouquet growing right out of the ground. Something interesting. That way you get a chance to be acquainted while you're walking. Maybe you know so good on the way back you can invite for ice cream."

No, no, won't listen. They have to break the tree down. Tear his arms and legs off like wolves. Jumping, Jumping. Who's gonna get the biggest branch? Makes me sick.

"Personally," I said, "I would be ashamed to give a lady flowers that I got for nothing. Flowers that I stole, I prefer better to buy. Shows more respect. Or else don't give."

All of a sudden that fellow, Cyrille, who had now the biggest bunch climbed down from the top branches and said to me, "I have to tie my shoelace. Hold my bouquet for a minute. I'll be back." In that minute a policeman was there.

"Awright. Awright," he said. "Defacing public property. Awright." He asked us our names and started writing them down on a piece of paper.

"What he does?" I asked Sergei.

"Gives us a summons."

"Summons?"

"We have to go in court."

"We're arrested?"

"Something like that. If we pay fine, everything be O.K. But if we ignore, throw away the summons, they chase us, lock us up."

"What's your name, buddy?" policeman asked me.

I explained the best I can I'm not picking, I'm only holding for the other fellow.

But he doesn't believe me. "Don't argue," he said. "Don't argue or I'll run you in right now."

I explained again. "Boys will tell you," I said. "I wasn't picking. Boys know I was only holding."

No, he doesn't believe them neither. "Don't alibi him," he said.

I'd be sorry to be a man like that policeman, suspicious that everybody is a liar. What's the use for a person to live if he can't trust nobody?

So he wrote a ticket for me, too, and went away. And still tying his shoe, that fellow Cyrille wasn't back yet.

"This is an awful, awful thing," I said.

"It's nothing." Sergei could laugh.

"Nothing! I lived my whole life at home and I was never in trouble. Now I'm six months in America and I'm a crook. Nothing, you think? How my father likes to hear such kind of news? What will our village say? First man from Kobiankari ever comes in the U.S.A.—for what? To go in prison!"

"Look," Sergei said. "You don't even have to go in court. Send the money. Plead guilty."

"But I'm not."

"You only say you are. Saves time."

"Then the policeman's right never to believe anybody. Say first, I didn't. Then, change around, say I did."

"If you won't plead guilty, you'll have to go in court and have a trial."

"Then I'll go."

"Lose a day's pay."

"I lose."

Sergei suggested how about we go to see old Mr. Cohen, he was years and years in the U.S.A. Maybe he can think of something.

"Listen," Mr. Cohen said, when we told him everything. "Take my advices. I been a citizen for forty-seven years with full papers. Go in court. When they ask you the first question say, 'Not guilty, Your Honor.'"

"Not guilty, Your Honor. What means 'Your Honor'?"

"Means the judge. All judges in U.S.A. named Your Honor."

"Not guilty, Your Honor. Then?"

"Just tell your story nice way."

"But with my broken words?"

"Say the best way you can. Probably judge gonna listen and try to understand you. Of course it can happen you get a mean judge, one that don't like foreigners to bother him. But very few those kind. If you get such a one, pay your fine, don't argue. But come and tell me."

"What you gonna do about it?"

"Why, next time, I vote against him, naturally. We don't keep him in office no more, if he don't act nice."

So next morning I went in court. Called the other names, Igor, Arkady, Sergei, Philip. Guilty. Guilty. Guilty. All sent money to pay their fines.

Now my name. I couldn't understand a word they asked me. I was nervous. My English was running out of my head like sand through a sieve. How they told me to call a judge? Your Honorable? No. Your Highness? No, that's Russian. Your?— They were asking me something. I had to answer. I took my courage in both hands and spoke. "Not guilty, Your Honesty."

Courtroom went wild. Laughing like hyenas. The judge pounded with the hammer. His face was red like a turkey's. What I done? I was sure I was going in Sing Sing and be thrown in the deepest-down dungeon.

But the judge was giving the audience hell first. "Word honesty—cause such mirth—contempt of court."

"Young man." Now it be my turn. "Address the Court as Sir."

"Yes, sir."

"Did I understand you to plead not guilty?"

"Yes, sir. I plead not guilty."

"This officer says you and your friends were violating an ordinance, destroying a tree. Breaking the limbs."

"Yes, sir. Some was picking. I wasn't."

"Have you any proof of this?"

"No, sir. Friends were with me, but they all pleaded guilty, sent you a fine. Cheaper than to lose a day's pay."

"Why didn't you do that?"

"Because if I'm guilty, I admit it, but if I'm not guilty, no man gonna make me say I am. Just as much a lie to say you guilty when you not as to say you innocent if you did wrong."

"Yes, that's correct. How long are you in the United States?"

"Six months."

"In court here before?"

"No, sir."

"Ever in trouble at home? Assault or kill a man?"

"Yes, sir."

"How many?"

"Hundreds. After the first year, I never counted them any more."

"Where was this?"

"In the war. I'm a sniper. It's my job to shoot all the Germans I see. Sometimes Bulgarians too."

"I see. I mean in civil life. When you were not a soldier, not in the army. Ever hurt or strike anybody?"

"Yes, sir. Once."

"What?"

"Knocked a man's teeths out. Few."

"Why?"

"Catched him giving poisoned meat to my dog to eat."

"Understandable. Only time?"

"Yes, sir."

"Did you actually see this man," His Honesty asked the policeman, "breaking the tree?"

"No, sir. Not exactly, but all the others admitted guilt and he was with them, holding a bunch of flowers."

"I believe he's a truthful man, Officer, and this time you were probably mistaken. Case dismissed."

And then His Honesty, big American judge, leaned over. And what do you think he said to me, ignorant, no speaking language, six months off a boat, greenhorn foreigner? "Young man, I like to shake hands with you."

And in front of that whole courtroom, he did.

# THE VERY FOREIGN AMBASSADORS

## by Walter Bastian

> This has the kind of surprise ending writers reach for and so seldom actually achieve.
>
> Walter Bastian, the author, is a U.S. Foreign Service officer currently on assignment in Washington, D. C., after a dozen years in foreign posts. I'd guess this story occurred to him after watching too many dignitaries parading up Pennsylvania Avenue.

He lay there in the master bedroom of Blair House—just across Pennsylvania Avenue from the White House—comfortably listening to the small sounds of his wife as she bustled about getting ready for the day. Through years of assignments in two-bit consulates and backwater capitals she had learned to make do, turn collars and cuffs, make her basic black dress hide the inadequacy of their budget when they had the two kids in college back home.

Then there was the miserable year when they had lived in the two-bedroom apartment while he received the mid-career honor of a course at the War College. Surrounded and pinned down by the military, they had survived. He had since made almost every right step by design or by luck: foreign-service inspector, political counselor, and then the area and language study course for the ambassadorship.

She had made every one of the transitions almost as effort-
lessly as he, and he recognized the fact that he owed a lot to
her, to her still striking appearance, to her poise, the instinctive
ability to say the right thing at the right time. As a special
concession they had even taken the briefing course together for
this post.

"Margaret," he called. They always spoke English nowadays
when they were alone. It was a trick they had picked up on
their very first assignment, using the foreign language together
until it became a part of their intimate personal life.

There was no answer and so he called again, "Margaret."
The rustling in the next room stopped. "You don't have to
clean up every damned thing. The Americans are civilized
enough, in spite of certain evidences to the contrary."

He was rather proud of the phrase even though it sounded
a little stiff. It was fluent, at least, and he remembered how it
had been during the first semester of the language course,
eight hours a day, every day of the week. And he could still
speak the barbarous tongue only with a guttural indistinctness
which the professor thought he would never dominate. But
here he was, and even the strangling aspirates sounded convincing.

He had insisted that his information officer put a few aspirates into his speech for good measure, certain that the press
would note them and be flattered at the way he spoke before
Congress. He touched his thorax appreciatively.

His wife came into the room, carrying her overnight bag.
Just like a damned ant, he thought, work for the sake of work,
no matter how many servants were about.

"George." It was the English approximation, just as Margaret was, but it permitted them to converse in front of Americans with that touch of domesticity to which Americans pay
such lip service.

"George," she said again. "I mean, Mr. Ambassador. If your
Excellency doesn't get himself out of bed, the chief of protocol will be here before you can get your ceremonials on. You

know it always takes you ten minutes just to put on the sash and medals."

He rolled over. Wretched bed was too short. "The Americans don't go much for this sash and medals stuff. Undemocratic and all that." But nevertheless he struggled out of bed obediently and went out into the anteroom. An elderly servant was laying out his things. He started as the ambassador entered.

"Sorry to frighten you, Richardson," he said amiably. This trick of remembering names came easily to him from years of experience. "I always look—and feel—like hell before I've had breakfast." As a matter of fact he found that he felt much better if he ate no breakfast whatsoever, but Americans made such a social business of refection that he thought this an unusually good touch.

In spite of what Margaret said, he managed to get himself into moderately good shape in short order. His ceremonials had been neatly pressed, and, as he viewed his tall, slender figure approvingly in the mirror, he formulated the opening conversational gambits which he might try during the ride from Blair House to the Capitol.

He smiled once at his reflection, the easy, over-rapid smile of the career diplomat, made sure that his speech was with him, the extra copy for the press. He would always remember with a rush of humiliation, even after all these years, the speech some sticky-handed aide had given him with two pages glued together by accident so that he omitted an entire section in the reading.

"Fortunately," Margaret had told him with what was meant to be assurance, "my husband is such an imposing figure that no one listens to what he says anyway."

Margaret came in from the other room, and Richardson announced the arrival of the chief of protocol at precisely the same moment. "Important individuals," she used to say, "set up vibrations, and so I'm always ready for them."

They swung down the stairs together, a tall couple who

would have attracted attention anywhere on earth, even in moderately sophisticated Washington.

He insisted on helping her into the open car himself, for he thought it good policy that they ride together, he pointing out the sights and she looking with enthusiasm. "Regular home folks," the Americans would say.

In between bows to the multitude and the exchanging of pleasantries with the chief of protocol as they rode down Pennsylvania Avenue, he rehearsed the concrete proposals in his speech. The bid for a Cultural Exchange agreement in order to give him an opportunity to show his professional skill at negotiation at minimum cost. A Public Law 480 bid for a Title II agreement for the alleviation of drought suffering through the use of agricultural surpluses. Finally an Export-Import Bank Loan. A neat little package.

In front of the Treasury Department the Marine Band was drawn up, and as he passed they sounded off in a reasonable approximation of his national anthem. A child dashed out of the crowd lining Fifteenth Street and tossed a bundle of flowers to him. He fielded them deftly, but out of the corner of his eye he could see someone grab the child and scold it. One of the Secret Service operatives in the car took the flowers from him and shredded the bouquet to assure himself that it contained no infernal machine. Other times and other customs. He was too much of an old pro, and so was Margaret, to show any surprise.

They turned left once again onto Pennsylvania Avenue with the Capitol building straight ahead of them and the large friendly crowds waving and applauding. He was a bit of a curiosity, but they were eager that he recognize their sincere desire for peace.

Then suddenly up ahead something fluttered from the balcony of an office building along the line of march. Even at a distance of more than two blocks they could see the crowd turning to look at what was apparently a huge banner, perhaps fifty feet square. Scrawled across the banner was a large, crudely drawn but unmistakable DDT bomb and the words, "Vermin, Go Home. This Planet Only for People."

It was contagious, he knew, this psychology of crowds, unpredictable as a meteor storm. He could almost feel the sudden change in the climate, the first whispers of hostility.

This was the way he sized up the situation as the car approached the ominously quiet crowd in front of the banner. This was one of those moments in which he could prove himself as an old pro, where the political appointees would blanch and bumble along. The years in the almost unnamed consulates in the least desirable cities of the galaxy had taught him to regroup his forces rapidly, to work always upon common understanding.

He leaned forward toward the chief of protocol. "With your permission," he said with the old professional smile, "I am afraid I must say a word or two to my wife in our native language. I find my English deserts me in moments such as this."

The chief of protocol looked at the banner and nodded miserably.

"My dear," the ambassador said, as if he were asking her to begin a grand waltz or be presented to a chief executive. The hairy anterior legs vibrated rapidly touching her mesothorax, metathorax, prothorax in a pattern of words and images so fast that the uncomplicated eye of the others in the open car could hardly follow the movements.

"My dear," the ambassador said, "do you remember the gesture we learned for just such an occasion?"

"The V for Victory sign?" she asked.

"No, my dear." He tapped her body with what seemed his usual deliberation. "No, I mean the one we practiced for use with the American masses?"

She nodded, and he bent over toward the chief of protocol. "Please stop the car," the ambassador asked. The automobile stopped almost directly in front of the impudent banner.

Balancing themselves on their posterior legs, they rose in the tonneau of the car, clinging with their middle legs to the rail which divided the front seat from the back seat. They were a stately couple, almost nine feet high, and all eyes were on them.

Deliberately then and smiling at the crowd of Americans, they clasped their anterior feet above their heads in the well-known and recognizable gesture of the victorious prize fighter and shook them.

For a second the crowd was dumfounded, but then as the full import of the gesture came to them, the crowd applauded. Arms stretched above heads and the gesture was repeated on every side.

"George," someone shouted from the crowd, "welcome to the good old U.S.A."

"Maggie," another voice shouted as the car moved off toward the Capitol, "we love you."

# THE HACK DRIVER

## by Sinclair Lewis

Sinclair Lewis was a restless, vivid, red-haired, dynamic
bean pole of a man. He first came to national promi-
nence when, at the age of thirty-five, he exploded an
angry novel in the faces of self-satisfied Americans. It
was *Main Street*, a startling exposure not only of the
smugness of the American small town but of a lot of
other things we'd carefully swept under the bed.

Another ten years passed, and Lewis wrote more
novels, and better ones. Then, in 1930, he brought
honor to his country by becoming the first American to
win the Nobel Prize for literature.

Many people think Lewis was at his best when he
came to a boil. He loved his country dearly; yet he saw
no reason why he should not point out its faults. He
did point them out—and little by little we began to see
them too.

But there was another side to Sinclair Lewis. There
was a part of him that grew wistful over the small-town
life he generally lambasted so vigorously. In his heart
he knew that lively men may be found in the dullest
places, and even the dullest places may become lively if
seen through the right pair of eyes.

"The Hack Driver," written in 1923, is a simple story.
It shows us an unfamiliar Sinclair Lewis, a Lewis good-
naturedly admitting that Main Street has its points, in-

cluding the point that it is sometimes smarter than
Broadway. It shows us Sinclair Lewis smiling.

I dare say there's no man of large affairs, whether he is bank
president or senator or dramatist, who hasn't a sneaking love
for some old rum hound in a frightful hat, living back in a
country shanty. (It was the Supreme Court Justice speaking. I
do not pretend to guarantee his theories or his story.)

He may be a Maine guide, or the old garageman who used
to keep the livery stable, or a perfectly useless innkeeper, but
your pompous big-city man will contrive to get back and see
him every year and secretly prefer him to all the highfalutin
leaders of the city. I don't know the philosophy of it; perhaps
it means that we retain a decent simplicity, no matter how
much we are tied to Things—to houses and motors and expensive wives.

When I was graduated from law school I suppose I was
about as artificial and idiotic and ambitious as most youngsters.
I wanted to climb, socially and financially. I wanted to be
famous. Imagine then how I felt when, after taking honors
and becoming fifteenth assistant clerk in the magnificent New
York law firm of Hodgins, Hodgins, Berkman and Taupe, I
was set not at preparing briefs but at serving summonses! Like
a cheap private detective!

I rejoiced one day when they sent me out forty miles or so
to a town called New Mullion, to serve a summons on one
Oliver Lutkins. This Lutkins had worked in the Northern
Woods, and he knew the facts about a certain timberland
boundary. We needed him as a witness, and he had dodged
service.

When I got off the train at New Mullion, my sudden affection for sweet and simple villages was dashed by the look of
the place and its rows of shops daubed with a sour brown.
There was one agreeable-looking man at the station—the expressman. He was a person of perhaps forty, red-faced, cheer-

ful, thick. He was very friendly and you knew at once he liked people and slapped them on the back out of pure, easy affection.

"I want," I told him, "to find a fellow named Oliver Lutkins."

"Him? I saw him 'round here 'twan't an hour ago. Hard fellow to catch, though—always chasing around on some phony business or other. Probably trying to get up a poker game in the back of Fritz Beinke's harness shop. I'll tell you, boy—any hurry about locating Lutkins?"

"Yes. I want to catch the afternoon train back." I was as impressively secret as a stage detective.

"I'll tell you. I've got a hack. We can drive around together and find Lutkins. I know most of the places where he generally hangs out."

He so immediately took me into the circle of his affection that I glowed with the warmth of it. I knew, of course, that he was drumming up business, but his kindness was real. I got him down to $2 an hour. He brought from his cottage an object like a black piano box on wheels.

He said, and almost shyly, "I don't want to butt in on your private business, young fellow, but my guess is that you want to collect some money from Lutkins—he never pays anybody a cent. He ain't a bad sort of a Yahoo, but he just naturally hates to loosen up on a coin of the realm. If you go asking for him—anybody can tell you come from the city, with that trick Fedora of yours—he'll suspect something and take a sneak. If you want me to, I'll go into Fritz Beinke's and ask for him, and you can keep out of sight behind me."

I loved him for it. In a burst I told the hack driver that I wanted to serve a summons on Lutkins. The driver listened. At the end he chuckled, "Well, we'll spring a little surprise on Brer Lutkins."

"Let's start, driver."

"Most folks around here call me Bill. Or Magnuson. William Magnuson, fancy carting and hauling."

At the somewhat gloomy harness shop we descended and went in. The room smelled of dressed leather. A scanty sort of man, presumably Mr. Beinke, was selling a horse collar to a farmer.

"Seen Nolly Lutkins around today? Friend of his looking for him," said Bill, with treacherous heartiness.

Beinke looked past him at my shrinking alien self; he hesitated and owned, "Yuh, he was in here a little while ago. Guess he's gone over to the Swede's to get a shave."

We sought the barber shop of "the Swede." Bill was again good enough to take the lead. He asked not only the Swede but two customers if they had seen Lutkins. The Swede decidedly had not; he raged, "I ain't seen him, and I don't want to, but if you find him you can just collect the dollar thirty-five he owes me."

At Gray's barber shop we missed Lutkins by only five minutes. He had just left—presumably for the poolroom. At the poolroom it appeared that he had merely bought a pack of cigarettes and gone on. Thus we pursued him, just behind him but never catching him, for an hour, till it was past one and I was hungry. "How about something to eat?" I suggested.

"Tell you what we'll do. There's an elegant view from Wade's Hill. We'll get the old woman to put us up a lunch— she won't charge you but half a dollar, and we'll go up there and have a Sunday-school picnic."

I knew that my friend Bill was not free from guile. But he was no more dishonest than I who charged the whole thing up to the firm, and it would have been worth paying him myself to have his presence. His country serenity, his natural wisdom, was a refreshing bath to the city-twitching youngster.

As we sat on the hilltop, looking across orchards and a creek which slipped among the willows, he talked of New Mullion, gave a whole gallery of portraits. He made them live. In that day I came to know New Mullion better than I did the city and to love it better.

We left that placid place of orchards and resumed the search for Oliver Lutkins. At last Bill cornered a friend of Lutkins who guessed Oliver'd "gone out to his ma's farm, three miles north."

We drove out there, mighty with strategy.

"I know Oliver's ma. She's a terror. She's a cyclone," Bill sighed. "We'll try bawling her out. But you better let me do it, boy."

We drove into a poor farmyard; we were faced by an enormous and cheerful old woman. My guardian snarled, "Remember me? I'm Bill Magnuson, the expressman. I want to find your son Oliver."

"I don't know anything about Oliver and I don't want to," she bellowed. She retired into the kitchen and we followed. From the old range she snatched a flatiron and marched on us clamoring, "You just search all you want to—providin' you don't mind getting burnt to a cinder!" She bellowed; she swelled; she laughed at our nervous retreat.

"Let's get out of this. She'll murder us," Bill groaned and, outside, "Did you see her grin? She was making fun of us. Can you beat that for nerve?"

It was nearly time for me to catch the afternoon train, and Bill drove me to the station. I worried very little over my failure to find Lutkins. I was too absorbed in the thought of Bill Magnuson. Really, I considered returning to New Mullion to practice law. If I had found Bill so deeply and richly human might I not come to love the yet uncharted Fritz Beinke and the Swede barber and a hundred other slow-spoken, simple, wise neighbors? I was excited, as one who has found a treasure.

But if I did not think much about Lutkins, the office did. I found them in a state next morning; the suit was ready to come to trial; they had to have Lutkins. I was ordered back to New Mullion, and with me they sent an ex-lumber-camp clerk who knew Lutkins.

When the train drew in at New Mullion, Bill was on the

platform. What was curious was that the old dragon, Lutkins's mother, was there talking to him, and they were not quarreling but laughing.

From the car steps I pointed them out to the lumber-camp clerk, and in young hero-worship I murmured, "There's a fine fellow, a real man."

"Meet him here yesterday?" asked the clerk.

"I spent the day with him."

"He help you hunt for Oliver Lutkins?"

"Yes, he helped me a lot."

"He must have! He's Lutkins himself!"

But what really hurt was that when I served the summons Lutkins and his mother laughed at me as though I were a bright boy of seven, and with loving solicitude they begged me to go to a neighbor's house and take a cup of coffee.

"I told 'em about you, and they're dying to have a look at you," said Lutkins joyfully. "They're about the only folks in town that missed seeing you yesterday."

# FOR US, THE LIVING

## by Alexander Woollcott

On November 19, 1863, Abraham Lincoln delivered the Gettysburg Address. Most of us know it by heart. But words can at times become so familiar that we have to be reminded of their meaning. Try reading the Gettysburg Address aloud—not declaiming it, but as if you were coming upon it for the first time. Then read what follows.

In this moving, reflective little essay Alexander Woollcott asks and answers a good question: To whom was Lincoln talking? You may say, "To the audience at Gettysburg, of course." But, as you will see from Woollcott's argument, there is some doubt as to that. Was he really talking to the audience? And did they hear him, either with their ears or their understandings?

Alexander Woollcott was often—and particularly with reference to his famous radio talks—accused of sentimentality. The charge was on occasion a just one. But I have never been able to see anything sentimental in this tribute to an American about whom reams of tosh have been written. When Woollcott wrote it, Hitler and Mussolini were successfully challenging the Gettysburg Address. In those dark days Woollcott's comment seemed especially meaningful to us. Is it less so today?

I have on purpose written this brief note in exactly two hundred and seventy-two words. They are the same number of words Lincoln used. But what a difference! Mine are perfectly good English words that say what they mean and no more. But Lincoln's two hundred and seventy-two words framed the vision of a whole people. The pen is not always mightier than the sword. Once in a while it can be.

If you could go back through the years—if, by virtue of some such gift as was the wonder and redemption of an old skinflint named Scrooge, you could go back through the long file of American years and play eavesdropper on one fateful moment in our history, which one would you choose?

Would you choose that moment in which the first starved and despairing settlers in Virginia saw, at long last, the governor's relief boat coming slowly 'round the bend in the muddy James? Or that moment in which, under the dripping trees at Saratoga, Gentleman Johnny Burgoyne surrendered his sword after the battle which had turned the tide of our own now sanctified revolution?

Or would you slip unnoticed into the multitude which stood in the November sunshine on Cemetery Hill at Gettysburg so that you might hear from his own lips that address by Abraham Lincoln which surely will live at least as long as this country does? Always in my own fond recourse to this pastime, that was my choice. But it may not have been a good one. For had I been at Gettysburg when Lincoln spoke, the chances are overwhelming that I would not have heard what he said.

In our own day it has been an ironic commonplace that that history-making speech made no impression at all on most of the reporters who filed it with the harried telegraph operators at Gettysburg. Nor indeed on most of the editors who, in composing their papers next day, merely gave their readers the impression that Mr. Lincoln "also spoke."

To be sure, the New York *Times* observed the occasion by printing an editorial headed "Two Great Speeches," but the

*Times* was referring to the stupefying two-hour oration with which Edward Everett had preceded Mr. Lincoln's address and to the stirring speech which Henry Ward Beecher had just made at the Academy of Music in Brooklyn.

It might be enjoyable and not unprofitable to glance here in passing at the more preposterous comments made by those already hostile to the speaker. In the nearby town of Harrisburg *The Patriot and Union* said, "We pass over the silly remarks of the President; for the credit of the nation we are willing that the veil of oblivion shall be dropped over them and that they shall no more be repeated or thought of."

The *Chicago Times* had this to say: "The cheek of every American must tingle with shame as he reads the silly, flat and dish-watery utterances of the man who has to be pointed out to intelligent foreigners as the President of the United States." One of those whose job it was to enlighten such foreigners, the American correspondent of *The London Times* kept them posted as follows: "The ceremony was rendered ludicrous by some of the sallies of that poor President Lincoln. Anything more dull and commonplace it wouldn't be easy to produce."

These, however, were but spiteful expressions of the same kind of angry partisanship which marked so much of the sniping at Lincoln while he lived and with which even the latest of his successors is by no means unfamiliar.

But here I am concerned only with the immediate effect upon the 15,000 who were actually present at Gettysburg. From the unconscious or reluctant testimony of many witnesses, one thing is clear. Few of them suspected for a moment that the world would long remember what was said there. Indeed, that is the basis of a celebrated and exceedingly sentimental short story called "The Perfect Tribute" in which Lincoln is presented as having left Gettysburg melancholy in the conviction that he had "failed."

The story could have been written only by someone who knew little about Lincoln and less about public speaking. But it is true that the first audience, however much *ex post facto* perceptiveness its members may later have laid claim to, were at the time quite unimpressed. Historians, with that wisdom-after-the-event which lends to posterity its smug air of superiority, have been amused to wonder why. I know why. I think it can be proved beyond all doubt that of the 15,000 only an inconsiderable few heard what Lincoln said.

It is easy to see why this must have been so. Even the most inexperienced playwright is careful to postpone past the first ten minutes any crucial line of his dialogue, not only because stragglers will still be rattling down the aisles but because there is such a thing as an arc of attention and, in the relation between the voice on the stage and the ears beyond the footlights, it takes a bit of time to establish that arc's trajectory.

Listen to any speaker at a dinner and note how inevitably he devotes his first two or three minutes to saying nothing at all, while his audience, with its varying rate of adjustment, is tuning in. The need for such purely vocal preliminaries is trebled when the gathering is held under the sky. Mr. Lincoln spoke not only in the open air but to a multitude of which many, having just escaped from the trap of a two-hour discourse, were, for reasons you are free to surmise, moving anxiously toward the exits. Some of these, as it dawned on them that the President had risen, turned in their tracks and started shoving their way back toward the rostrum.

So it was not only to a huge crowd in the open air that he spoke, but to one that was not even stationary. He would have had to talk at least five minutes before even those within reach of his voice could have really begun to listen. The address is made up of ten sentences. It has only 272 words. After he had been speaking for two minutes and thirty-five seconds, Mr. Lincoln sat down. Most of those present could not have taken in a word he said.

Now all this I know from my own platform experience. Of course, it was an old story to him who had held the difficult

Cooper Union audience in thrall, who had gone down with
Douglas into the dust of the arena, and who had spoken by
torchlight to many a milling crossroads crowd. No one this
country ever produced—not Patrick Henry, nor Henry Ward
Beecher, nor Woodrow Wilson—knew better than Lincoln
how to make an audience listen. If he did not make the one at
Gettysburg listen, it must have been for a reason you will find
suggested by an anecdote Edna Ferber tells us.

Once, as a guest of the William Lyon Phelpses in New
Haven, she heard her host invoke the blessing of God on the
excellent menu by muttering confidentially into his soup plate.
After the "Amen," Mrs. Phelps complained that she had not
heard a word. "My dear," he replied, "I wasn't speaking to
you." Is it not clear that, if Mr. Lincoln did not trouble to
make the crowd at Gettysburg hear him, it is because he was
not speaking to them?

To whom, then? My own inescapable notion is that, over
the heads of the audience, he was also talking to Americans as
yet unborn.

. . . *whether that nation, or any nation so conceived and so
dedicated, can long endure*. . . .

Have these words, for example, at any time since they were
first spoken, ever had such painful immediacy as they have
seemed to have in our own anxious era? Yes, he was talking
to you and to me. Of this there is no real question in my mind.
The only question—in an age when beggars on horseback the
world around are challenging all that Lincoln had and was—
the only question is whether we will listen. . . . *It is for us,
the living, rather, to be dedicated here*. . . .

For whom was the speech meant? Why, the answer is in his
own words. For us. *For us, the living*. For us to resolve and see
to it—*that government of the people, by the people, for the
people, shall not perish from the earth*.

## LINCOLN'S GETTYSBURG ADDRESS

*Four score and seven years ago our fathers brought forth on this continent a new nation conceived in liberty and dedicated to the proposition that all men are created equal.*

*Now we are engaged in a great civil war testing whether that nation, or any nation so conceived and so dedicated, can long endure. We are met on a great battle-field of that war. We have come to dedicate a portion of that field as a final resting place for those who here gave their lives that that nation might live. It is altogether fitting and proper that we should do this.*

*But, in a larger sense, we can not dedicate, we can not consecrate, we can not hallow this ground. The brave men, living and dead, who struggled here have consecrated it far above our poor power to add or detract. The world will little note nor long remember what we say here, but it can never forget what they did here. It is for us the living rather to be dedicated here to the unfinished work which they who fought here have thus far so nobly advanced. It is rather for us to be here dedicated to the great task remaining before us—that from these honored dead we take increased devotion to that cause for which they gave the last full measure of devotion—that we here highly resolve that these dead shall not have died in vain, that this nation under God shall have a new birth of freedom, and that government of the people, by the people, for the people, shall not perish from the earth.*

# THE BRASS CANNON

## by Robert Benchley

> Everyone knows Benchley's "Treasurer's Report" (see page 186), but this rich dead-pan anecdote may be less familiar. I've extracted it from a Benchley piece called A Vanishing Art, which deals with the business of putting ships in bottles. "The Brass Cannon" should be read very quietly and gravely, and the punch line should be delivered the same way.

One is reminded (and, let us be quite frank about it, when I say "one is reminded" I mean "I am reminded") of the business troubles of the man who polished the commemorative brass cannon in Ypsilanti, Mich. (I have always heard that it was Ypsilanti, Mich., but I am willing to retract if it is not true.) It seems that the residents of Ypsilanti, Mich., shortly after the Civil War decided that some sort of monument or Denkmal should be placed in a public square to remind future generations of Michigan's part in the great struggle. So a large brass commemorative cannon was placed on the common (if there is a common in Ypsilanti) and a veteran of the war was engaged, at a nominal salary, to keep this cannon in good condition. He was to polish it twice a week and see that small boys did not hide in it. Aside from this, his time was his own.

This business routine went on for twenty-five years. The

veteran was faithful at his task of polishing the commemorative brass cannon and its splendor and shining surface were
the admiration of every one who visited Ypsilanti, Mich., during those twenty-five years, to say nothing of the natives. "The
commemorative brass cannon of Ypsilanti, Mich.," became a
byword throughout the state for expressing how shiny a commemorative brass cannon could be made.

One evening, during the veteran's twenty-sixth year of service, he came home to supper at his usual hour (4:30), but his
wife noticed that he was more depressed than was his wont.
He hardly touched his food and sat in moody contemplation
of the backs of his polish-stained hands. His wife was worried.

"What is it, Joe?" she asked. "What is the matter?"

"Oh, nothing, my dear," said her husband, and turned in a
brave attempt to finish his cutlet.

"Come, come," said the companion of his twenty-five years
of labor (he had married immediately on getting the job of
polishing the commemorative brass cannon), "I know that
something is wrong. You are depressed."

The gray-haired man put down his knife and looked his wife
in the eye.

"You're right," he said, as he took her hand in his. "I am depressed. Things haven't been going very well down at the cannon lately."

"You don't mean that you're fired, Joe!" she said fearfully.

"No, no! Never fear about that," was his reply. "They
couldn't fire me. I know too much. They would be afraid that
I might make trouble. But I am discouraged about my work. I
don't seem to be getting ahead. For twenty-five years I have
been polishing that cannon and putting everything that I had
into making it bright and shiny. I have done my job well—no
one can deny that. But recently I have got to thinking. What
is it leading to? Where am I getting? Where is the future in
polishing commemorative brass cannons?" And the old man
broke down and cried.

His wife was silent for a minute. Then she stroked his head and said, "I know, Joe. I have worried a little myself. And I have figured it out this way. In the last twenty-five years we have saved a little money. I have put aside a dollar here and a dollar there when you didn't know about it. We have quite a tidy little nest egg in the bank now, and here is my suggestion: Let's take that money, buy a cannon, and go into business for ourselves!"

# THE CHASER*

## by John Collier

> This is one of the best bits of *macabric-à-brac* (if I may
> borrow a phrase from myself) John Collier ever wrote.
> I do not endorse its morality but I do think it's an in-
> genious bit of devilish foolery, with all the sting at the
> very end of the tail. Some years ago, when I was an
> itinerant platform reader, this story was one of the most
> successful pieces in my repertoire. All the credit goes to
> the author, for this is so neatly written and so well con-
> ceived for reading aloud that for proper effect no great
> artistry is required. However, if you think that any of
> your audience might just possibly be stumped by the
> familiar French phrase uttered by the old man at the
> end, substitute "I'll be seeing you."

Alan Austen, as nervous as a kitten, went up certain dark and
creaky stairs in the neighborhood of Pell Street, and peered
about for a long time on the dim landing before he found the
name he wanted written obscurely on one of the doors.

He pushed open this door, as he had been told to do, and
found himself in a tiny room, which contained no furniture
but a plain kitchen table, a rocking chair, and an ordinary
chair. On one of the dirty buff-colored walls were a couple of
shelves, containing in all perhaps a dozen bottles and jars.

An old man sat in the rocking chair, reading a newspaper.
Alan, without a word, handed him the card he had been given.

* Originally appeared in *The New Yorker*

"Sit down, Mr. Austen," said the old man very politely. "I am glad to make your acquaintance."

"Is it true," asked Alan, "that you have a certain mixture that has—er—quite extraordinary effects?"

"My dear sir," replied the old man, "my stock in trade is not very large—I don't deal in laxatives and teething mixtures—but such as it is, it is varied. I think nothing I sell has effects which could be precisely described as ordinary."

"Well, the fact is—" began Alan.

"Here, for example," interrupted the old man, reaching for a bottle from the shelf. "Here is a liquid as colorless as water, almost tasteless, quite imperceptible in coffee, milk, wine, or any other beverage. It is also quite imperceptible to any known method of autopsy."

"Do you mean it is a poison?" cried Alan, very much horrified.

"Call it a glove-cleaner if you like," said the old man indifferently. "Maybe it will clean gloves. I have never tried. One might call it a life-cleaner. Lives need cleaning sometimes."

"I want nothing of that sort," said Alan.

"Probably it is just as well," said the old man. "Do you know the price of this? For one teaspoonful, which is sufficient, I ask five thousand dollars. Never less. Not a penny less."

"I hope all your mixtures are not as expensive," said Alan apprehensively.

"Oh dear, no," said the old man. "It would be no good charging that sort of price for a love potion, for example. Young people who need a love potion very seldom have five thousand dollars. Otherwise they would not need a love potion."

"I am glad to hear that," said Alan.

"I look at it like this," said the old man. "Please a customer with one article, and he will come back when he needs another. Even if it *is* more costly. He will save up for it, if necessary."

"So," said Alan, "you really do sell love potions?"

"If I did not sell love potions," said the old man, reaching for another bottle, "I should not have mentioned the other matter to you. It is only when one is in a position to oblige that one can afford to be so confidential."

"And these potions," said Alan. "They are not just—just—er—"

"Oh, no," said the old man. "Their effects are permanent, and extend far beyond the mere casual impulse. But they include it. Oh, yes, they include it. Bountifully, insistently. Everlastingly."

"But consider the spiritual side," said the old man.

"I do, indeed," said Alan.

"For indifference," said the old man, "they substitute devotion. For scorn, adoration. Give one tiny measure of this to the young lady—its flavor is imperceptible in orange juice, soup, or cocktails—and however gay and giddy she is, she will change altogether. She will want nothing but solitude, and you."

"I can hardly believe it," said Alan. "She is so fond of parties."

"She will not like them any more," said the old man. "She will be afraid of the pretty girls you may meet."

"She will actually be jealous?" cried Alan in a rapture. "Of me?"

"Yes, she will want to be everything to you."

"She is already. Only she doesn't care about it."

"She will, when she has taken this. She will care intensely. You will be her sole interest in life."

"Wonderful!" cried Alan.

"She will want to know all you do," said the old man. All that has happened to you during the day. Every word of it. She will want to know what you are thinking about, why you smile suddenly, why you are looking sad."

"That is love!" cried Alan.

"Yes," said the old man. "How carefully she will look after

you! She will never allow you to be tired, to sit in a draft, to neglect your food. If you are an hour late, she will be terrified. She will think you are killed, or that some siren has caught you."

"I can hardly imagine Diana like that!" cried Alan, overwhelmed with joy.

"You will not have to use your imagination," said the old man. "And, by the way, since there are always sirens, if by any chance you *should*, later on, slip a little, you need not worry. She will forgive you, in the end. She will be terribly hurt, of course, but she will forgive you—in the end."

"That will not happen," said Alan fervently.

"Of course not," said the old man. "But, if it did, you need not worry. She would never divorce you. Oh, no! And, of course, she herself will never give you the least, the very least, grounds for—uneasiness."

"And how much," said Alan, "is this wonderful mixture?"

"It is not as dear," said the old man, "as the glove-cleaner, or life-cleaner, as I sometimes call it. No. That is five thousand dollars, never a penny less. One has to be older than you are, to indulge in that sort of thing. One has to save up for it."

"But the love potion?" said Alan.

"Oh, that," said the old man, opening the drawer in the kitchen table, and taking out a tiny, rather dirty-looking phial. "That is just a dollar."

"I can't tell you how grateful I am," said Alan, watching him fill it.

"I like to oblige," said the old man. "Then customers come back, later in life, when they are rather better off, and want more expensive things. Here you are. You will find it very effective."

"Thank you again," said Alan. "Goodbye."

"*Au revoir*," said the old man.

# MY FINANCIAL CAREER

## by Stephen Leacock

This is an oldie but still good, even though banks today
are rather different from what they were in Leacock's
time. Nowadays every bank official is a smiling, wel-
coming Committee of One and all depositors are treated
as if they were angels from Heaven. The great trick in a
funny piece such as this is to have a comic blackout
close. There is one here; but Leacock spoiled it just a
tiny bit by adding the last two short paragraphs. Humor
has quickened its tempo during the last thirty years or
so. Maybe we're quicker, too; at any rate, we don't need
to have the point underlined for us, as the author under-
lines it here. But the rest of it still makes me laugh.

When I go into a bank I get rattled. The clerks rattle me; the
wickets rattle me; the sight of the money rattles me; everything
rattles me.

The moment I cross the threshold of a bank and attempt to
transact business there, I become an irresponsible idiot.

I knew this beforehand, but my salary had been raised to
fifty dollars a month and I felt that the bank was the only
place for it.

So I shambled in and looked timidly round at the clerks. I
had an idea that a person about to open an account must
needs consult the manager.

I went up to a wicket marked "Accountant." The accountant was a tall, cool devil. The very sight of him rattled me. My voice was sepulchral.

"Can I see the manager?" I said, and added solemnly, "alone." I don't know why I said "alone."

"Certainly," said the accountant, and fetched him.

The manager was a grave, calm man. I held my fifty-six dollars clutched in a crumpled ball in my pocket.

"Are you the manager?" I said. God knows I didn't doubt it.

"Yes," he said.

"Can I see you," I asked, "alone?" I didn't want to say "alone" again, but without it the thing seemed self-evident.

The manager looked at me in some alarm. He felt that I had an awful secret to reveal.

"Come in here," he said, and led the way to a private room. He turned the key in the lock.

"We are safe from interruption here," he said; "sit down."

We both sat down and looked at each other. I found no voice to speak.

"You are one of Pinkerton's men, I presume," he said.

He had gathered from my mysterious manner that I was a detective. I knew what he was thinking, and it made me worse.

"No, not from Pinkerton's," I said, seeming to imply that I came from a rival agency.

"To tell the truth," I went on, as if I had been prompted to lie about it, "I am not a detective at all. I have come to open an account. I intend to keep all my money in this bank."

The manager looked relieved but still serious; he concluded now that I was a son of Baron Rothschild or a young Gould.

"A large account, I suppose," he said.

"Fairly large," I whispered. "I propose to deposit fifty-six dollars now and fifty dollars a month regularly."

The manager got up and opened the door. He called to the accountant.

"Mr. Montgomery," he said unkindly loud, "this gentleman

is opening an account, he will deposit fifty-six dollars. Good morning."

I rose.

A big iron door stood open at the side of the room.

"Good morning," I said, and stepped into the safe.

"Come out," said the manager coldly, and showed me the other way.

I went up to the accountant's wicket and poked the ball of money at him with a quick convulsive movement as if I were doing a conjuring trick.

My face was ghastly pale.

"Here," I said, "deposit it." The tone of the words seemed to mean, "Let us do this painful thing while the fit is on us."

He took the money and gave it to another clerk.

He made me write the sum on a slip and sign my name in a book. I no longer knew what I was doing. The bank swam before my eyes.

"Is it deposited?" I asked in a hollow, vibrating voice.

"It is," said the accountant.

"Then I want to draw a check."

My idea was to draw out six dollars of it for present use. Someone gave me a checkbook through a wicket and someone else began telling me how to write it out. The people in the bank had the impression that I was an invalid millionaire. I wrote something on the check and thrust it in at the clerk. He looked at it.

"What! are you drawing it all out again?" he asked in surprise. Then I realized that I had written fifty-six instead of six. I was too far gone to reason now. I had a feeling that it was impossible to explain the thing. All the clerks had stopped writing to look at me.

Reckless with misery, I made a plunge.

"Yes, the whole thing."

"You withdraw your money from the bank?"

"Every cent of it."

"Are you not going to deposit any more?" said the clerk, astonished.

"Never."

An idiot hope struck me that they might think something had insulted me while I was writing the check and that I had changed my mind. I made a wretched attempt to look like a man with a fearfully quick temper.

The clerk prepared to pay the money.

"How will you have it?" he said.

"What?"

"How will you have it?"

"Oh"—I caught his meaning and answered without even trying to think—"in fifties."

He gave me a fifty-dollar bill.

"And the six?" he asked dryly.

"In sixes," I said.

He gave it to me and I rushed out.

As the big door swung behind me I caught the echo of a roar of laughter that went up to the ceiling of the bank. Since then I bank no more. I keep my money in cash in my trousers pocket and my savings in silver dollars in a sock.

# ABOUT THE EDITOR

CLIFTON FADIMAN *has perhaps done more than anyone else alive to interest the general American public in the pleasures of good reading. There is hardly a medium of communication in which he has not made his mark. His name first came to the fore when he was literary critic for* The New Yorker. *Since the heyday of "Information Please," he has also been prominent in radio and television. Today he is best known as an editor of anthologies such as* Reading I've Liked *and* The American Treasury; *as public speaker and platform reader; and as essayist, appearing regularly in* Holiday. *His department in* This Week *has provided millions with pleasurable reading experiences. For almost two decades he has been one of the judges of the Book-of-the-Month Club. His books of essays,* Party of One *and* Any Number Can Play, *are known to large audiences, as is* Fantasia Mathematica, *to which he is now preparing a sequel volume. One of his outstanding recent successes was his guide to the great books of the Western world,* The Lifetime Reading Plan. *Mr. Fadiman is on the board of editors of the* Encyclopædia Britannica *and is on the advisory board of* Encyclopædia Britannica Films, Inc.